OFFICIAL TOURIST BOARD PU

C000045928

Britain's Camping
& Caravan Parks
2007

visit**Britain**

Contents

Gaze out over Derwentwater, Cumbria, at dawn

VisitBritain

VisitBritain is the organisation created to
market Britain to the rest of the world, and
England to the British.

Formed by the merger of the British Tourist
Authority and the English Tourism Council,
its mission is to build the value of tourism
by creating world-class destination brands
and marketing campaigns.

It will also build partnerships with – and
provide insights to – other organisations
which have a stake in British and English

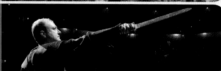

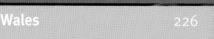

This guide is packed with information from where to stay, to how to get there and what to see and do. **In fact, everything you need to know to enjoy Britain.**

The guide that gives you more

endless
possibilities
for
relaxing
short breaks
and
fun-filled
holidays

Explore the grassy sand dunes above Constantine Bay, Cornwall

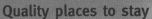

Quality places to stay

Choose from a wide range of quality-assessed sites to suit all budgets and tastes. This guide contains an exclusive listing of all touring, camping and holiday parks plus holiday villages in England, Scotland and Wales participating in The British Graded Holiday Parks Scheme.

Regional information

Every region has its own unique attractions – in each section we highlight a selection of interesting ideas for memorable days out. Regional maps show their location as well as National Trails and sections of the National Cycle Network. For even more ideas go online at visitbritain.com.

You'll also find contact details for regional tourism organisations together with a list of free and saleable tourism publications.

Useful indexes

Indexes at the back make it easy to find sites that match your requirements – and if you know the name of the site use the park index.

Tourist information centres

For local information phone or call in to a tourist information centre. Location and contact details can be found at the beginning of each regional section. Alternatively, you can text **TIC LOCATE** to 64118 to find your nearest tourist information centre.

How to use
this guide

In this new, fully updated camping and caravan parks guide, you'll find a great choice of touring, camping and holiday parks plus holiday villages in England, Scotland and Wales.

Relax and spend time with the family

Each site has been assessed by VisitBritain's assessors under The British Graded Holiday Parks Scheme so that you can book with confidence knowing all parks in the guide have been checked and rated for quality.

Detailed entries include descriptions, prices and facilities. You'll also find special offers and themed breaks to suit your tastes, interests and budget.

Finding a place to stay is easy
Regional entries
The guide is divided into eleven regional sections and entries are listed alphabetically by place name within each region. (Additionally ALL parks/holiday villages participating in The British Graded Holiday Parks Scheme, which include those that have not taken a paid entry, are listed at the back of the guide, again by region.)

Colour maps
Use the colour maps, starting on page 17, to pinpoint the location of all sites featured in the regional sections. Then refer to the place index at the back of the guide to find the page number. The index also includes tourism areas such as the New Forest and the Cotswolds.

Indexes
The indexes, listed on page 277, will help you find the right place to stay. If you require a swimming pool, for example, there is an index that lists all parks with this facility.

Ratings and awards
at a glance

Reliable, rigorous, easy to use – look out for the following ratings and awards to help you choose with confidence:

Ratings made easy

★	Acceptable quality
★★	Good quality
★★★	Very good quality
★★★★	Excellent quality
★★★★★	Exceptional quality

**rest assured
with our
official
quality
ratings**

Star ratings

Parks are awarded a rating of one to five stars following an assessment of the quality, cleanliness, maintenance and condition of the various facilities provided. It is not necessary to provide a wide range of facilities in order to achieve a high rating, as the emphasis is on the quality of what is actually provided rather than a rating restricted by a lack of facilities. See page 278 for an explanation of each star rating.

Designators

A range of designators is available to show the type of park at a glance. Proprietors choose the one that fits their business most accurately and descriptions can be found overleaf. **Holiday Villages** are also rated from one to five stars.

Enjoy England Awards for Excellence

The prestigious and coveted Enjoy England Awards for Excellence showcase the very best in English tourism. Run by VisitBritain in association with England's regions, they include a Caravan Holiday Park of the Year category (see page 15).

National Accessible Scheme

Sites with a National Accessible rating provide access and facilities for guests with special visual, hearing and mobility needs (see page 12).

Walkers and Cyclists Welcome

Parks participating in these Enjoy England schemes actively encourage walking and cycling. Proprietors go out of their way to make special provision for guests who enjoy these activities.

David Bellamy Conservation Award

This special award is a signpost to parks that are making real achievements in protecting our environment (see page 14).

Visitor Attraction Quality Assurance

Attractions achieving high standards in all aspects of the visitor experience, from initial telephone enquiry to departure, receive this Enjoy England award and are visited every year by professional assessors.

Caravan Holiday Home Award Scheme

VisitBritain, VisitScotland and Visit Wales run award schemes for individual holiday caravan homes on highly graded caravan parks. In addition to complying with standards for Holiday Parks, these exceptional caravans must have a shower or bath, toilet, mains electricity and water heating (at no extra charge) and a fridge (many also have a colour TV).

designators
explained

Parks vary greatly in style and in the facilities they offer. The following will help you decide which is right for you whether you are looking for an overnight caravan stop or an open-air family holiday with all the extras.

Camping Park	These sites only have pitches available for tents.
Touring Park	If you are planning to travel with your own caravan, motor home or tent, then look for a Touring Park.
Holiday Park	If you want to hire a caravan holiday home for a short break or longer holiday, or are looking to buy your own holiday home, a Holiday Park is the right choice. They range from small, rural sites to larger parks with all the added extras, such as a pool.

Many parks will offer a combination of these designators.

Holiday Village	Holiday villages usually comprise a variety of types of accommodation, with the majority in custom-built rooms, chalets for example. The option to book on a bed and breakfast, or dinner, bed and breakfast basis is normally available. A range of facilities, entertainment and activities are also provided which may, or may not, be included in the tariff.

Holiday Villages must meet a minimum entry requirement for both the provision and quality of facilities and services, including fixtures, fittings, furnishings, decor and any other extra facilities. Progressively higher levels of quality and customer care are provided at each star level.

Accommodation
entries explained

Each entry contains detailed information to help you decide if it is right for you. This information has been provided by the proprietors themselves, and our aim has been to ensure that it is as objective and factual as possible.

RELUBBUS, Cornwall Map ref 2B3

★★★★★
HOLIDAY, TOURING
& CAMPING PARK
ROSE AWARD

St Michael's Country Park
Relubbus, Penzance TR20 9ER **t** (01336) 763398 **f** (01336) 763340
e stmichaels@surfbay.co.uk **w** stmichaelspark.co.uk

🚐 (124) £15.00-£20.00
🚏 (90) £15.00-£18.50
⛺ (40) £9.60-£15.00
🏠 (10) £230.00-£450.00
254 touring pitches

open All year
payment Credit/debit card, cash/cheques, euros

Exceptional family park close to the resort of Penzance and an excellent touring base for discovering Cornwall. Spacious pitches are level and shaded by trees. Close to woodland and plentiful walking routes, the site is well suited to dog owners and ramblers. Children's clubs and evening entertainment in peak season.

⊕ *From Helston on A394, turn right onto B3280. At Relubbus cross over bridge. St Michael's is 0.5 miles on left.*

♥ *10% discount off a 4 night stay in September.*

General 🛢 🖼 🚗 📷 ⛽ 🚿 🛁 🛒 ✕ Leisure: 🍷 📺 🎣 ⛰ ⛵ 🛶 ∪ 🎾 ♪ 🎵 🏛

Sample enhanced entry

1 Listing under town or village with map reference

2 Star rating

3 Designator

4 Award (if applicable)

5 Site name, address, telephone and fax numbers, email and website address

6 Indicates when the site is open and payment accepted.

7 Description

8 Prices per pitch per night for touring pitches; per unit per week for caravan holiday homes

9 Accessible rating where applicable

10 Walkers/Cyclists Welcome where applicable

11 Travel directions

12 Special promotions

13 At-a-glance facility symbols

**A key to symbols can be found on the back-cover flap.
Keep it open for easy reference.**

National
Accessible Scheme

Finding suitable sites is not always easy, especially if you have to seek out wheelchair-friendly pathways or large print signs. Use the **National Accessible Scheme** to help you make your choice.

accessible accommodation for a comfortable stay

tourismforall

The National Accessible Scheme forms part of the Tourism for All Campaign that is being promoted by VisitBritain and national/regional tourism organisations. Additional help and guidance on finding suitable holiday accommodation for those with special needs can be obtained from:

Tourism for All
c/o Vitalise
Shap Road Industrial Estate,
Kendal LA9 6NZ

information helpline 0845 124 9971
reservations 0845 124 9973
(lines open 9-5 Mon-Fri)
f (01539) 735567
e info@tourismforall.org.uk
w tourismforall.org.uk

Proprietors of parks taking part in the National Accessible Scheme have gone out of their way to ensure a comfortable stay for guests with special hearing, visual or mobility needs. These exceptional places are full of extra touches to make everyone's visit trouble-free, from handrails and ramps to level-access showers. Members of the staff may have attended a disability awareness course and will know what assistance will really be appreciated.

Appropriate National Accessible symbols are included in the guide entries for English and Scottish sites. If you have additional needs or special requirements we strongly recommend that you make sure your chosen site can meet these before you confirm your reservation. The index at the back of the guide gives a full list of sites that have received a National Accessible rating.

Wales

Caravan holiday homes and parks in Wales should have an Access Statement available to visitors. Sites have been invited to join the National Accessible Scheme from summer 2006 and the new symbols will feature in Camping and Caravan Parks 2008.

Scotland

 Category 1
Accessible to a wheelchair user travelling independently.

 Category 2
Accessible to a wheelchair user travelling with assistance.

 Category 3
Accessible to a wheelchair user able to walk a few paces and up a maximum of three steps.

The criteria VisitBritain and national/regional tourism organisations have adopted do not necessarily conform to British Standards or to Building Regulations. They reflect what the organisations understand to be acceptable to meet the practical needs of guests with special mobility or sensory needs and encourage the industry to increase access to all.

England

Mobility Symbols

 Typically suitable for a person with sufficient mobility to climb a flight of steps but who would benefit from fixtures and fittings to aid balance.

 Typically suitable for a person with restricted walking ability and for those who may need to use a wheelchair some of the time and can negotiate a maximum of three steps.

 Typically suitable for a person who depends on the use of a wheelchair and transfers unaided to and from the wheelchair in a seated position. This person may be an independent traveller.

 Typically suitable for a person who depends on the use of a wheelchair in a seated position. This person also requires personal/mechanical assistance to aid transfer (eg carer, hoist).

 Access Exceptional is awarded to establishments that meet the requirements of independent wheelchair users or assisted wheelchair users shown above and also fulfil more demanding requirements with reference to the British Standards BS8300:2001.

Visual Impairment Symbols

 Typically provides key additional services and facilities to meet the needs of visually impaired guests.

 Typically provides a higher level of additional services and facilities to meet the needs of visually impaired guests.

Hearing Impairment Symbols

 Typically provides key additional services and facilities to meet the needs of guests with hearing impairment.

 Typically provides a higher level of additional services and facilities to meet the needs of guests with hearing impairment.

David Bellamy
Conservation Award

'**These well-deserved awards are a signpost to parks which are making real achievements in protecting our environment.** Go there and experience wrap-around nature...you could be amazed at what you find!'
says Professor David Bellamy.

More than 500 gold, silver and bronze parks were named this year in the David Bellamy Conservation Awards, organised in conjunction with the British Holiday and Home Parks Association. These parks are recognised for their commitment to conservation and the environment through their management of landscaping, recycling policies, waste management, the cultivation of flora and fauna and the creation of habitats designed to encourage a variety of wildlife onto the park. Links with the local community and the use of local materials is also an important consideration.

Parks participating in the scheme are assessed for the awards by holidaymakers who complete postcards to be returned to David Bellamy, an inspection by a local, independent Environmental Consultant and David Bellamy's own study of the parks environmental audit completed when joining the scheme.

An index of award-winning parks featured in the regional pages of this guide can be found on page 300.

Awards
for Excellence

enjoy**England**
Awards for
Excellence
——2007——

Enjoy England Awards for Excellence are all about telling the world what a fantastic place England is to visit, whether it's for a day trip, a weekend break or a fortnight's holiday.

The Awards, now in their 18th year, are run by VisitBritain in association with England's regional tourism organisations. This year there are 13 categories, including Caravan Holiday Park of the Year, Tourist Information Centre of the Year and awards for the best tourism website and the best tourism experience.

Winners of the 2006 Caravan Holiday Park of the Year Award

- GOLD WINNER
  Seafield Caravan Park, Seahouses, *Northumberland*

- SILVER WINNER
  Sandy Balls Holiday Centre, Fordingbridge, *Hampshire*

  Camping and Caravanning Club Site Sandringham, Sandringham, *Norfolk*

Winners of the 2007 awards will receive their trophies at a ceremony in April 2007. The day will celebrate excellence in tourism in England.
For more information about the awards visit enjoyengland.com.

**experience
the very
best of
the best**

Come and visit the Lee Valley Regional Park, there are great places to stay.

Perfectly placed for London, Essex and Hertfordshire the Lee Valley Regional Park has 3 camping and caravan sites to choose from.

You'll enjoy modern facilities, great prices and our 10,000 acres of Park to explore!

Lee Valley Campsite, Chingford, London
Situated on the edge of Epping Forest and close to historic Waltham Abbey, this site is easily accessible from the M25 and around 40 minutes from central London by public transport.
Tel: 020 8529 5689
Fax: 020 8559 4070
E-mail: scs@leevalleypark.org.uk

Lee Valley Caravan Park, Dobbs Weir, Hoddesdon, Herts
Enjoy peace and tranquillity next to this riverside site with good fishing, walking and boating nearby.
Get to London by train.
Tel/fax: 01992 462090
E-mail: caravanpark@leevalleypark.org.uk

Lee Valley Camping and Caravan Park, Edmonton, London
Not only is this peaceful site within easy reach of central London, the site boosts a 12 screen cinema and 18-hole golf course.
Tel: 020 8803 6900
Fax: 020 8884 4975
E-mail: leisurecomplex@leevalleypark.org.uk

For more information all about the Park and what you can do call
01992 702 200 or visit
www.leevalleypark.org.uk

Open spaces and sporting places

Map 1

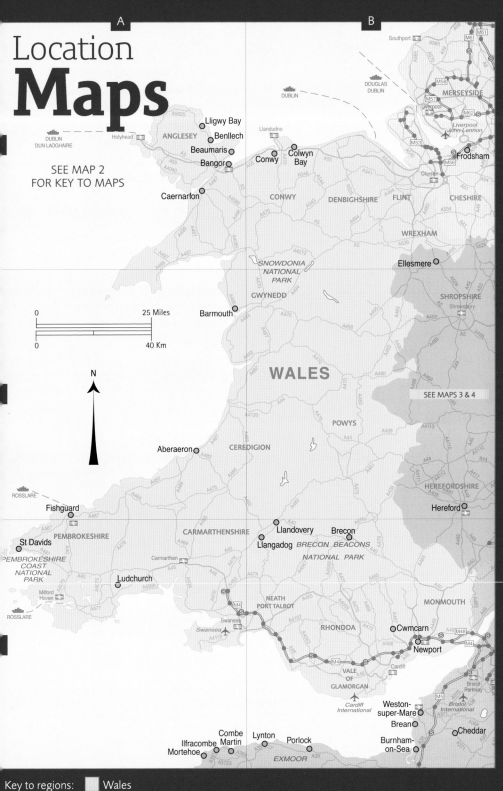

Location
Maps

SEE MAP 2
FOR KEY TO MAPS

0   25 Miles

0   40 Km

N

WALES

SEE MAPS 3 & 4

Key to regions: ▨ Wales

Every place name featured in the regional accommodation sections of this guide has a map reference to help you locate it on the maps which follow. For example, to find Bournemouth, which has 'Map ref 3B3', turn to Map 3 and refer to grid square B3.

All place names appearing in the regional sections are shown in black type on the maps. This enables you to find other places in your chosen area which may have suitable accommodation – the place index (at the back of this guide) gives page numbers.

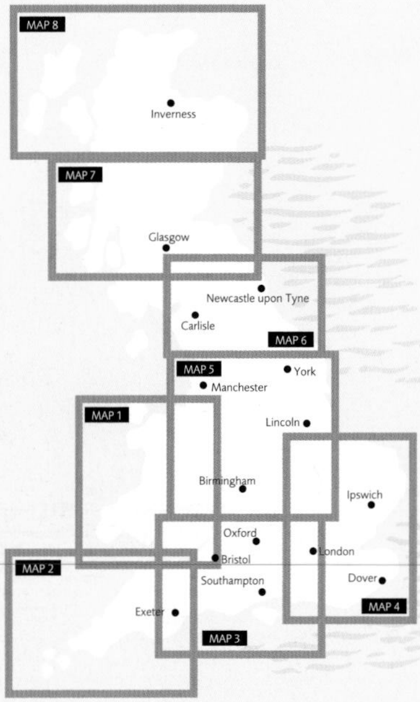
MAP 8
Inverness
MAP 7
Glasgow
Newcastle upon Tyne
Carlisle
MAP 6
MAP 5
York
Manchester
MAP 1
Lincoln
Birmingham
Ipswich
Oxford
Bristol
London
MAP 2
Southampton
Dover
Exeter
MAP 4
MAP 3

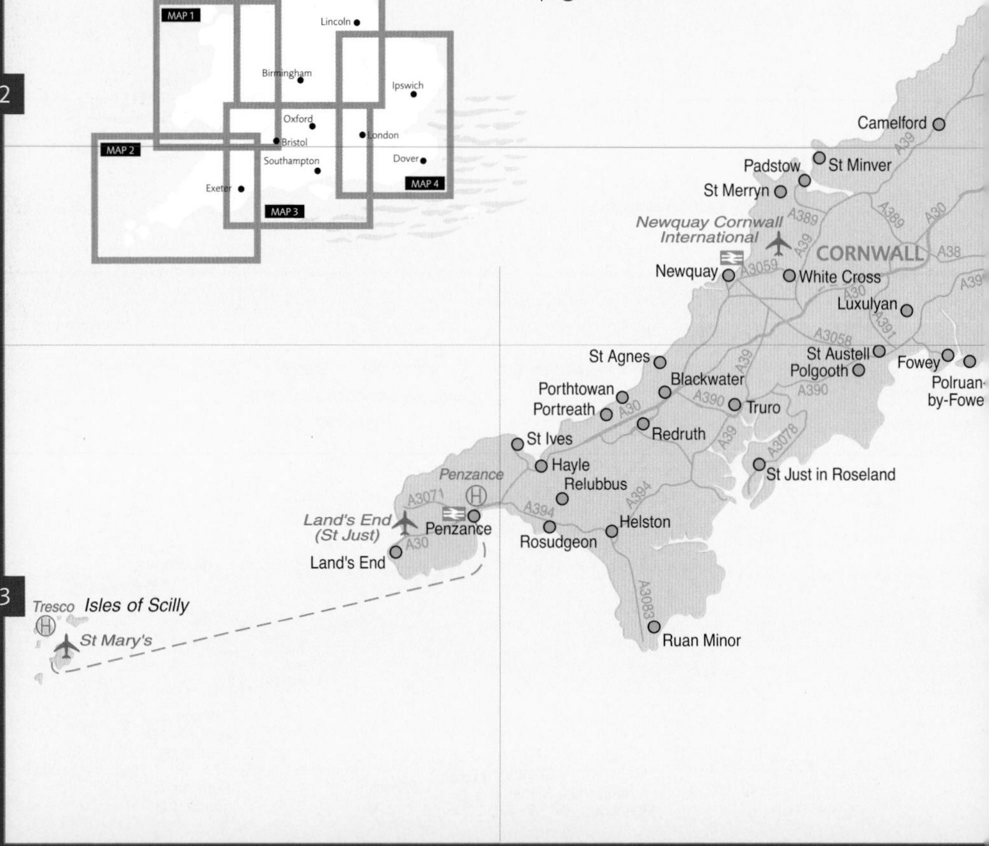
A
B
1
2
3
Camelford
Padstow
St Minver
St Merryn
Newquay Cornwall International
CORNWALL
Newquay
White Cross
Luxulyan
St Agnes
St Austell
Polgooth
Fowey
Polruan-by-Fowe
Blackwater
Porthtowan
Portreath
Truro
Redruth
St Ives
Hayle
St Just in Roseland
Penzance
Relubbus
Land's End (St Just)
Penzance
Helston
Rosudgeon
Land's End
Ruan Minor
Tresco
Isles of Scilly
St Mary's
A39
A389
A30
A38
A3059
A3058
A391
A390
A3078
A394
A3071
A3083

Key to regions: South West England

Map 2

Map 3

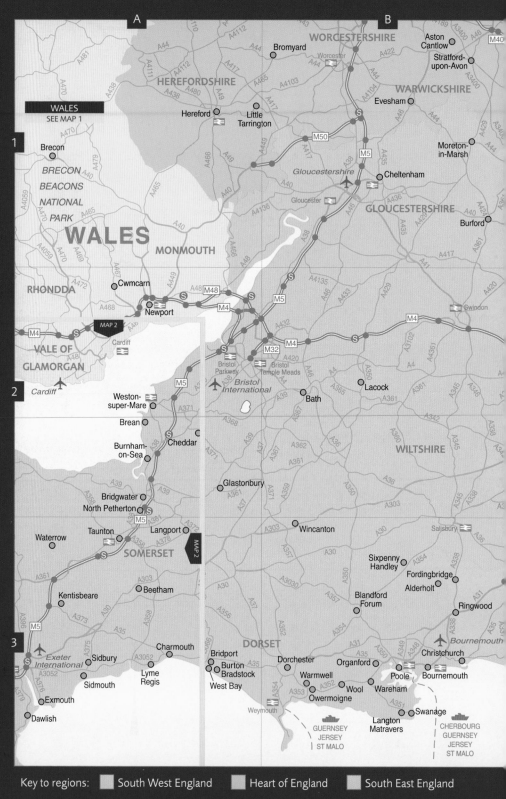

Key to regions: ▮ South West England ▮ Heart of England ▮ South East England

Map 3

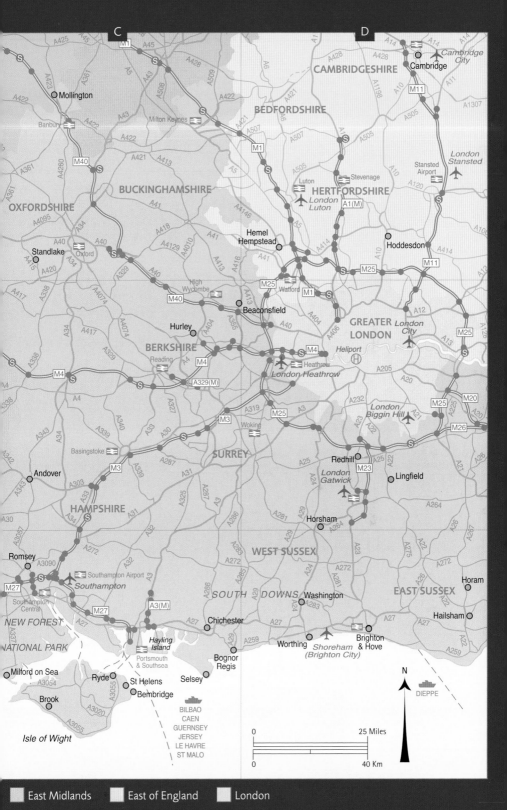

East Midlands East of England London

All place names in black offer parks in this guide

Map 4

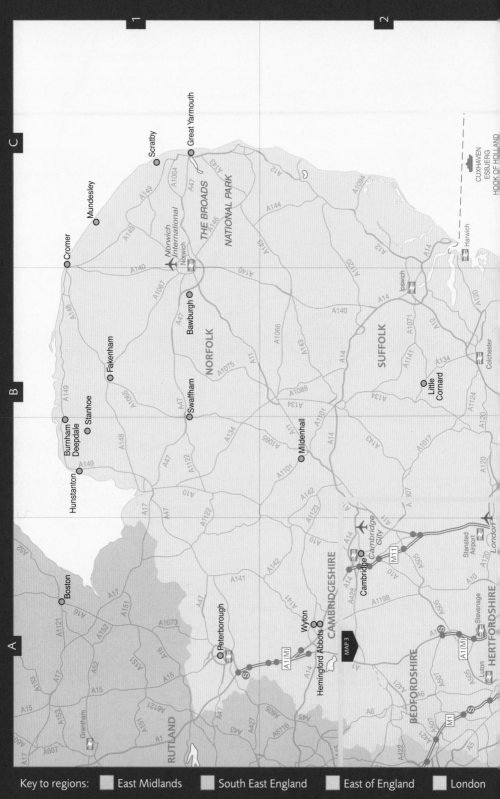

Key to regions: ■ East Midlands ■ South East England ■ East of England ■ London

Map 4

Map 5

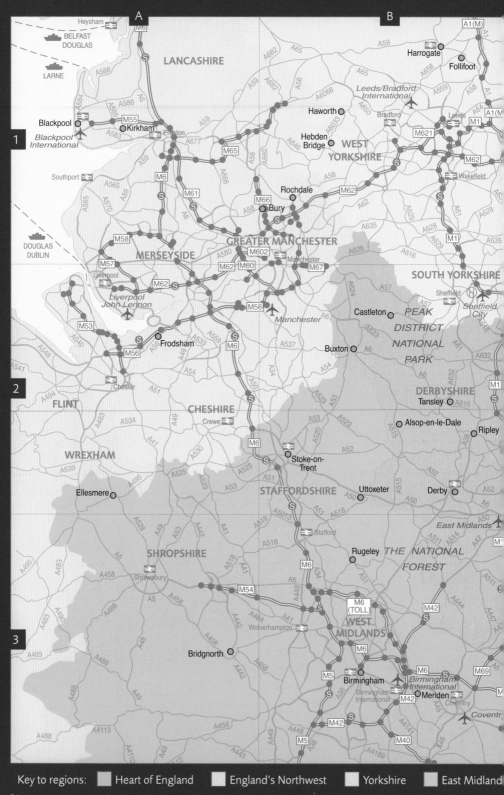

Key to regions: ▮ Heart of England ▮ England's Northwest ▮ Yorkshire ▮ East Midland

Map 5

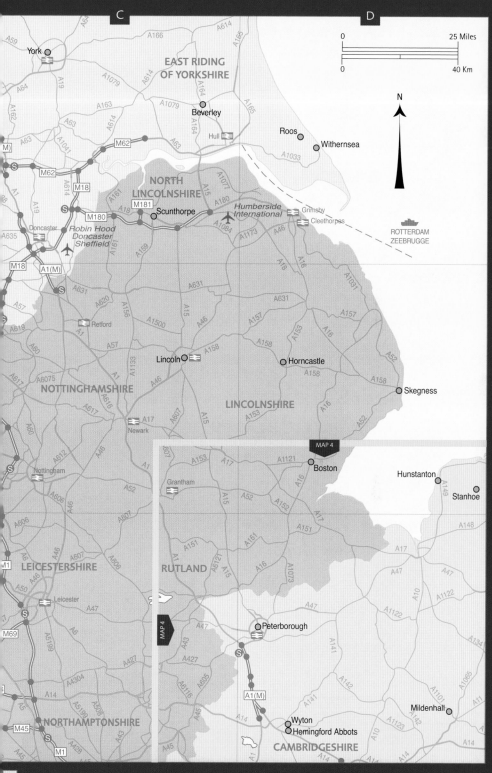

Map 6

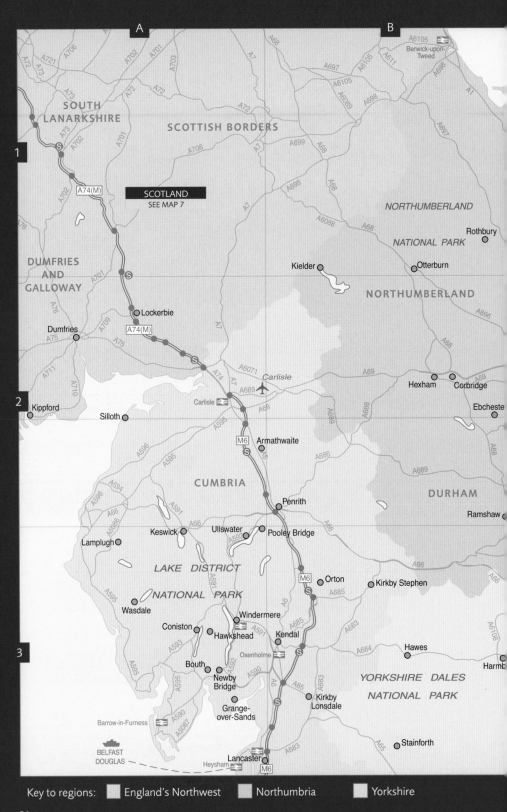

Key to regions: England's Northwest   Northumbria   Yorkshire

Map 6

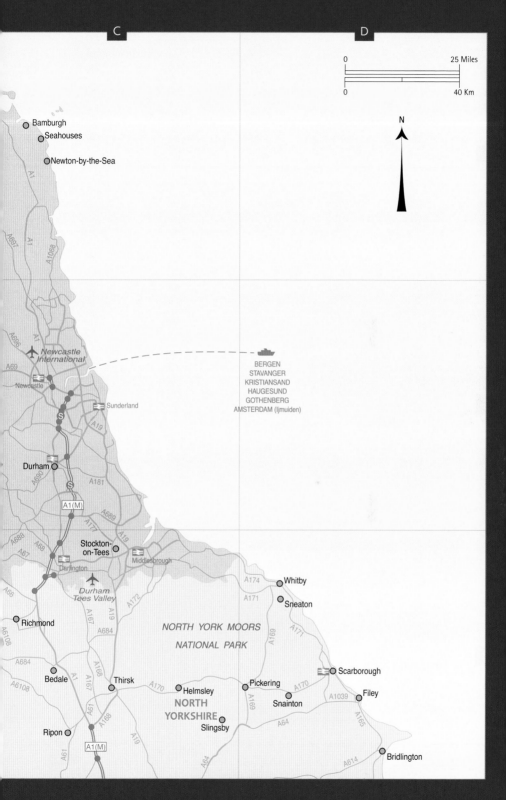

C

D

0   25 Miles

0   40 Km

N

Bamburgh
Seahouses
Newton-by-the-Sea

Newcastle International

BERGEN
STAVANGER
KRISTIANSAND
HAUGESUND
GOTHENBERG
AMSTERDAM (Ijmuiden)

Newcastle

Sunderland

Durham

A1(M)

Stockton-on-Tees

Darlington

Middlesbrough

Durham Tees Valley

Richmond

NORTH YORK MOORS

NATIONAL PARK

Whitby

Sneaton

Scarborough

Bedale

Thirsk

Helmsley

Pickering

Filey

NORTH YORKSHIRE

Snainton

Ripon

Slingsby

A1(M)

Bridlington

Map 7

Map 7

Map 8

A   B

1

2

WESTERN ISLES

Stornoway

Gairloch

Kinlochewe

Benbecula

HIGHLAND

3

Kyle of
Lochalsh

Balmacara

Barra

Key to regions: Scotland

Map 8

C　　　　　　　　　　　　　D

0　　　　　　　　　　　　25 Miles

0　　　　　　　　　　　　40 Km

N

John O'Groats

Thurso　　A836

A838

A836　　A836

A897　　A9

Wick

Wick

A9

A9

A839

A839　　Brora

A836

A837

A9

A949

A836

A9

A96

A832

A96

A941

A96　　A95　　A98　　A981　　A90

A9　　A96　　A98　　A950

Inverness

A832　　Culloden　　A940　　A947　　A948　　A90

A862

Inverness

A9　　A939　　A920　　A947　　A90

A920

MORAY

A938　　A941　　A97

A95　　ABERDEENSHIRE　　A96

A939　　A97　　A920

A944　　Aberdeen

A9　　A944　　Aberdeen

A93

A986　　A97　　A980　　A90

CAIRNGORMS

NATIONAL PARK　　Braemar　　A957

England's Northwest

Blackpool and Lancashire › Chester and Cheshire
Cumbria – The Lake District › Liverpool and Merseyside › Manchester

Having a ball in Blackpool

England's Northwest
visitenglandsnorthwest.com

Cheshire and Warrington Tourism Board
(01244) 402111
visitchester.com

Cumbria Tourism
(015398) 22222
golakes.co.uk
lakedistrictoutdoors.co.uk

The Lancashire & Blackpool Tourist Board
(01257) 226600
visitlancashire.com

Marketing Manchester
(0161) 237 1010
visitmanchester.com

The Mersey Partnership
(0151) 227 2727
visitliverpool.com

**majestic
lakes,
sunset
sands,
cutting-edge
cities**

Main The calming serenity of
The Lake District **Left** Amble
around Chester and meet the
locals; admire great works of
art in The Lowry, Manchester;
relive childhood memories at
The World of Beatrix Potter
Attraction, Bowness-on-
Windermere; visit the Fab
Four's old haunts in Liverpool

Explore Cumbria's soaring peaks or discover the rounded hills and plains of Cheshire. Relax on inland waterways or on Lancashire's sandy beaches. Experience the buzz of Manchester and Liverpool or **the thrill of a rollercoaster ride in Blackpool.**

Explore England's Northwest

Take to the water

Be inspired by the mighty peaks and glorious watery scenes in Cumbria – The Lake District. Take your chances at the Windermere Outdoor Adventure Activities Centre and hop in a canoe, relax in a wayfarer or slice through the waters on a powerboat. Test your climbing skills or swing through the trees in Grizedale Forest on the Go Ape! adventure trail. Alternatively, find your feet on one of the National Trails.

Clear your mind, relax and be mesmerised by the setting sun from Friar's Crag beside Derwentwater. Or take a stroll around Long Meg and Her Daughters near Penrith – one of the largest stone circles in the country – where you can almost hear the spirit of Wordsworth uttering his profound verse.

City culture

Discover the Manchester waterfront at the impressive Quays. Enjoy a play, wander the galleries or dine out in a restaurant at The Lowry, a veritable centre of culture and entertainment. Marvel at the impressive 'B of the Bang' sculpture – the tallest in the UK – and discover how Mancunians lived a hundred or so years ago at the Museum of Science & Industry in Manchester.

Head out of town, roam the Cheshire countryside and admire picturesque black-and-white timbered buildings or listen to the water lapping the edge of your boat on Cheshire's waterways. Amble around Chester Cathedral and find yourself awestruck by the impressive spires and intricate arches.

Take a ferry across the Mersey and visit Liverpool – the European Capital of Culture for 2008. Hop off at Albert Dock, stroll in to the Tate Liverpool and be enthralled by the vast and intriguing array of modern art on display. Do we have lift-off? Head to Spaceport in Merseyside and explore all the universe in this fantastic virtual space adventure.

Thrills and skills

Cruise peacefully through the River Caves at Pleasure Beach, Blackpool, or feel your heart thumping as you plummet down the traditional big dipper (as you feel your stomach flip, imagine one World Record breaker riding it solidly for three months!) Pick out your favourite amongst the sparkling Autumn Illuminations, enjoy high tea in the glitzy Blackpool Tower Ballroom or make your way to one of the nearby beaches and feel the fresh sea breeze fill your lungs.

Learn a new skill and entice a few slimy friends out of the ground at the annual World Worm-Charming Championships near Nantwich in Cheshire. Explore Amazonian life or take a deep breath and swim with the sharks at the Blue Planet Aquarium in Cheshire Oak.

Beauty in many forms

Bask in the Victorian beauty of Port Sunlight Village on Merseyside and catch the scent of the colourful flowers scattered all around. Listen to stories of Liverpool's seafaring heritage at the Merseyside Maritime Museum or follow the remarkable 30-mile Irwell Sculpture Trail that runs from the Salford Quays to the Pennines.

Seek inner peace in the beautiful landscaped gardens or spot roaming fallow deer at Tatton Park in Cheshire. Visit Ness Botanic Gardens – residing in its own microclimate – and delight in the picturesque surroundings awash with dazzling colours and idyllic waterfalls.

Places to **visit**

0   50 miles

0   75 kms

7

72

HADRIAN'S WALL PATH

Solway Coast
Carlisle
Silloth

7

PENNINE BRIDLEWAY

PENNINE WAY

Maryport

Penrith

North Pennines

Workington

71

Keswick

71

Whitehaven

LAKE DISTRICT

Kirkby Stephen

Ambleside
Dalegarth   Windermere

Ravenglass

68

Grange-over-Sands

6

Ulverston

Arnside & Silverdale

Kirkby Lonsdale

Barrow-in-Furness

Lancaster

Forest of Bowland

Blackpool

Blackburn

Preston

Southport

Chorley

PENNINE BRIDLEWAY

62

Manchester

Liverpool

Neston

Knutsford

Ellesmere Port

Macclesfield

Chester

Nantwich

National Park

Area of Outstanding Natural Beauty

Heritage Coast

National Trails
nationaltrail.co.uk

National Trails approved but
not yet open

3   Sections of the
National Cycle Network
nationalcyclenetwork.org.uk

The Beatles Story
Liverpool, Merseyside
(0151) 709 1963
beatlesstory.com
The history of the Fab Four

Blue Planet Aquarium
Cheshire Oaks, Cheshire
(0151) 357 8800
blueplanetaquarium.com
Take a dip with the sharks

Bowland Wild Boar Park
near Preston, Lancashire
(01995) 61554
wildboarpark.co.uk
Feed animals amid beautiful countryside

Camelot Theme Park
Chorley, Lancashire
(01257) 453044
camelotthemepark.co.uk
Explore King Arthur's magical land

Chester Cathedral
Cheshire
(01244) 324756
chestercathedral.com
Outstanding architecture and famous choir

Go Ape! High Ropes Forest Adventure
Grizedale Forest, Cumbria
0870 428 5330
goape.co.uk
Swing through the forest trees

Imperial War Museum North
Manchester
(0161) 836 4000
north.iwm.org.uk
Spectacular and fascinating museum

Long Meg and her Daughters
near Penrith, Cumbria
(015394) 44444
henge.org.uk
Impressive Bronze Age stone circle

The Lowry
Manchester
0870 787 5780
thelowry.com
Centre of culture and entertainment

Merseyside Maritime Museum
Liverpool, Merseyside
(0151) 478 4499
liverpoolmuseums.org.uk
Learn about Liverpool's seafaring heritage

The Museum of Science & Industry in Manchester
(0161) 832 2244
msim.org.uk
Step into Manchester's past

Ness Botanic Gardens
Cheshire
(0151) 353 0123
nessgardens.org.uk
Picturesque colourful gardens and waterfall

Pleasure Beach, Blackpool
Lancashire
0870 444 5566
blackpoolpleasurebeach.com
Breathtaking rides and spectacular shows

South Lakes Wild Animal Park
Dalton-in-Furness, Cumbria
(01229) 466086
wildanimalpark.co.uk
Unique safari and conservation park – meet and handle a variety of animals

Spaceport
Liverpool, Merseyside
(0151) 330 1333
spaceport.org.uk
Fantastic virtual space adventure that's out of this world!

Speke Hall, Gardens and Woodland (NT)
Liverpool, Merseyside
(0151) 427 7231
spekehall.org.uk
Tudor mansion and fine wooded estate

Tate Liverpool
Liverpool, Merseyside
(0151) 702 7400
tate.org.uk/liverpool
Four glorious floors of modern art

Tatton Park (NT)
Knutsford, Cheshire
(01625) 534400
tattonpark.org.uk
Explore the 1,000-acre deer park

Wildfowl and Wetland Trust Martin Mere
near Southport, Lancashire
(01704) 895181
wwt.org.uk
Home to ducks, geese and swans

Windermere Outdoor Adventure Activities Centre
Cumbria
(015394) 47183
southlakelandleisure.org.uk/windermere
A haven of watersports activities

Wythenshawe Hall
Northenden,
Greater Manchester
(0161) 998 2331
manchestergalleries.org
Splendid Tudor house

Tourist information centres

When you arrive at your destination, visit a tourist information centre for help with accommodation and information about local attractions and events, or email your request before you go.

Accrington	Blackburn Road	(01254) 872595	leisure@hyndburnbc.gov.uk
Alston Moor	Front Street	(01434) 382244	alston.tic@eden.gov.uk
Altrincham	20 Stamford New Road	(0161) 912 5931	tourist.information@trafford.gov.uk
Ambleside	Market Cross	(015394) 32582	amblesidetic@southlakeland.gov.uk
Appleby-in-Westmorland	Boroughgate	(017683) 51177	tic@applebytown.org.uk
Ashton-under-Lyne	Wellington Road	(0161) 343 4343	tourist.information@mail.tameside.gov.uk
Barnoldswick	Fernlea Avenue	(01282) 666704	tourist.info@pendle.gov.uk
Barrow-in-Furness	Duke Street	(01229) 894784	touristinfo@barrowbc.gov.uk
Birkenhead	Woodside Ferry Terminal, Wirral	(0151) 647 6780	touristinfo@wirral.gov.uk
Blackburn	50-54 Church Street	(01254) 53277	visit@blackburn.gov.uk
Blackpool	1 Clifton Street	(01253) 478222	tic@blackpool.gov.uk
Blackpool*	Central Promenade	(01253) 478222	tic@blackpool.gov.uk
Bolton	Le Mans Crescent	(01204) 334321	tourist.info@bolton.gov.uk
Bowness	Glebe Road	(015394) 42895	bownesstic@lake-district.gov.uk
Brampton*	Market Place	(01697) 73433	tourism@carlisle-city.gov.uk
Broughton in Furness	The Square	(01229) 716115	email@broughton-tic.fsnet.co.uk
Burnley	Croft Street	(01282) 664421	tic@burnley.gov.uk
Bury	Market Street	(0161) 253 5111	touristinformation@bury.gov.uk
Carlisle	Greenmarket	(01228) 625600	tourism@carlisle-city.gov.uk
Chester (Town Hall)	Northgate Street	(01244) 402111	tis@chestercc.gov.uk
Chester Visitor Centre	Vicars Lane	(01244) 402111	tis@chestercc.gov.uk
Cleveleys	Victoria Square	(01253) 853378	cleveleystic@wyrebc.gov.uk
Clitheroe	12-14 Market Place	(01200) 425566	tourism@ribblevalley.gov.uk
Cockermouth	Market Street	(01900) 822634	email@cockermouth-tic.fsnet.co.uk
Congleton	High Street	(01260) 271095	tourism@congleton.gov.uk
Coniston	Ruskin Avenue	(015394) 41533	
Egremont	12 Main Street	(01946) 820693	email@egremont-tic.fsnet.co.uk
Ellesmere Port	Kinsey Road	(0151) 356 7879	cheshireoaks-tic@hotmail.co.uk
Fleetwood	The Esplanade	(01253) 773953	fleetwoodtic@wyrebc.gov.uk
Garstang	High Street	(01995) 602125	garstangtic@wyrebc.gov.uk
Grange-over-Sands	Main Street	(015395) 34026	grangetic@southlakeland.gov.uk
Kendal	Highgate	(01539) 725758	kendaltic@southlakeland.gov.uk
Keswick	Market Square	(017687) 72645	keswicktic@lake-district.gov.uk

Kirkby Lonsdale	24 Main Street	(01524) 271437	kltic@southlakeland.gov.uk
Kirkby Stephen	Market Street	(017683) 71199	ks.tic@eden.gov.uk
Knutsford	Toft Road	(01565) 632611	ktic@macclesfield.gov.uk
Lancaster	29 Castle Hill	(01524) 32878	lancastertic@lancaster.gov.uk
Liverpool (Maritime Museum)	Albert Dock	(0151) 233 2008	info@visitliverpool.com
Liverpool	John Lennon Airport	(0151) 907 1057	info@visitliverpool.com
Liverpool 08 Place	Whitechapel	(0151) 233 2008	08place@liverpool.gov.uk
Lytham St Annes	67 St Annes Road West	(01253) 725610	touristinformation@fylde.gov.uk
Macclesfield	Town Hall	(01625) 504114	Informationcentre@macclesfield.gov.uk
Manchester Visitor Information Centre	Lloyd Street	0871 222 8223	touristinformation@ marketing-manchester.co.uk
Maryport	Senhouse Street	(01900) 812101	maryporttic@allerdale.gov.uk
Millom*	Station Road	(01229) 774819	millomtic@copelandbc.gov.uk
Morecambe	Marine Road Central	(01524) 582808	morecambetic@lancaster.gov.uk
Nantwich	Church Walk	(01270) 610983	touristi@crewe-nantwich.gov.uk
Northwich	1 The Arcade	(01606) 353534	tourism@valeroyal.gov.uk
Oldham	12 Albion Street	(0161) 627 1024	ecs.tourist@oldham.gov.uk
Pendle Heritage Centre	Park Hill	(01282) 661701	heritage.centre@pendle.gov.uk
Penrith	Middlegate	(01768) 867466	pen.tic@eden.gov.uk
Preston	Lancaster Road	(01772) 253731	tourism@preston.gov.uk
Rheged		(01768) 860034	tic@rheged.com
Rochdale	The Esplanade	(01706) 864928	tic@rochdale.gov.uk
Saddleworth	High Street, Uppermill	(01457) 870336	ecs.tourist@oldham.gov.uk
Salford	Salford Quays	(0161) 848 8601	tic@salford.gov.uk
Sedbergh	72 Main Street	(015396) 20125	tic@sedbergh.org.uk
Silloth-on-Solway	Liddell Street	(016973) 31944	sillothtic@allerdale.gov.uk
Southport	112 Lord Street	(01704) 533333	info@visitsouthport.com
Southwaite	M6 Service Area	(016974) 73445	southwaitetic@visitscotland.com
St Helens	Chalon Way East	(01744) 755150	info@sthelenstic.com
Stockport	30 Market Place	(0161) 474 4444	tourist.information@stockport.gov.uk
Ullswater	Glenridding	(017684) 82414	ullswatertic@lake-district.gov.uk
Ulverston	County Square	(01229) 587120	ulverstontic@southlakeland.gov.uk
Warrington	Academy Way	(01925) 632571	informationcentre@warrington.gov.uk
Whitehaven	Market Place	(01946) 852939	tic@copelandbc.gov.uk
Wigan	Trencherfield Mill	(01942) 825677	tic@wlct.org
Wilmslow	Rectory Fields	(01625) 522275	i.hillaby@macclesfield.gov.uk
Windermere	Victoria Street	(015394) 46499	windermeretic@southlakeland.gov.uk
Workington	21 Finkle Street	(01900) 606699	workingtontic@allerdale.gov.uk

seasonal opening

Alternatively, you can text **TIC LOCATE** to **64118** to find your nearest tourist information centre

Find out **more**

Relax in the beautiful gardens at
Tatton Park, Knutsford

There are various publications and
guides about England's Northwest
available from the following
Tourist Boards or by logging on to
visitenglandsnorthwest.com or calling
(01257) 226600:

Cheshire and Warrington Tourism Board
Grosvenor Park Lodge, Grosvenor Park Road
Chester CH1 1QQ
t (01244) 402111
e info@cwtb.co.uk
w visitchester.com

Cumbria Tourism
Windermere Road, Staveley, Kendal LA8 9PL
t (015398) 22222
e info@cumbriatourism.org
w golakes.co.uk or lakedistrictoutdoors.co.uk

**The Lancashire & Blackpool
Tourist Board**
St George's House, St George's Street
Chorley PR7 2AA
t (01257) 226600 (Brochure request)
e info@visitlancashire.com
w visitlancashire.com

**Marketing Manchester – The Tourist
Board for Greater Manchester**
Churchgate House, 56 Oxford Street
Manchester M1 6EU
t (0161) 237 1010
   Brochure request: 0870 609 3013
e touristinformation@marketing-manchester.co.uk
w visitmanchester.com

**The Mersey Partnership – The Tourist
Board for Liverpool and Merseyside**
12 Princes Parade, Liverpool L3 1BG
t (0151) 227 2727
f (0151) 227 2325
   Accommodation booking service:
   0845 601 1125
e info@visitliverpool.com
w visitliverpool.com

Travel **info**

By road:
Motorways intersect within the region
which has the best road network in the
country. Travelling north or south use the
M6, and east or west the M62.

By rail:
Most Northwest coastal resorts are
connected to InterCity routes with trains
from many parts of the country, and there
are through trains to major cities and towns.

By air:
Fly into Liverpool John Lennon, Manchester
or Blackpool airports.

where to stay in
England's Northwest

All place names in the blue bands are shown on the maps at the front of this guide.

A complete listing of all VisitBritain assessed parks in England appears at the back.

Accommodation symbols
Symbols give useful information about services and facilities. Inside the back-cover flap you can find a key to these symbols. Keep it open for easy reference.

ARMATHWAITE, Cumbria Map ref 6A2

★★★★
TOURING PARK
🚐 (63)　£8.50–£19.60
🚐 (63)　£8.50–£19.60
63 touring pitches

See Ad on inside back cover

Englethwaite Hall Caravan Club Site
Armathwaite, Carlisle CA4 9SY　t (01228) 560202　w caravanclub.co.uk

payment Credit/debit cards, cash/cheques

Tranquil site, scattered with rhododendrons. Walkers will love this beautiful, uncrowded area. Open March to November.

⊕ Exit M6/A6 onto B6263, in 1.75 miles turn right. Site on right in about 2.75 miles.

♥ Special member rates mean you can save your membership subscription in less than a week. Visit our website to find out more.

General P 🚭 🚻 🞊 🐾 🛉. Leisure ⌁

BLACKPOOL, Lancashire Map ref 5A1

★★★★
HOLIDAY &
TOURING PARK
🚐　£14.00–£19.00
🚐　£14.00–£19.00
🏠 (18) £150.00–£490.00
44 touring pitches

Newton Hall Caravan Park
Staining Road, Blackpool FY3 0AX　t (01253) 882512　f (01253) 893101　e reception@newtonhall.net
w partingtons.com

Family park ideally situated in open country, 2.5 miles from Blackpool town centre. Caravans and flats for hire. New leisure complex. Regular live entertainment. No pets. Loads to do. Open 1 March to 15 November.

payment Credit/debit cards, cash/cheques

General 🚽 🖭 🛏 P 🚭 🚻 🞊 🐾 🍴 🎡 🛒 ✕ ☼　Leisure 🎣 📺 🍺 🎵 🔍 🎢 ⌁

BOUTH, Cumbria Map ref 6A3

★★★★★
HOLIDAY &
TOURING PARK
ROSE AWARD
🚐 (26)　£12.50–£20.00
🚐 (4)　£12.50–£20.00
🏠 (3) £195.00–£495.00
30 touring pitches

Black Beck Caravan Park
Bouth, Ulverston LA12 8JN　t (01229) 861274　f (01229) 861041　e reception@blackbeck.com

Black Beck is situated within the Lake District National Park, nestled in the beautiful Rusland Valley between the southern tips of Lake Windermere and Coniston. Surrounded by spectacular woodland scenery.

payment Credit/debit cards, cash/cheques

General 🖭 P 🚭 🚻 🍴 🐾 🎡 🛒 🐾 ☼　Leisure 🎢 ⌣ ⌁

BURY, Greater Manchester Map ref 5B1

★★★★★
TOURING PARK
(75) £12.50–£25.10
(75) £12.50–£25.10
75 touring pitches

See Ad on inside back cover

Burrs Country Park Caravan Club Site

Woodhill Road, Bury BL8 1BN **t** (0161) 761 0489 **w** caravanclub.co.uk

payment Credit/debit cards, cash/cheques

On a historic mill site, Burrs has much to offer, including relaxing river and countryside walks as well as easy access into Manchester. Open March to November.

From A676 (signposted Ramsbottom), follow signs for Burrs Country Park.

Special member rates mean you can save your membership subscription in less than a week. Visit our website to find out more.

General

CONISTON, Cumbria Map ref 6A3

★★★★★
HOLIDAY PARK
ROSE AWARD
(6) Min £13.00
(15) £200.00–£530.00

Crake Valley Holiday Park

Lake Bank, Water Yeat, Ulverston LA12 8DL **t** (01229) 885203 **f** (01229) 885203
e crakevalley@coniston1.fslife.co.uk **w** crakevalley.co.uk

Small, top-graded holiday park. Caravans and lodges for hire in secluded setting opposite Coniston Water. Ideal base for touring the Lakes. Open March to January.

payment Cash/cheques

General

CONISTON, Cumbria Map ref 6A3

★★★★★
TOURING PARK
(280) £11.00–£24.00
(280) £11.00–£24.00
280 touring pitches

See Ad on inside back cover

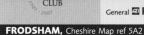

Park Coppice Caravan Club Site

Park Gate, Coniston LA21 8LA **t** (015394) 41555 **w** caravanclub.co.uk

payment Credit/debit cards, cash/cheques

Landscaped site set in 63 acres of National Trust woodland. Lake for watersports, on-site play areas, orienteering courses and Red Squirrel Nature Trail. Open March to November.

Follow A593, 1.5 miles south of Coniston village. Final approach from the north or south is narrow in places.

Special member rates mean you can save your membership subscription in less than a week. Visit our website to find out more.

General Leisure

FRODSHAM, Cheshire Map ref 5A2

★★★★
HOLIDAY PARK
(10) £209.00–£563.00

Ridgeway Country Holiday Park

The Ridgeway, Frodsham WA6 6XQ **t** (01928) 734981 **f** (01928) 734981 **e** sue@ridgewaypark.com
w ridgewaypark.com

An ideal base for exploring the scenic countryside, yet within close proximity to Liverpool and Chester. Prices weekly for the lodges and caravans. Open 1 March to 2 January. Short-break prices available.

payment Credit/debit cards, cash/cheques

General Leisure

Look at the maps

Colour maps at the front pinpoint the location of all parks found in the regional sections.

GRANGE-OVER-SANDS, Cumbria Map ref 6A3

★★★★
HOLIDAY & TOURING PARK
ROSE AWARD

(3) £11.00–£14.00
(3) £11.00–£14.00
(5) £9.00–£12.00
(2) £250.00–£350.00
8 touring pitches

Greaves Farm Caravan Park

Field Broughton, Grange-over-Sands LA11 6HR **t** (015395) 36329 & (015395) 36587

Small, quiet site two miles north of Cartmel. A convenient base for Lake District touring, and under personal supervision of the owner. Directions given with booking confirmation. Open March to October.

payment Cash/cheques

General

GRANGE-OVER-SANDS, Cumbria Map ref 6A3

★★★★★
TOURING PARK

(130) £12.50–£25.10
(130) £12.50–£25.10
130 touring pitches

See Ad on inside back cover

CENTENARY THE CARAVAN CLUB 1907–2007

Meathop Fell Caravan Club Site

Meathop, Grange-over-Sands LA11 6RB **t** (015395) 32912 **w** caravanclub.co.uk

open All year
payment Credit/debit cards, cash/cheques

Peaceful site, ideal for exploring the southern Lake District. Kendal, famous for its mint cake, is within easy reach; Grange-over-Sands and Ulverston are close by.

M6 jct 36, A590 to Barrow. After about 3.25 miles take slip road and follow A590 to Barrow. At 1st roundabout follow International Camping signs. Steep approach.

Special member rates mean you can save your membership subscription in less than a week. Visit our website to find out more.

General Leisure

HAWKSHEAD, Cumbria Map ref 6A3

★★★★
HOLIDAY, TOURING & CAMPING PARK

(25) £16.50–£20.00
£13.50–£15.75
(75) £13.50–£15.75
(20) £235.00–£480.00
100 touring pitches

The Croft Caravan and Camp Site

North Lonsdale Road, Hawkshead, Ambleside LA22 0NX **t** (015394) 36374 **f** (015394) 36544
e enquiries@hawkshead-croft.com **w** hawkshead-croft.com

Quiet family site at Hawkshead village, close to shops etc. Flat, grassy and well sheltered holiday homes for hire. Open mid-March to mid-November.

payment Credit/debit cards, cash/cheques

General Leisure

KENDAL, Cumbria Map ref 6B3

★★★★
HOLIDAY, TOURING & CAMPING PARK

(26) £11.50–£17.00
(26) £11.50–£17.00
(5) £6.50–£17.00
26 touring pitches

Waters Edge Caravan Park

Crooklands, Milnthorpe LA7 7NN **t** (015395) 67708 **w** watersedgecaravanpark.co.uk

payment Credit/debit cards, cash/cheques

Small, friendly site set in open countryside close to M6. Lake District, Morecambe, Yorkshire Dales within easy reach. All hardstanding pitches. Reception area with small shop. Lounge, bar, pool room, patio area. Modern shower block with laundry and washing-up facilities. Local pub/restaurant within 300yds. Open 1 March to 14 November.

Leave M6 at jct 36, take A65 to Kirkby Lonsdale, the A65 to Crooklands. Site approx 0.75 miles on the right.

General Leisure

KESWICK, Cumbria Map ref 6A3

★★★★
TOURING &
CAMPING PARK

🚐 £10.00–£15.00
🚐(3) £10.00–£15.00
🅰 (30) £9.50–£11.50
3 touring pitches

Castlerigg Farm Camping & Caravan Site

Castlerigg, Keswick CA12 4TE t (017687) 72479 e info@castleriggfarm.com w castleriggfarm.com

A quiet, family-run site with exceptional views. Ideal as a base for walking. Approximately 20 minutes' walk to Keswick. Open March to November. Site located on left of lane.

payment Cash/cheques

General P 🚗 🛗 🚹 🖵 🕞 ☉ 🛢 🅿 🐕 Leisure ✈ ▶ 🚵 🚤

KESWICK, Cumbria Map ref 6A3

★★★★
HOLIDAY, TOURING
& CAMPING PARK

🚐(53) £13.60–£15.90
🚐(53) £11.99–£14.60
🅰 (120) £10.90–£13.50
🚏(7) £180.00–£440.00

Castlerigg Hall Caravan & Camping Park

Castlerigg Hall, Keswick CA12 4TE t (017687) 74499 e info@castlerigg.co.uk w castlerigg.co.uk

payment Credit/debit cards, cash/cheques

Situated 1.5 miles south east of the pretty market town of Keswick, our elevated position commands wonderful panoramic views of Derwentwater and the surrounding fells. Formerly a Lakeland hill farm, Castlerigg Hall has been sympathetically developed into a quality touring park. Many scenic walks are available directly from the park. Open April to October.

General P 🚗 🛗 🚹 🖵 🕞 ☉ 🛢 🅿 🐕 Leisure 📺 ◑ 🚤

KIRKBY LONSDALE, Cumbria Map ref 6B3

★★★★★
HOLIDAY, TOURING
& CAMPING PARK

🚐(17) £10.00–£22.00
🚐 £10.00–£22.00
🅰 (12) £12.00–£14.00
17 touring pitches

Woodclose Caravan Park

Kirkby Lonsdale LA6 2SE t (01524) 271597 f (01524) 272301 e info@woodclosepark.com
w woodclosepark.com

payment Cash/cheques

A quiet, picturesque, exclusive site situated between the Lakes and the Dales, a short walk from Kirkby Lonsdale. All pitches are supplied with electric and TV hook-up points. The camping field is sheltered and secluded. Children's play area and shop. David Bellamy Gold Award. Open March to October.

⊕ M6 jct 36, follow A65 for approx 6 miles. The park entrance can be found just past Devil's Bridge on the left-hand side.

General P 🚗 🛗 🚹 🕞 ☉ 🛢 🅿 🐕 ☼ Leisure ⚠ ∪ ✈ ▶

KIRKBY STEPHEN, Cumbria Map ref 6B3

★★★★★
TOURING &
CAMPING PARK

🚐(43) £14.50–£16.50
🚐(43)
🅰 (15)
58 touring pitches

Pennine View Caravan Park

Station Road, Kirkby Stephen CA17 4SZ t (017683) 71717
e pennineviewcaravanpark@googlemail.com

Family-run caravan park on edge of small market town of Kirkby Stephen, just off A685. Easy reach of Lake District and Yorkshire Dales. Open March to October.

payment Credit/debit cards, cash/cheques

General 🖵 P 🚗 🛗 🚹 🕞 ☉ 🛢 🅿 Leisure ⚠ 🚵

KIRKHAM, Lancashire Map ref 5A1

★★★★★
HOLIDAY PARK
⌂ (2)   £240.00–£400.00

Mowbreck Holiday and Residential Park

Mowbreck Lane, Preston PR4 3HA   t (01772) 682494   f (01772) 672986

No noisy amusement arcades. Relax in this picturesque setting. Mowbreck Park is family run to the highest standards. Ideal location to enjoy the Fylde coast. Just one hour from Manchester and North Yorkshire.

open All year except Christmas
payment Cash/cheques

General ⌖⊡ ⛺ ⛺.   Leisure ∪ ⟍ ⟊

LAMPLUGH, Cumbria Map ref 6A3

★★★★
TOURING PARK
⌂ (53)   £8.50–£19.60
⌂ (53)   £8.50–£19.60
53 touring pitches

See Ad on inside back cover

Dockray Meadow Caravan Club Site

Lamplugh CA14 4SH   t (01946) 861357   w caravanclub.co.uk

payment Credit/debit cards, cash/cheques

Site close to lesser-known lake beauties including Cogra Moss and Ennerdale. Within easy reach of Keswick. Open March to November.

✤ From A66 turn onto A5086. In 6.5 miles turn left at signpost for Lamplugh Green. Turn right at signpost for Croasdale. Site on left.

❤ Special member rates mean you can save your membership subscription in less than a week. Visit our website to find out more.

General P ⊕ ☼ ⊞ ⛺   Leisure ⟍

LANCASTER, Lancashire Map ref 6A3

★★★
TOURING &
CAMPING PARK
⌂ (30)   £10.00–£13.00
⌂ (5)   £10.00–£13.00
⚐ (5)   £5.00–£9.50
40 touring pitches

New Parkside Farm Caravan Park

Denny Beck, Lancaster LA2 9HH   t (01524) 770723   w ukparks.co.uk/newparkside

Family-run site on a working farm in an Area of Outstanding Natural Beauty. Excellent base for exploring Morecambe Bay, the Lake District and Yorkshire Dales.

payment Cash/cheques

General ⊞P ⊕ ☼ ⊕ ⊙ ⛺ ⛺. ☼   Leisure ⟍

NEWBY BRIDGE, Cumbria Map ref 6A3

★★★★★
HOLIDAY PARK
ROSE AWARD
⌂ (7)   £175.00–£465.00

Newby Bridge Country Caravan Park

Canny Hill, Newby Bridge LA12 8NF   t (015395) 31030   f (015395) 30105
e info@cumbriancaravans.co.uk   w cumbriancaravans.co.uk

Situated in a delightfully secluded setting on the outskirts of Newby Bridge within easy walking distance of Lake Windermere. One- and two-bedroom luxury caravans for hire – weekly or short breaks. Open 1 March to 31 October.

payment Credit/debit cards, cash/cheques, euros

General ⌖⊡P ⊕ ☼ ⊕ ⊞⊡ ⊞ ✕ ⛺ ☼   Leisure ∪ ⟍

Check it out

Information on parks listed in this guide has been supplied by proprietors. As changes may occur you should remember to check all relevant details at the time of booking.

ORTON, Cumbria Map ref 6B3

★★★★
HOLIDAY &
TOURING PARK

🚐(67) £10.50–£16.00
🚲(70) £10.50–£16.00
70 touring pitches

Westmorland Caravan Site

Orton, Penrith CA10 3SB t (01539) 711322 f (01539) 624944 e caravans@westmorland.com
w tebaycaravanpark.co.uk

Peaceful, level hardstands, hook-ups, overnight
halt area. Launderette, free hot water, and
showers, restaurant, shops and fuel adjacent.
Open March to October

payment Credit/debit cards, cash/cheques

General 🖵 🚗 P 🔌 🌡 🍴 🐾 🌙 ☉ 📠 🔋 ✕ 🐕 🦮. Leisure ◢ 🚲

PENRITH, Cumbria Map ref 6B2

★★★★★
HOLIDAY &
TOURING PARK

🚐(45) £15.00–£18.00
🚲(7) £15.00–£18.00
52 touring pitches

Flusco Wood Caravan Park

Flusco, Penrith CA11 0JB t (017684) 80020 e admin@fluscowood.co.uk w fluscowood.co.uk

payment Cash/cheques

A very high-standard and quiet woodland touring
caravan park with fully serviced pitches and centrally
heated amenity building. Short drive to many
attractions and places of interest in the Lake District.
Open April to October.

⊕ M6 jct 40, travel west on A66 towards Keswick. After about
4 miles turn right (signposted Flusco). Entrance along lane
on the left.

♥ Luxury pine holiday lodges for sale. Reduction on prices for
pre-booked stays of 1 week or more.

General 🖵 🚗 P 🔌 🌡 🍴 🐾 🌙 ☉ 📠 🔋 🐕 🦮. Leisure ⚠ ∪ ◢ 🚲

POOLEY BRIDGE, Cumbria Map ref 6A3

★★★★
CAMPING PARK

🚲   £12.00–£18.00
⛺(90) £12.00–£18.00

Waterside House Campsite

Waterside House, Howtown, Penrith CA10 2NA t (017684) 86332 f (017684) 86332
e enquire@watersidefarm-campsite.co.uk w watersidefarm-campsite.co.uk

payment Cash/cheques

Beautiful lakeside location on working farm with
excellent toilet, shower and laundry facilities.
Mountain bike, Canadian canoe and boat hire. Boat
storage available. Open March to October inclusive.

⊕ M6 jct 40, A66 to Keswick (1 mile), then A592 (Ullswater
and Pooley Bridge). Right at church, right again along
Howtown Road (1 mile). 2nd site on right.

General 🚗 P 🌡 🍴 🐾 ☉ 📠 🔋 🐕 ☼ Leisure ⚠ ∪ ◢ 🚲

Key to symbols

Symbols at the end of each entry help you pick
out the services and facilities which are most
important for your stay. A key to the symbols can
be found inside the back-cover flap. Keep this
open for easy reference.

ROCHDALE, Greater Manchester Map ref 5B1

★★★
HOLIDAY, TOURING
& CAMPING PARK

🚐(30)   £10.00–£14.00
🚐(10)   £10.00–£14.00
⛺ (10)   £8.00–£14.00
50 touring pitches

Hollingworth Lake Caravan Park

Roundhouse Farm, Hollingworth Lake, Littleborough OL15 0AT t (01706) 378661

open All year
payment Cash/cheques

A popular, five-acre park adjacent to Hollingworth Lake, at the foot of the Pennines, within easy reach of many local attractions. Backpackers walking the Pennine Way are welcome at this family-run park.

⊕ *From M62. Jct 21 Milnrow. Follow Hollingworth Lake Country Park signs to the Fishermans Inn/The Wine Press. Take Rakewood Road then 2nd on right.*

General 🔲 P 🔌 🝙 🝙 🝙 🝙 ⊙ 🝙🝙 🝙 ☼   Leisure ∪ ♪

SILLOTH, Cumbria Map ref 6A2

★★
HOLIDAY &
TOURING PARK

🚐   £4.50–£18.00
🚐   £4.50–£18.00
⛺   £4.50–£18.00
🏠(50) £95.00–£625.00
150 touring pitches

Solway Holiday Village

Skinburness Drive, Silloth, Wigton CA7 4QQ t (016973) 31236 f (016973) 32553
e solway@hagansleisure.co.uk w hagansleisure.co.uk

open All year except Christmas
payment Credit/debit cards, cash/cheques

Located in the seaside Victorian town of Silloth, this 120-acre family park has something for everyone and offers an ideal touring centre for the Scottish Borders and Lake District. Indoor pool, kids' club, indoor and outdoor play areas, small animal farm, themed bars with live entertainment, tennis courts, golf and gymnasium.

⊕ *M6 jct 41 to Wigton. Follow signs to Silloth (B5302). In Silloth, right at Raffa Club, follow road for 0.5 miles, holiday park on right.*

♥ *Touring pitches from £4.50. Bring a friend and get 50% off. Loyalty discounts for repeat bookings.*

General 🔲 P 🔌 🝙 🝙 🝙 🝙🝙 🝙 ✕ 🝙 ☼   Leisure 🝙 📺 🝙 🎵 🝙 🝙 🝙 ∪ 🝙 🝙 🝙

ULLSWATER, Cumbria Map ref 6A3

★★★★★
HOLIDAY &
TOURING PARK

🚐(38) £15.00–£21.50
🚐   £15.00–£21.50
38 touring pitches

Waterfoot Caravan Park

Pooley Bridge, Penrith CA11 0JF t (017684) 86302 f (017684) 86728
e enquiries@waterfootpark.co.uk w waterfootpark.co.uk

payment Cash/cheques

Situated in the grounds of a Georgian mansion overlooking Ullswater. The park has an excellent touring area with a mix of hardstanding and lawned areas. The reception and shop are open daily. Licensed bar and games room with pool table. Children's play area. David Bellamy Gold Award. Open March to November.

⊕ *M6 jct 40, follow signs marked Ullswater Steamers. West on A66 for 1 mile. Left at roundabout onto A592 (Ullswater). Pass Dalemain; Waterfoot is under 2 miles on right.*

♥ *Private boat-launching area available.*

General 🔲 P 🔌 🝙 🝙 🝙 ⊙ 🝙🝙 🝙 🝙 🝙 ☼   Leisure 🝙 🝙 🝙 ∪ ♪

Check it out
Please check prices, quality ratings and other details when you book.

WASDALE, Cumbria Map ref 6A3

★★★★
HOLIDAY, TOURING
& CAMPING PARK

🚐 (9)   £12.00–£14.00
🛖 (41)   £12.00–£14.00
50 touring pitches

Church Stile Holiday Park

Church Stile Farm, Wasdale CA20 1ET t (01946) 726252 f (01946) 726028
e churchstile@campfarm.fsnet.co.uk w churchstile.com

Small family-run park in woodland clearing.
Nature/woodland walk with viewing point.
Magnificent scenery and plenty of walks. Families,
couples and walkers welcome. Considerate
campers only. Open mid-March to 31 October.

payment Credit/debit cards, cash/cheques

General P 🔌 🅿 🛉 🍳 🕞 ⊙ 🔟 🏇 ☼   Leisure ⚠ ⌒ 🛶

WINDERMERE, Cumbria Map ref 6A3

★★★★★
HOLIDAY &
TOURING PARK

🚐 (43)   £10.00–£26.00
🚐   £10.00–£26.00
43 touring pitches

Hill of Oaks and Blakeholme Caravans

Tower Wood, Windermere LA23 3PJ t (015395) 31578 f (015395) 30431
e enquiries@hillofoaks.co.uk w hillofoaks.co.uk

payment Cash/cheques

Award-winning caravan park situated on the shores
of Windermere. Very much family orientated, the
park has a play area and nature walks through the
woodland. The site has six jetties, boat launching and
access to watersport activities. Shop and disabled
facilities. Children's play area. David Bellamy Gold
Award. Open March to November.

⊕ M6 jct 36, head west on A590 towards Barrow and Newby
Bridge. At roundabout turn right, onto A592. Park is approx
3 miles on the left-hand side.

General P 🔌 🅿 🛉 🕞 ⊙ 🍴 🔟 🐾 ☼ Leisure ⚠ ∪ ⌒

Help before you go

ℹ️ **When it comes to your next British
break, the first stage of your journey
could be closer than you think.**

You've probably got a tourist information centre nearby
which is there to serve the local community – as well as
visitors. Knowledgeable staff will be happy to help you,
wherever you're heading.

Many tourist information centres can provide you with
maps and guides, and it's often possible to book
accommodation and travel tickets too.

Across the country there are more than 700 TICs.
You'll find the address of your nearest centre in your
local phone book, or look at the beginning of each
regional section in this guide.

North East England

County Durham > Northumberland
Tees Valley > Tyne and Wear

Strolling through the waves towards Bamburgh Castle, Northumbria

One NorthEast Tourism Team
Stella House, Gold Crest Way, Newburn
Riverside, Newcastle upon Tyne NE15 8NY
0870 160 1781
visitnorthumbria.com

uncrowded beaches, top entertainment, tempting flavours

Main Stunning night-time views of The Sage Gateshead **Left** The powerful beauty of High Force, near Middleton-in-Teesdale; Up for the challenge on the Hadrian's Wall Path; dazzling fountains at The Alnwick Garden, Northumberland; fantastic views of Durham Cathedral

Discover the beauty of unspoilt coastlines and breathtaking countryside, feel revived by the crisp, fresh air and experience limitless nightlife in the cities. **There's so much diversity, you'll want to come back for more.**

Explore
North East England

Outdoor living

Feel exhilarated by the vast wide-open spaces of the North East. Feel the refreshing spray on your face at High Force – the highest unbroken waterfall in the country. Take up the challenge and walk one of the many National Trails through either of the National Parks. Feeling strong? Follow in Roman footsteps along the 84-mile Hadrian's Wall Path. If you're with the kids, why not walk a section of it and call in at Segedunum Roman Fort, Baths & Museum, then hop on the Hadrian's Wall Bus for a scenic tour.

Watch red squirrels scavenging the undergrowth and admire the stunning simple beauty of Kielder Water. Lose yourself in the enchantment of the surrounding forest and be inspired by the impressive visual arts and sculpture trail. Stand and gaze in awe from the base of the magnificent Angel of the North or take a day trip to The Alnwick Garden in Northumberland for a truly magical experience within the walls of this redeveloped haven.

Bright lights, big city

Treat yourself to a spending spree in Newcastle: browse Europe's largest indoor shopping complex, the MetroCentre, find all the high street shops at Eldon Square, or seek out something individual in the boutiques and markets. Relax in one of the numerous pavement cafes – cappuccino in hand – and treat yourself to an exquisite meal, taking your pick from dishes spanning the globe.

Take in a play at The Sage Gateshead – a truly magnificent building staging outstanding theatrical performances and live music.

Head to NewcastleGateshead Quayside to see spectacular architecture, and party the night away in one of the many nightclubs.

Castle central

Admire the intricate carvings as you amble softly through the aisles of Durham Cathedral and visit Durham Castle – a Norman fortress that lies just behind it. View the fabulous art collection within Raby Castle or take a trip to Barnard Castle, and then wander the streets of the picturesque town that surround it.

Whisk the kids into a world where the past comes to life at Beamish, The North of England Open Air Museum. Give them a pioneering eco experience at Nature's World or allow them to be inspired at Seven Stories, the Centre for Children's Books in Ouseburn Valley.

Adventure seeking

Take your chances with the rapids at the Four Seasons Teesside White Water Centre; push the boat out and hire a log cabin in the grounds so you can really get a feel for white-water rafting. Relax with a pair of binoculars at Farne Island – perfect for birdwatching – or take a boat trip and spot wading puffins.

Spin those spokes in Hamsterley Forest – a veritable haven for mountain bikers and indeed all manner of cyclists. Varied colours mark routes in terms of difficulty, making this ideal for all levels of riders. Alternatively, kick off your shoes and relax on the stunning Northumberland or Durham Heritage Coasts. Appreciate the uncrowded beaches and sample a local dish in a cosy pub.

Places to **visit**

0   50 miles

0   75 kms

Berwick-upon-Tweed

Holy Island/
Lindisfarne
Bamburgh

Wooler   **1**   *Northumberland Coast*

68

PENNINE
WAY   Alnwick

Kielder Water
and Forest Park   NORTHUMBERLAND

Druridge   Druridge Bay

Bellingham

HADRIAN'S
WALL PATH   Tynemouth
South Shields
72   Newcastle   Sunderland
PENNINE
BRIDLEWAY   Gateshead
Derwent Reservoir
7
North   Stanhope   **14**   Durham
Pennines

Middleton-   **1**   Hartlepool
in-Teesdale   Middlesbrough
Stockton-on-Tees   Saltburn-by-the-Sea
PENNINE   Barnard   CLEVELAND
WAY   Castle   Darlington   WAY

National Park

Area of Outstanding Natural Beauty

Heritage Coast

National Trails
nationaltrail.co.uk

National Trails approved but
not yet open

Sections of the
National Cycle Network
nationalcyclenetwork.org.uk

The Alnwick Garden
Northumberland
(01665) 511350
alnwickgarden.com
Magnificent and contemporary

The Angel of the North
NewcastleGateshead,
Tyne and Wear
(0191) 433 3000
gateshead.gov.uk/angel
Outstanding hillside sculpture

**Baltic Centre for
Contemporary Art**
Gateshead, Tyne and Wear
(01914) 781810
balticmill.com
Diverse international art

Barnard Castle
County Durham
(01833) 690909
teesdalediscovery.com
*Inspiring ruins of majestic
Norman castle*

Beamish, The North of England Open Air Museum
Stanley, County Durham
(01913) 704000
beamish.org.uk
Let the past come to life

Blue Reef Aquarium
Tynemouth, Tyne and Wear
(01912) 581031
bluereefaquarium.co.uk
Gaze from the underwater tunnel

Centre for Life
Newcastle upon Tyne,
Tyne and Wear
(01912) 438210
life.org.uk
A hands-on experience for all

Discovery Museum
Newcastle upon Tyne,
Tyne and Wear
(01912) 326789
twmuseums.org.uk/discovery
Explore world-changing inventions

Durham Castle
(01913) 344106
durhamcastle.com
Fine example of motte and bailey

Durham Cathedral
(01913) 864266
durhamcathedral.co.uk
Beautiful Norman architecture

Four Seasons Teesside White Water Centre
Stockton-on-Tees, Tees Valley
(01642) 678000
4seasons.co.uk
Prepare for a white-knuckle ride

Hadrian's Wall Path National Trail
Hexham, Northumberland
(01912) 691600
nationaltrail.co.uk/hadrianswall
An essential and historic 84-mile trail

Hamsterley Forest
County Durham
(01388) 488312
hamsterley-trailblazers.co.uk
Cycling adventures for all ages and abilities

Kielder Water and Forest Park
Northumberland
(01434) 220643
kielder.org
Divine views and an abundance of nature

Nature's World
Middlesbrough,
County Durham
(01642) 594895
naturesworld.org.uk
A pioneering eco experience that could change you

Raby Castle
Darlington, County
Durham
(01833) 660202
rabycastle.com
Medieval castle with outstanding walled gardens and surrounding park

Seven Stories, the Centre for Children's Books
NewcastleGateshead,
Tyne and Wear
0845 271 0777
sevenstories.org.uk
Celebrating children's books

Segedunum Roman Fort Baths & Museum
Wallsend, Tynedale
(0191) 236 9347
twmuseums.org.uk
The most excavated fort in Britain

The Sage Gateshead
Tyne and Wear
(01914) 434666
thesagegateshead.org
Pioneering centre for musical discovery

Wet n' Wild
North Shields, Tyne and Wear
(01912) 961333
wetnwild.co.uk
Indoor waterpark with whirlpools

Tourist information centres

When you arrive at your destination, visit a tourist information centre for help with accommodation and information about local attractions and events, or email your request before you go.

Adderstone	Adderstone Garage	(01668) 213678	adderstone@hotmail.com
Alnwick	2 The Shambles	(01665) 510665	alnwicktic@alnwick.gov.uk
Amble*	Queen Street Car Park	(01665) 712313	ambletic@alnwick.gov.uk
Barnard Castle	Woodleigh Flatts Road	(01833) 690909	tourism@teesdale.gov.uk
Bellingham	Main Street	(01434) 220616	bellinghamtic@btconnect.com
Berwick-upon-Tweed	106 Marygate	(01289) 330733	tourism@berwick-upon-tweed.gov.uk
Bishop Auckland	Market Place	(01388) 604922	bishopauckland.tourisminfo@durham.gov.uk
Corbridge*	Hill Street	(01434) 632815	corbridgetic@btconnect.com
Craster*	Craster Car Park	(01665) 576007	crastertic@alnwick.gov.uk
Darlington	13 Horsemarket	(01325) 388666	tic@darlington.gov.uk
Durham	2 Millennium Place	(0191) 384 3720	touristinfo@durhamcity.gov.uk
Gateshead (Central Library)	Prince Consort Road	(0191) 433 8400	tic@gateshead.gov.uk
Gateshead (Visitor Centre, Quayside)	St Mary's Church	(0191) 478 4222	tourism@gateshead.gov.uk
Guisborough	Church Street	(01287) 633801	guisborough_tic@redcar-cleveland.gov.uk
Haltwhistle	Station Road	(01434) 322002	haltwhistletic@btconnect.com
Hartlepool	Church Square	(01429) 869706	hpooltic@hartlepool.gov.uk
Hexham	Wentworth Car Park	(01434) 652220	hexham.tic@tynedale.gov.uk
Middlesbrough	99-101 Albert Road	(01642) 729700	middlesbrough_tic@middlesbrough.gov.uk
Middleton-in-Teesdale	10 Market Place	(01833) 641001	middletonplus@compuserve.com
Morpeth	Bridge Street	(01670) 500700	tourism@castlemorpeth.gov.uk
Newcastle International Airport		(0191) 214 4422	niatic@hotmail.com
Newcastle upon Tyne (Grainger St)	132 Grainger Street	(0191) 277 8000	tourist.info@newcastle.gov.uk
Newcastle upon Tyne (Guildhall)	Quayside	(0191) 277 8000	tourist.info@newcastle.gov.uk
North Shields	Royal Quays Outlet Shopping	(0191) 200 5895	ticns@northtyneside.gov.uk
Once Brewed*	Military Road	(01434) 344396	tic.oncebrewed@nnpa.org.uk
Otterburn	Otterburn Mill	(01830) 520093	tic@otterburnmill.co.uk
Peterlee	4 Upper Yoden Way	(0191) 586 4450	touristinfo@peterlee.gov.uk
Redcar	West Terrace	(01642) 471921	redcar_tic@redcar-cleveland.gov.uk
Rothbury*	Church Street	(01669) 620887	tic.rothbury@nnpa.org.uk
Saltburn-by-the-Sea	Station Square	(01287) 622422	saltburn_tic@redcar-cleveland.gov.uk
Seahouses*	Seafield car park	(01665) 720884	seahousestic@berwick-upon-tweed.gov.uk
South Shields	Ocean Road	(0191) 454 6612	museum.tic@southtyneside.gov.uk
South Shields (Amphitheatre)*	Sea Road	(0191) 455 7411	foreshore.tic@southtyneside.gov.uk
Stanhope	Durham Dales Centre	(01388) 527650	durham.dales.centre@durham.gov.uk
Stockton-on-Tees	Church Road	(01642) 528130	touristinformation@stockton.gov.uk
Sunderland	50 Fawcett Street	(0191) 553 2000	tourist.info@sunderland.gov.uk
Whitley Bay	Park Road	(0191) 200 8535	ticwb@northtyneside.gov.uk
Wooler*	12 Padgepool Place	(01668) 282123	woolertic@berwick-upon-tweed.gov.uk

* *seasonal opening*

Alternatively, you can text **TIC LOCATE** to **64118** to find your nearest tourist information centre

Find out **more**

Further publications are available from One NorthEast Tourism Team (unless otherwise stated) by logging on to **visitnorthumbria.com** or calling **0870 160 1781:**

› **Holiday and Short Breaks Guide**
Information on the region, including hotels, bed and breakfast and self-catering accommodation, caravan and camping parks and attractions. Call 0870 160 1781.

› **Cycling Guide**
For information on day rides, traffic-free trails and challenging routes call 0870 160 1778 for your free cycling guide.

› **Gardens Guide**
For your free guide to the region's inspirational gardens call 0870 225 5380.

› **Walking Guide**
For information on walking in North East England call 0870 225 0129 for your free walking guide.

› **Group Travel Guide**
Packed with everything tour planners need to know when planning a group visit – group hotels, attractions, destinations, itinerary suggestions, Blue Badge Guides, coach-parking locations and events. Call 0870 428 0810.

› **Educational Visits Guide**
Information for teachers planning school visits, including attractions with links to National Curriculum subjects, suitable accommodation, itinerary suggestions and events. Call (0191) 229 6845.

› **Tailored to Suit**
Aimed at group organisers, this guide includes a selection of themed itineraries offering suggestions for day tours, short breaks and long-stay holidays which can be tailored to suit the needs of the group. Call 0870 428 0810.

Travel **info**

By road:
There is excellent motorway access via the A1/A1M and A69 and A66 connecting to the M6. Within North East England you will find fast, modern interconnecting roads between all the main centres, a vast network of scenic, traffic-free country roads, which make motoring a pleasure, and frequent local bus services which operate to towns and villages.

By rail:
Direct train services operate from most cities in Britain to Newcastle's Central Station. The London to Edinburgh InterCity service stops at Darlington, Durham, Newcastle and Berwick upon Tweed. Trains make the journey between London and Newcastle in just over three hours. The London to Middlesbrough journey (changing at Darlington) takes three hours, Birmingham to Darlington just under three hours, Bristol to Durham five hours and Sheffield to Newcastle just over two hours. Regional services to areas of scenic beauty operate frequently, allowing the traveller easy access. The Tyne and Wear Metro makes it possible to travel to many destinations within the Tyne and Wear area, such as Gateshead, South Shields, Whitley Bay, Sunderland, Newcastle City Centre and Newcastle International Airport, in minutes.

By air:
Fly into Durham Tees Valley or Newcastle International airports.

where to stay in
North East England

All place names in the blue bands are shown on the maps at the front of this guide.

A complete listing of all VisitBritain assessed parks in England appears at the back.

Accommodation symbols
Symbols give useful information about services and facilities. Inside the back-cover flap you can find a key to these symbols. Keep it open for easy reference.

BAMBURGH, Northumberland Map ref 6C1

★★
HOLIDAY, TOURING
& CAMPING PARK

🚐(80)   £12.00–£15.00
🚍(80)   £12.00–£15.00
🅰 (80)   £12.00–£15.00
80 touring pitches

Bradford Kaims Caravan Park

Bradford House, Bamburgh NE70 7JT **t** (01668) 213432 **f** (01668) 213891 **e** lwrob@tiscali.co.uk **w** bradford-leisure.co.uk

Beautiful walking country. Close to Bamburgh, Seahouses, Wooler and Cheviot Hills. Pre-booking advised during school holidays. Open March to November. Bradford Kaims Caravan Park is signposted from the B1341.

payment Credit/debit cards, cash/cheques

General 🔌 🅖 🍴 🅟 ☉ 📞🖂 🛂 🐕 ☼   Leisure ♦ ⚲

BAMBURGH, Northumberland Map ref 6C1

★★★★
HOLIDAY, TOURING
& CAMPING PARK
ROSE AWARD

🚐(150)   £11.00–£19.50
🚍(150)   £11.00–£19.50
🅰 (30)   £11.00–£23.50
🏠 (27) £235.00–£540.00
150 touring pitches

Meadowhead's Waren Caravan and Camping Park

Waren Mill, Belford NE70 7EE **t** (01668) 214366 **f** (01668) 214224 **e** waren@meadowhead.co.uk **w** meadowhead.co.uk

payment Credit/debit cards, cash/cheques

Nestled in coastal countryside with great views to Holy Island and Bamburgh Castle. Waren offers restaurant-bar, splash-pool and play facilities. Our happy environment is great if you wish to stay on-site but we also make a great base from which to explore Northumberland's coast and castles, from Alnwick to Berwick. Open 17 March to 31 October.

⊕ *Follow B1342 from A1 to Waren Mill towards Bamburgh. By Budle turn right, follow Meadowhead's Waren Caravan and Camping Park signs.*

♥ *Please see website for promotions and details of our new wigwams too!*

General P 🔌 🅖 🍴 🆒🖂 ☉ 📞🖂 🛂 ✗ 🐕 ☼   Leisure ⚡ 📺 🍴 ♦ ⚲

Check it out

Information on parks listed in this guide has been supplied by proprietors. As changes may occur you should remember to check all relevant details at the time of booking.

CORBRIDGE, Northumberland Map ref 6B2

★★★
TOURING & CAMPING PARK

(40) £10.00–£14.00
(40) £10.00–£14.00
(40) £4.00–£10.00
40 touring pitches

Well House Farm – Corbridge

Newton, Stocksfield NE43 7UY **t** (01661) 842193 **e** info@wellhousefarm.co.uk
w wellhousefarm.co.uk

Peaceful family-run site on a farm near Corbridge one mile south of Hadrian's Wall. Ideal for exploring Northumberland and surrounding areas. Open April to October.

payment Cash/cheques

General Leisure

DURHAM, County Durham Map ref 6C2

★★★★★
TOURING & CAMPING PARK

(77) £12.50–£25.10
(77) £12.50–£25.10
77 touring pitches

See Ad on inside back cover

Grange Caravan Club Site

Meadow Lane, Durham DH1 1TL **t** (0191) 384 4778 **w** caravanclub.co.uk

open All year
payment Credit/debit cards, cash/cheques

An open, level site, this is a lovely location for a short break and an ideal stopover en route to or from Scotland.

A1(M) jct 62, A690 towards Durham. Turn right after 50m. Signposted Maureen Terrace and brown caravan sign.

Special member rates mean you can save your membership subscription in less than a week. Visit our website to find out more.

General Leisure

DURHAM, County Durham Map ref 6C2

★★★★
HOLIDAY, TOURING & CAMPING PARK
ROSE AWARD

(35) £14.50–£16.50
(35) £14.50–£16.50
(10) £12.50–£16.50
(3) £295.00–£365.00
45 touring pitches

Strawberry Hill Farm Camping & Caravanning Park

Running Waters, Old Cassop, Durham DH6 4QA **t** (0191) 372 3457 **f** (0191) 372 2512
e howarddunkerley@strawberryhillfarm.freeserve.co.uk **w** strawberry-hill-farm.co.uk

Situated in open countryside with magnificent, panoramic views. Ideally situated to explore the World Heritage site of the castle and cathedral. For further details please see website. Open March to December.

payment Credit/debit cards, cash/cheques, euros

General

EBCHESTER, County Durham Map ref 6B2

★★★★
TOURING & CAMPING PARK

(31) £8.00–£9.00
(5) £8.00–£9.00
(6) £6.00–£10.00
31 touring pitches

Byreside Caravan Site

Hamsterley Colliery, Newcastle upon Tyne NE17 7RT **t** (01207) 560280

Site on family-run farm, adjacent to Derwent walk and cycle track. Easy access to both Durham and Northumberland countryside.

open All year
payment Cash/cheques

General

Check the maps

Colour maps at the front pinpoint all the places you will find accommodation entries in the regional sections. Pick your location and then refer to the place index at the back to find the page number.

Fallowfield Dene Caravan and Camping Park

★★★★
TOURING &
CAMPING PARK

🚐(32) £14.50–£15.50
🚎(6) £14.50–£15.50
🅰 (10) £8.50–£24.50
42 touring pitches

Acomb, Hexham NE46 4RP **t** (01434) 603553 **f** (01434) 603553 **e** den@fallowfielddene.co.uk
w fallowfielddene.co.uk

In unspoilt countryside, 1.5 miles from the village of Acomb. The site is within easy reach of Hadrian's Wall and many places of interest. Open March to November.

payment Credit/debit cards, cash/cheques

General 🔲 P 🔌 🕒 🚻 🔁 🅿 ☉ 🔔 🔘 🔁 🛴 Leisure ∪

Hexham Racecourse Caravan Site

★★★
TOURING &
CAMPING PARK

🚐(40) £10.00–£12.00
🚎(30) £10.00–£12.00
🅰 (16) Min £6.00
40 touring pitches

Yarridge Road, High Yarridge, Hexham NE46 2JP **t** (01434) 606847 **f** (01434) 605814
e hexrace@aol.com **w** hexham-racecourse.co.uk

Set in beautiful open countryside with panoramic views. Close to Hadrian's Wall, and within travelling distance of Northumberland, County Durham, Cumbria and Tyneside.

payment Cash/cheques

General P 🔌 🕒 🚻 🅿 ☉ 🔁 🔘 🐾 🔩. Leisure 🔵 ⚠ ▶

Kielder Water Caravan Club Site

★★★★
TOURING &
CAMPING PARK

🚐(83) £8.50–£19.60
🚎(83) £8.50–£19.60
83 touring pitches

See Ad on inside back cover

Leaplish Waterside Park, Falstone, Hexham NE48 1AX **t** (01434) 250278 **w** caravanclub.co.uk

payment Credit/debit cards, cash/cheques

This is a gently sloping site, with some pitches overlooking the beautiful Kielder Water – Britain's largest man-made lake. A fabulous site for an active holiday. Open March to October.

⊕ *From east on A69. Past Hexham, right onto A6079. Approx 3 miles, left onto B6320. In Bellingham, left to Kielder Water. Right, signposted Leaplish Waterside Park. Site on right.*

♥ *Special member rates mean you can save your membership subscription in less than a week. Visit our website to find out more.*

General 🔌 🕒 🚻 🔁 🅿 ☉ 🔘 🔩 ☼

See under Kielder

Newton Hall Caravan Park

★★★★
HOLIDAY &
TOURING PARK

🚐(15) £11.00–£18.00
🚎(15) £11.00–£18.00
🏚(3) £245.00–£540.00
15 touring pitches

Newton-by-the-Sea, Alnwick NE66 3DZ **t** (01665) 576239 **f** (01665) 576900
e ianpatterson@newtonholidays.co.uk **w** newtonholidays.co.uk

Small level park close to sandy beaches. Large children's play area.

open All year
payment Credit/debit cards, cash/cheques

General 🔩 🔲 🔩 P 🔌 🕒 🚻 🅿 ☉ 🔘 🔩 Leisure 🔵 ∪ ⌐ ▶

North East England

OTTERBURN, Northumberland Map ref 6B1

★★★★
HOLIDAY, TOURING
& CAMPING PARK

⊕(36) £9.50–£13.00
🚐(36) £9.50–£13.00
⚑(36) £9.50–£13.00
🏠(2) £200.00–£375.00
36 touring pitches

Border Forest Caravan Park

Cottonshopeburnfoot, Rochester, Otterburn NE19 1TF **t** (01830) 520259 **w** borderforest.com

Border Forest Caravan Park was established in 1989. Small, secluded park owned and operated by the Flanagan family. On the A68, the east side of Kielder Forest Park. Open March to October.

payment Credit/debit cards, cash/cheques, euros

General 🖥 P 🔌 🕛 🚻 🚲 🦮 🛗 🔥 🛁 📮   Leisure ∪ ✈ 🚴

RAMSHAW, County Durham Map ref 6B2

★★★
HOLIDAY, TOURING
& CAMPING PARK

⊕(40) £12.00–£15.00
🚐(40) £12.00–£15.00
40 touring pitches

Craggwood Caravan Park

Gordon Lane, Ramshaw, Bishop Auckland DL14 0NS **t** (01388) 835866 **f** (01388) 835866
e billy6482@btopenworld.com **w** craggwoodcaravanpark.co.uk

Craggwood Caravan Park is set in approximately 60 acres with lovely views, woodland and a river running through the park. Open 1 March to 31 October.

payment Credit/debit cards, cash/cheques

General 🖥 P 🔌 🕛 🚻 🚲 🦮 🛗 📮 ✂ ✕ 🛁 🔥 ☼   Leisure ⚑ ∪ ✈

ROTHBURY, Northumberland Map ref 6B1

★★★
TOURING PARK

⊕(84) £7.90–£17.10
🚐(84) £7.90–£17.10
84 touring pitches

See Ad on inside back cover

CARAVAN
CLUB
2007

Nunnykirk Caravan Club Site

Nunnykirk, Morpeth NE61 4PZ **t** (01669) 620762 **w** caravanclub.co.uk

payment Credit/debit cards, cash/cheques

The peace and tranquillity of this site makes it a haven for wildlife. Space, fresh air and open countryside abound. Hill-walkers will enjoy the splendour of the nearby Simonside Hills. Open April to October.

⊕ *From B6342, cross bridge at foot of 1:8 hill and turn right into private road. Site on right in 0.25 miles.*

♥ *Special member rates mean you can save your membership subscription in less than a week. Visit our website to find out more.*

General P 🔌 🕛 🦮   Leisure ✈

SEAHOUSES, Northumberland Map ref 6C1

★★★★★
HOLIDAY &
TOURING PARK
ROSE AWARD

⊕(18) £18.00–£35.00
🚐(18) £18.00–£35.00
🏠(37) £295.00–£620.00
18 touring pitches

Seafield Caravan Park

Seafield Road, Seahouses NE68 7SP **t** (01665) 720628 **f** (01665) 720088 **e** info@seafieldpark.co.uk
w seafieldpark.co.uk

payment Credit/debit cards, cash/cheques

Luxurious holiday homes for hire on Northumberland's premier park. Fully appointed caravans. Superior, fully serviced touring pitches. Prices include full use of Ocean Club facilities (www.ocean-club.co.uk).

⊕ *Take the B1340 from Alnwick for 14 miles. East to coast.*

♥ *Seasonal discounts available on 3-, 4- and 7-day breaks.*

General 🖥 P 🔌 🕛 🚻 🚲 🦮 ⊙ 🛗 ✕ 🛁 🔥 ☼   Leisure 🎣 ⚑ ∪ ✈ ▶

STOCKTON-ON-TEES, Tees Valley Map ref 6C3

★★★★★
TOURING PARK
(115) £9.50–£21.40
(115) £9.50–£21.40
115 touring pitches

See Ad on inside back cover

THE
CARAVAN
CLUB

White Water Caravan Club Park

Tees Barrage, Stockton-on-Tees TS18 2QW **t** (01642) 634880 **w** caravanclub.co.uk

open All year
payment Credit/debit cards, cash/cheques

Pleasantly landscaped site, part of the largest white-water canoeing and rafting course built to an international standard in Britain. Nearby Teesside Park for shopping, restaurants etc.

⊕ *Come off the A66 Teesside Park. Follow Teesdale sign, go over Tees Barrage Bridge, turn right. Site 200yds on the left.*

♥ *Special member rates mean you can save your membership subscription in less than a week. Visit our website to find out more.*

General 🖭 P 🔌 🖰 🍴 🚐 📶 ☉ 🧻 🛏 ☼ Leisure ♣ ⊿ ♪ ►

Country ways

The Countryside Rights of Way Act gives people new rights to walk on areas of open countryside and registered common land.

To find out where you can go and what you can do, as well as information about taking your dog to the countryside, go online at countrysideaccess.gov.uk.

And when you're out and about...

Always follow the Country Code

- **Be safe – plan ahead and follow any signs**
- **Leave gates and property as you find them**
- **Protect plants and animals, and take your litter home**
- **Keep dogs under close control**
- **Consider other people**

Help
before you go

When it comes to your next British break, the first stage of your journey could be closer than you think.

You've probably got a tourist information centre nearby which is there to serve the local community – as well as visitors. Knowledgeable staff will be happy to help you, wherever you're heading.

Many tourist information centres can provide you with maps and guides, and it's often possible to book accommodation and travel tickets too.

Across the country there are more than 700 TICs. You'll find the address of your nearest centre in your local phone book, or look at the beginning of each regional section in this guide.

Yorkshire

East Yorkshire › North Yorkshire › South Yorkshire › West Yorkshire

Fascinating marine life at The Deep, Hull

Yorkshire Tourist Board
312 Tadcaster Road
York YO24 1GS
0870 609 0000
info@ytb.org.uk
yorkshirevisitor.com

proud heritage, big attractions, lush dales

Main Stunning views across Yorkshire fields **Left** Come face to face with the past at Jorvik – The Viking City, York; family fun at Spurn Point Nature Reserve, Humberside; contemporary displays at Sheffield's Millennium Galleries; balancing on the limestone pavement at Malham Cove, North Yorkshire

With its rolling hills and dramatic, lush green landscapes, England's biggest county boasts some of the most picturesque pockets to be found in the country. Along with lively cities and ancient, ruined abbeys, **Yorkshire is rich in both history and culture.**

Explore
Yorkshire

A sea of green

Experience the spine-tingling desolation of the Yorkshire moors as they sweep you into the world of Emily Brontë's Wuthering Heights. Coupled with a visit to the Brontë Parsonage Museum, where the works of the remarkable sisters came to life, Brontë Country is truly inspiring.

Lose yourself in the 30,000 acres of stunning countryside encompassing the Bolton Abbey Estate, traverse woodland and riverside paths and soak up the incredible vistas. Or head to the vibrant coastal town of Scarborough – the country's first seaside resort – and immerse yourself in marine life at the Sea Life Centre.

Eye it up

Allow the innovative space at Sheffield's Millennium Galleries to guide you on a journey of art throughout the ages. Or take a trip to Bradford and experience art of a different nature at the National Museum of Photography, Film & Television, the country's most visited museum outside the capital. Be amazed by the new interactive exhibition, Experience TV, and discover how television comes to life.

At Yorkshire Sculpture Park in West Bretton, you will discover that no two visits are ever the same. Changing weather and seasons will alter your perception of this unique park, where art is integrated into the landscape in a complementary fashion.

Take time to soak up some of the rich heritage that Yorkshire has to offer. Pay the 11th-century Middleham Castle a visit and discover the childhood home of Richard III, or hunt for ghosts in the ruins of the majestic Rievaulx Abbey and admire its graceful arches and elegant structure.

Put your boots on

Pull on your hiking boots and explore the 1,000 square miles of National Parks (the Yorkshire Dales, the North York Moors and the Peak District). Stride out along the Pennine or Dales Way or take a leisurely stroll along one of the many trails across this vast expanse of beautiful countryside.

Gaze in awe at the mighty Malham Cove – a curved crag of limestone formed after the last ice age – and attempt to understand this truly magnificent spectacle. Pick your way across the disected limestone pavement running across the surface of the cove – a result of chemical weathering – and admire the simplistic beauty of the eroded channels.

The charming fishing village of Robin Hood's Bay near Whitby is the perfect place to relax and dip into the rock pools that surround the delightful sandy beaches. Or take your binoculars up the 400-feet chalk cliffs of the Flamborough Headland Heritage Coast and spot the intriguing selection of wildlife.

But above all, don't forget about the wonderful tastes the region has to offer. Sup a true pint of Yorkshire bitter and nibble on a chunk of Wensleydale, or warm your cockles with a selection of traditional pies and Yorkshire pudding. And, for that sweet tooth, there's always Bakewell tart for dessert.

Places to **visit**

0 |——————————| 50 miles
0 |——————————| 75 kms

Whitby

NORTH YORK MOORS

PENNINE WAY 71

PENNINE BRIDLEWAY

CLEVELAND WAY

Scarborough

65

YORKSHIRE DALES

Helmsley

Filey

68

Howardian Hills

DALES WAY Ripon

Nidderdale

Bridlington

Harrogate   York

Skipton   YORKSHIRE WOLDS WAY

Ilkley

1

Haworth Leeds

Bradford Kingston upon Hull

PENNINE BRIDLEWAY Wakefield 67

65

62

Withernsea

Huddersfield

PEAK DISTRICT

Doncaster

Rotherham

Sheffield

Aerial Extreme
Bedale, North Yorkshire
(01845) 567100
aerialextreme.co.uk
Swing high above the forest floor

Bolton Abbey Estate
North Yorkshire
(01756) 718009
boltonabbey.com
Beautiful setting, ruins and stepping stones

Brontë Parsonage Museum
Haworth, West Yorkshire
(01535) 642323
bronte.info
Former home of the inspiring literary sisters in quaint village setting

The Deep
Hull, East Yorkshire
(01482) 381000
thedeep.co.uk
Learn the history of the oceans

The Henry Moore Institute
Leeds, West Yorkshire
(0113) 246 7467
henry-moore-fdn.co.uk
Unique building housing art exhibitions

Jorvik – The Viking City
York, North Yorkshire
(01904) 543402
vikingjorvik.com
Viking history comes to life

National Park

Area of Outstanding Natural Beauty

Heritage Coast

National Trails
nationaltrail.co.uk

National Trails approved
but not yet open

3 Sections of the
National Cycle Network
nationalcyclenetwork.org.uk

Magna Science Adventure Centre
Rotherham, South Yorkshire
(01709) 723123
magnatrust.org.uk
An extraordinary science adventure

Malham Cove and Gordale Scar
North Yorkshire
(01729) 830363
malhamdale.com
Awe-inspiring rock formations

Middleham Castle
North Yorkshire
0870 333 1181
english-heritage.org.uk
Impressive 11th-century ruined castle

Millennium Galleries
Sheffield, South Yorkshire
(0114) 278 2600
sheffieldgalleries.org.uk
Innovative and diverse art space

National Museum of Photography, Film & Television
Bradford, West Yorkshire
0870 701 0200
nmpft.org.uk
With a spectacular 3D IMAX cinema and interactive television gallery

North Yorkshire Moors Railway
(01751) 473799
northyorkshiremoorsrailway.com
Heritage railway steaming through stunning scenery

Rievaulx Abbey
near Helmsley, North Yorkshire
(01439) 798228
yorkshirevisitor.com
Awe-inspiring ruined abbey in tranquil valley

Royal Armouries Museum
Leeds, West Yorkshire
(0113) 220 1916
armouries.org.uk
Jousting tournaments and fabulous exhibitions

Sea Life Centre
Scarborough, East Yorkshire
(01723) 373414
sealife.co.uk
Marine life at your fingertips

Sheffield Botanical Gardens
South Yorkshire
(0114) 267 6496
sbg.org.uk
Lanscaped gardens of historical interest

Sheffield Ski Village
South Yorkshire
(0114) 276 9459
sheffieldskivillage.co.uk
Europe's largest artificial ski complex

Underground RAF Bunker Tours
Withernsea, East Yorkshire
(01964) 630208
rafholmpton.co.uk
Explore the past, deep underground

York Minster
North Yorkshire
(01904) 557216
yorkminster.org
Huge, stunning, medieval gothic cathedral

Yorkshire Sculpture Park
West Bretton, West Yorkshire
(01924) 832631
ysp.co.uk
Open-air gallery in beautiful grounds

Tourist information centres

When you arrive at your destination, visit a tourist information centre for help with accommodation and information about local attractions and events, or email your request before you go.

Aysgarth Falls	Aysgarth Falls National Park Centre	(01969) 662910	aysgarth@ytbtic.co.uk
Barnsley	Central Library	(01226) 206757	barnsley@ytbtic.co.uk
Batley	Bradford Road	(01924) 426670	batley@ytbtic.co.uk
Beverley	34 Butcher Row	(01482) 867430	beverley.tic@eastriding .gov.uk
Bradford	City Hall	(01274) 739067	tourist.information@bradford.gov.uk
Bridlington	25 Prince Street	(01262) 673474	bridlington.tic@eastriding.gov.uk
Brigg	Market Place	(01652) 657053	brigg.tic@northlincs.gov.uk
Cleethorpes	42-43 Alexandra Road	(01472) 323111	cleethorpes@ytbtic04.freeserve.co.uk
Danby*	Lodge Lane	(01439) 772737	moorscentre@northyorkmoors-npa.gov.uk
Doncaster	38-40 High Street	(01302) 734309	tourist.information@doncaster.gov.uk
Filey*	John Street	(01723) 383637	fileytic@scarborough.gov.uk
Grassington	Hebden Road	(01756) 752774	grassington@ytbtic.co.uk
Guisborough	Church Street	(01287) 633801	guisborough_tic@redcar-cleveland.gov.uk
Halifax	Piece Hall	(01422) 368725	halifax@ytbtic.co.uk
Harrogate	Crescent Road	(01423) 537300	tic@harrogate.gov.uk
Hawes	Station Yard	(01969) 666210	hawes@ytbtic.co.uk
Haworth	2/4 West Lane	(01535) 642329	haworth@ytbtic.co.uk
Hebden Bridge	New Road	(01422) 843831	hebdenbridge@ytbtic.co.uk
Helmsley	Castlegate	(01439) 770173	helmsley@ytbtic.co.uk
Holmfirth	49-51 Huddersfield Road	(01484) 222444	holmfirth.tic@kirklees.gov.uk
Hornsea*	120 Newbegin	(01964) 536404	hornsea.tic@eastriding.gov.uk
Horton in Ribblesdale	Pen-y-ghent Cafe	(01729) 860333	horton@ytbtic.co.uk
Huddersfield	3 Albion Street	(01484) 223200	huddersfield.tic@kirklees.gov.uk
Hull	1 Paragon Street	(01482) 223559	tourist.information@hullcc.gov.uk
Humber Bridge	Ferriby Road	(01482) 640852	humberbridge.tic@eastriding.gov.uk
Ilkley	Station Road	(01943) 602319	ilkley@ytbtic.co.uk
Ingleton*	The Community Centre Car Park	(015242) 41049	ingleton@ytbtic.co.uk
Knaresborough	9 Castle Courtyard	08453 890177	kntic@harrogate.gov.uk
Leeds	The Arcade, City Station	(0113) 242 5242	tourinfo@leeds.gov.uk
Leeming Bar	The Great North Road	(01677) 424262	leeming@ytbtic.co.uk
Leyburn	4 Central Chambers	(01969) 623069	leyburn@ytbtic.co.uk
Malham		(01969) 652380	malham@ytbtic.co.uk
Malton	58 Market Place	(01653) 600048	maltontic@btconnect.com
Otley	Nelson Street	(01943) 462485	otleytic@leedslearning.net
Pateley Bridge*	18 High Street	08453 890179	pbtic@harrogate.gov.uk
Pickering	The Ropery	(01751) 473791	pickering@ytbtic.co.uk
Redcar	West Terrace	(01642) 471921	redcar_tic@redcar-cleveland.gov.uk

Reeth	The Green	(01748) 884059	reeth@ytbtic.co.uk
Richmond	Friary Gardens	(01748) 850252	richmond@ytbtic.co.uk
Ripon*	Minster Road	08453 890178	ripontic@harrogate.gov.uk
Rotherham Visitor Centre	40 Bridgegate	(01709) 835904	tic@rotherham.gov.uk
Saltburn-by-the-Sea	Station Square	(01287) 622422	saltburn_tic@redcar-cleveland.gov.uk
Scarborough	Brunswick Centre	(01723) 383636	tourismbureau@scarborough.gov.uk
Scarborough (Harbourside)	Sandside	(01723) 383636	harboursidetic@scarborough.gov.uk
Scunthorpe	Carlton Street	(01724) 297354	brigg.tic@northlincs.gov.uk
Selby	52 Micklegate	(01757) 212181	selby@ytbtic.co.uk
Settle	Cheapside	(01729) 825192	settle@ytbtic.co.uk
Sheffield	Winter Garden	(0114) 221 1900	visitor@sheffield.gov.uk
Skipton	35 Coach Street	(01756) 792809	skipton@ytbtic.co.uk
Sutton Bank	Sutton Bank	(01845) 597426	suttonbank@ytbtic.co.uk
Thirsk	49 Market Place	(01845) 522755	thirsktic@hambleton.gov.uk
Todmorden	15 Burnley Road	(01706) 818181	todmorden@ytbtic.co.uk
Wakefield	9 The Bull Ring	0845 601 8353	tic@wakefield.gov.uk
Wetherby	17 Westgate	(01937) 582151	wetherbytic@leedslearning.net
Whitby	Langborne Road	(01723) 383637	whitbytic@scarborough.gov.uk
Withernsea*	131 Queen Street	(01964) 615683	withernsea.tic@eastriding.gov.uk
York (De Grey Rooms)	Exhibition Square	(01904) 621756	tic@york-tourism.co.uk
York (Railway Station)	Station Road	(01904) 621756	kg@ytbyork.swiftserve.net

*seasonal opening

Alternatively, you can text **TIC LOCATE** to **64118** to find your nearest tourist information centre

Find out **more**

The following publications are available from Yorkshire Tourist Board by logging on to **yorkshirevisitor.com** or calling **0870 609 0000**

Yorkshire Accommodation Guide 2007
Information on Yorkshire and northern Lincolnshire, including hotels, self catering, camping and caravan parks.

Make Yorkshire Yours Magazine
This entertaining magazine is full of articles and features about what's happening in Yorkshire, including where to go and what to do.

Travel **info**

By road:
Motorways: M1, M62, M606, M621, M18, M180, M181, A1(M). Trunk roads: A1, A19, A57, A58, A59, A61, A62, A63, A64, A65, A66.

By rail:
InterCity services to Bradford, Doncaster, Harrogate, Kingston upon Hull, Leeds, Sheffield, Wakefield and York. Frequent regional railway services city centre to city centre, including Manchester Airport service to Scarborough, York and Leeds.

By air:
Fly into Durham Tees Valley, Humberside, Leeds/Bradford International or Robin Hood, Doncaster, Sheffield.

where to stay in
Yorkshire

All place names in the blue bands are shown on the maps at the front of this guide.

A complete listing of all VisitBritain assessed parks in England appears at the back.

Accommodation symbols
Symbols give useful information about services and facilities. Inside the back-cover flap you can find a key to these symbols. Keep it open for easy reference.

BEDALE, North Yorkshire Map ref 6C3

★★★★
TOURING &
CAMPING PARK

🚐 (25)   Min £9.00
🚐 (25)   Min £9.00
🛖 (25)   £6.00–£9.00
🚐 (3)   Min £120.00
25 touring pitches

Pembroke Caravan Park
19 Low Street, Leeming Bar, Northallerton DL7 9BW t (01677) 422652

Small sheltered site catering for touring vans, including motor caravans and tents. Excellent A1 night halt. Open March to October.

payment Cash/cheques

General 🖾 🛋 P 🔌 🕁 🖀 🕼 ☺ 🖺 🐂 ☼   Leisure ∪ ♪ ⊁

BEVERLEY, East Riding of Yorkshire Map ref 5C1

★★★★★
HOLIDAY PARK

🚐 (5)   Min £170.00

Barmston Farm Caravan Park
Barmston Farm, Barmston Lane, Woodmansey, Beverley HU17 0TP t (01482) 863566 & 07970 042587 e enquiry@barmstonfarm.co.uk w barmstonfarm.co.uk

open All year
payment Cash/cheques

Small, quiet, friendly site. Caravans positioned around a pond with open countryside views. In an adjacent field there is a well-stocked, two-acre fishing lake.

⊕ *Follow A1174 from Beverley, 3 miles to Woodmansey. Church on sharp bend, site at bottom of lane, next to church.*

General P 🕼 🕮 🔅   Leisure ∪ ♪

Check it out

Information on parks listed in this guide has been supplied by proprietors. As changes may occur you should remember to check all relevant details at the time of booking.

BRIDLINGTON, East Riding of Yorkshire Map ref 6D3

★★★★
HOLIDAY, TOURING
& CAMPING PARK

🚐 £16.00–£19.00
🚎 £16.00–£19.00
⚊ (20) £16.00–£19.00
🚍 (10) £184.00–£440.00
175 touring pitches

South Cliff Caravan Park

Wilsthorpe, Bridlington YO15 3QN t (01262) 671051 f (01262) 605639
e southcliff@eastriding.gov.uk w southcliff.co.uk

Situated 300yds from clean, safe, sandy beaches, one mile south of Bridlington. Bus service to Bridlington, also a shop, takeaway and leisure complex including bars, children's lounge and restaurant. Open March to November.

payment Credit/debit cards, cash/cheques

General P 🕭 🕿 🛜 📶 ⊙ 📠 🗐 🎇 ✕ ☼ Leisure 📺 🍷 ♫ ♦ 🎢 ∪ 🎣 ►

FILEY, North Yorkshire Map ref 6D3

★★★★★
HOLIDAY PARK

🚐 £10.00–£16.00
🚎 £10.00–£16.00
⚊ (25) £10.00–£16.00
60 touring pitches

Orchard Farm Holiday Village

Stonegate, Hunmanby, Filey YO14 0PU t (01723) 891582 f (01723) 891582

Family park on edge of village location with easy access to resorts of Filey, Scarborough and Bridlington. Amenities include children's play area, fishing lake and entertainment during peak season. Open March to October.

payment Cash/cheques

General ⊞ P 🕭 🕿 🛜 📶 ⊙ 📠 🗐 🎇 ⛺ ☼ Leisure 🎣 📺 🍷 ♫ ♦ 🎢 🎣

FOLLIFOOT, North Yorkshire Map ref 5B1

★★★★
TOURING PARK

🚐 (71) £8.50–£19.60
🚎 (71) £8.50–£19.60
⚊ on application
71 touring pitches

See Ad on inside back cover

Great Yorkshire Showground Caravan Club Site

Wetherby Road, Harrogate HG3 1TZ t (01423) 560470 w caravanclub.co.uk

payment Credit/debit cards, cash/cheques

A flat, pleasantly open site, very convenient to visit Harrogate, the floral capital of Yorkshire. Not only does the town have splendid examples of municipal gardens, but it also hosts two major flower shows. Open March to November.

⊕ *Turn left off A661 (Wetherby-Harrogate). Site on right in 400yds.*

♥ *Special member rates mean you can save your membership subscription in less than a week. Visit our website to find out more.*

General P 🕭 🕿 ⛺ Leisure ►

HARMBY, North Yorkshire Map ref 6B3

★★★
TOURING &
CAMPING PARK

🚐 (98) £9.50–£21.40
🚎 (98) £9.50–£21.40
⚊ on application
98 touring pitches

See Ad on inside back cover

Lower Wensleydale Caravan Club Site

Harmby, Leyburn DL8 5NU t (01969) 623366 w caravanclub.co.uk

payment Credit/debit cards, cash/cheques

Set within the hollow of a disused quarry, now overrun with wild flowers and mosses. This site offers charming pitching areas. Many interesting attractions nearby and wonderful walking country. Open March to November.

⊕ *From east on A684, turn right 0.75 miles past railway bridge; turn immediately left and follow signs to site entrance.*

♥ *Special member rates mean you can save your membership subscription in less than a week. Visit our website to find out more.*

General P 🕭 🕿 🚐 📶 🗐 ⛺ Leisure 🎣

HARROGATE, North Yorkshire Map ref 5B1

★★★★★
HOLIDAY &
TOURING PARK

🚐 (200) £13.00–£15.00
🚎 (57) £13.00–£15.00
200 touring pitches

High Moor Farm Park

Skipton Road, Felliscliffe, Harrogate HG3 2LT **t** (01423) 563637 **f** (01423) 529449
e highmoorfarmpark@btconnect.com

Secluded site surrounded by trees on the edge of
the Yorkshire Dales. Open April to October.

payment Credit/debit cards, cash/cheques

General 🖵 💷 P 🔌 🗓 🍴 🕮 🌣 ⊙ 🏧 🛒 ✕ 🐕 🐾 Leisure 🎣 🍽 🔍 ⚲ ♪ ▸

HARROGATE, North Yorkshire Map ref 5B1

★★★★★
HOLIDAY, TOURING
& CAMPING PARK
ROSE AWARD

🚐 £15.00–£29.00
🚎 £15.00–£29.00
Å £15.00–£29.00
141 touring pitches

Rudding Holiday Park

Follifoot, Harrogate HG3 1JH **t** (01423) 870439 **f** (01423) 870859 **e** holiday-park@ruddingpark.com
w ruddingpark.com

payment Credit/debit cards, cash/cheques, euros

Award-winning campsite. Just three miles south of
Harrogate, in peaceful setting, offering Deer House
pub, swimming pool, golf course, driving range and
shop. Closed February. Self-catering timber lodges
also available.

⊕ *Three miles south of Harrogate, to the north of the A658*
between its junction with the A61 to Leeds and the A661 to
Wetherby.

♥ *Peak season: 7 nights for the price of 6. Off-peak season: 4*
nights for the price of 3.

General 🖵 💷 P 🔌 🗓 🍴 🕮 🌣 ⊙ 🏧 🛒 ✕ 🐕 🐾 ☼ Leisure 🎣 📺 🍽 🔍 ⚲ ∪ ♪ ▸

HAWES, North Yorkshire Map ref 6B3

★★
HOLIDAY, TOURING
& CAMPING PARK

🚐 (25) Min £10.50
🚎 (5) Min £10.00
Å (40) Max £10.00
🏚 (2) £160.00–£205.00
70 touring pitches

Bainbridge Ings Caravan and Camping Site

Hawes DL8 3NU **t** (01969) 667354 **e** janet@bainbridge-ings.co.uk **w** bainbridge-ings.co.uk

Quiet, clean, well-organised, family-run site.
Pitches situated around the edge of open fields
with magnificent views. Ten-minute walk into
Hawes. Excellent centre for walking and touring
the Dales.

payment Cash/cheques

General P 🔌 🗓 🍴 🕮 ⊙ 🏧 🐕 ☼ Leisure ♪

HAWORTH, West Yorkshire Map ref 5B1

★★★★
HOLIDAY, TOURING
& CAMPING PARK

🚐 £11.00–£16.50
🚎 (2) £10.00–£15.00
Å (15) Max £7.50
🏚 (2) £100.00–£295.00
60 touring pitches

Upwood Holiday Park

Blackmoor Road, Oxenhope, Haworth, Keighley BD22 9SS **t** (01535) 644242 **f** (01535) 647913
e caravans@upwoodholidaypark.fsnet.co.uk **w** upwoodholidaypark.fsnet.co.uk

payment Credit/debit cards, cash/cheques

A family-owned park pleasantly situated close to the
Yorkshire Dales National Park – an ideal base from
which to explore the area by car or on foot. Large,
modern toilet facilities, comfortable lounge bar
serving snacks, games room with pool and table
tennis, small shop for essential items.

General 💷 P 🔌 🗓 🍴 🕮 ⊙ 🏧 🛒 ✕ 🐕 🐾 ☼ Leisure 📺 🍽 🎵 🔍 ⚲ ∪ ♪ ▸ 🚲 🏞

★★★★
TOURING PARK
🚐(45)   £8.50–£19.60
🚎(45)   £8.50–£19.60
45 touring pitches

See Ad on inside back cover

Lower Clough Foot Caravan Club Site

Cragg Vale, Hebden Bridge HX7 5RU   t (01422) 882531   w caravanclub.co.uk

payment Credit/debit cards, cash/cheques

Pretty site, set in a grassy enclave, well screened by mature trees and bordered by a stream. Good for walkers. Open March to November.

⊕ *Turn off A646 onto B6138. Site on right in 1 mile.*

♥ *Special member rates mean you can save your membership subscription in less than a week. Visit our website to find out more.*

General P 🔌 🚰 🔲 🐕   Leisure ✈ ↑

★★★★★
TOURING &
CAMPING PARK
🚐(60)   £12.50–£16.50
🚎(60)   £12.50–£16.50
▲ (60)   £12.50–£16.50
60 touring pitches

Foxholme Touring Caravan Park

Harome, Helmsley YO62 5JG   t (01439) 771241   f (01439) 771744

Adults-only park.   **payment** Cash/cheques

General 🔲 🛁 P 🔌 🚰 🚻 🔲 🕻 ☉ 📵 🐕 🚱.

★★★★★
TOURING &
CAMPING PARK
🚐   £12.50–£16.50
🚎   £12.50–£16.50
▲   £12.50–£16.50
🏠(1) £155.00–£195.00
129 touring pitches

Golden Square Caravan and Camping Park

Oswaldkirk, Helmsley, York YO62 5YQ   t (01439) 788269   f (01439) 788236
e barbara@goldensquarecaravanpark.freeserve.co.uk   w goldensquarecaravanpark.com

Secluded site with magnificent view of North York Moors. Award-winning, heated toilet block (refurbished 2006), bathroom, disabled room, shop. Indoor/outdoor play areas. Sports centre nearby. De luxe and seasonal pitches. Storage compound.

payment Cash/cheques, euros

General 🔲 🛁 P 🔌 🚰 🚻 🔲 🕻 ☉ 📵 🛒 🐕 🚱   Leisure ♦ ⛰ ∪ ✈ ↑ 🚴

★★★★
HOLIDAY, TOURING
& CAMPING PARK
🚐(55)   £14.50
🚎(55)   £14.00
▲ (20)   £11.00
55 touring pitches

Wayside Caravan Park

Pickering YO18 8PG   t (01723) 512373   f (01723) 512373   e waysideparks@freenet.co.uk
w waysideparks.co.uk

Sheltered, quiet, south-facing park, delightfully located with lovely country views. A walker's paradise. Steam railway. Castle Howard nearby. Whitby, Scarborough and York within a 45-minute drive. Open March to October.

payment Credit/debit cards, cash/cheques

General 🔲 🛁 P 🔌 🚰 🚻 🔲 🕻 ☉ 📵 🛒 🐕 🚱. ☼   Leisure ⛰ ∪ ✈ ↑ 🚴 ⛺

You're welcome at our Sites!
For details of Caravan Club sites in this region, where high standards, excellent facilities and a warm welcome are assured, please see our website

THE CARAVAN CLUB
www.caravanclub.co.uk

RICHMOND, North Yorkshire Map ref 6C3

★★★★
HOLIDAY, TOURING
& CAMPING PARK

🚐 £15.00–£20.00
🏕 £15.00–£20.00
⛺ (40) £5.00–£15.00
🏠 (2) £200.00–£345.00
217 touring pitches

Brompton Caravan Park

Easby, Richmond DL10 7EZ **t** (01748) 824629 **f** (01748) 826383
e brompton.caravanpark@btinternet.com **w** bromptoncaravanpark.co.uk

A family-run, peaceful riverside park, set in 14.5
acres, two miles from Richmond. There is a good
children's playground, takeaway and fishing
available on site.

open All year except Christmas
payment Credit/debit cards, cash/cheques

General 🏕🖳🏗P🔌🕭🚽🖵🌞 Leisure ⚓∪🎯

RIPON, North Yorkshire Map ref 6C3

★★★★
TOURING &
CAMPING PARK

🚐 (30) £8.50–£16.00
🏕 (20) £8.50–£16.00
⛺ (40) £6.50–£14.00
90 touring pitches

Sleningford Watermill Caravan & Camping

North Stainley, Ripon HG4 3HQ **t** (01765) 635201 **e** sleningford@hotmail.co.uk
w ukparks.co.uk/sleningford

payment Credit/debit cards, cash/cheques

A beautiful and tranquil riverside site in semi-
wooded parkland, five miles north-west of Ripon and
three miles south-east of Masham on the A6108.
Ideal for bird and wild-flower enthusiasts. On-site fly-
fishing and white-water canoeing. Open April to
October.

⊕ *A1 South-A61 to Ripon, then north for 5 miles. A1 North-
B6267 to West Tanfield, then left on A6108 for 0.5 miles.*

♥ *Special rates Mon-Thu at certain times during season.*

General 🏕🖳🏗P🔌🕭🚽🖵🌞 Leisure ⚓🏔🔍∪🎯🎣

RIPON, North Yorkshire Map ref 6C3

★★★★
HOLIDAY, TOURING
& CAMPING PARK

🚐 (60) £10.50–£15.50
🏕 (5) £10.50–£15.50
⛺ (40) £9.50–£13.50
100 touring pitches

Woodhouse Farm Caravan & Camping Park

Winksley, Ripon HG4 3PG **t** (01765) 658309 **e** woodhouse.farm@talk21.com
w woodhousewinksley.com

Spacious family park with two coarse-fishing
lakes, restaurant/bar, new amenity block, shop
and play areas. Open March to October.

payment Credit/debit cards, cash/cheques

General 🖳P🔌🕭🚽🖵✖🌞 Leisure 📺🍴⚓🏔∪🎯

ROOS, East Riding of Yorkshire Map ref 5D1

★★★★
HOLIDAY, TOURING
& CAMPING PARK
ROSE AWARD

🚐 (16) £10.00–£15.00
🏕 (2) £10.00–£15.00
🏠 (26) £135.00–£375.00
18 touring pitches

Sand-le-Mere Caravan & Leisure Park

Seaside Lane, Tunstall, Hull HU12 0JQ **t** (01964) 670403 **f** (01964) 671099
e info@sand-le-mere.co.uk **w** sand-le-mere.co.uk

A great place to stay, with its natural park and
mere leading to a gentle slope to the beach. No
cliffs to climb.

payment Credit/debit cards, cash/cheques,
euros

General P🔌🕭🖵✖🌞 Leisure ⚡📺🍴🎵⚓∪🎯🚲

Check the maps

Colour maps at the front pinpoint all the places you will find accommodation
entries in the regional sections. Pick your location and then refer to the place
index at the back to find the page number.

SCARBOROUGH, North Yorkshire Map ref 6D3

★★★★★
TOURING & CAMPING PARK

£11.50–£24.00
£11.50–£24.00
£9.00–£18.00
200 touring pitches

Cayton Village Caravan Park

Mill Lane, Cayton Bay, Scarborough YO11 3NN **t** (01723) 583171 **e** info@caytontouring.co.uk
w caytontouring.co.uk

payment Credit/debit cards, cash/cheques

The very best of coast and country. Luxurious facilities, adventure playground, site shop, dog walk. Seasonal pitches, supersites, hardstanding and storage. Open March to October. Half a mile to beach, three miles to Scarborough, four miles to Filey. Next to village with pubs, chip shop, post office and bus service.

⊕ *A64; take B1261 to Cayton village. 2nd left after Blacksmiths Arms into Mill Lane. Park is 150yds on left.*

♥ *Low-season savers: 7 nights – £7 discount, any 4 nights Sun-Thu inclusive – £4 discount, Senior Citizen 7-night special – £10 discount.*

General P ☼ Leisure

SCARBOROUGH, North Yorkshire Map ref 6D3

★★★★
HOLIDAY, TOURING & CAMPING PARK
ROSE AWARD

(50) £14.00–£22.00
(50) £10.00–£22.00
(100) £10.00–£18.00
(40) £120.00–£475.00
150 touring pitches

Crows Nest Caravan Park

Gristhorpe, Filey YO14 9PS **t** (01723) 582206 **f** (01723) 582206
e enquiries@crowsnestcaravanpark.com **w** crowsnestcaravanpark.com

This family-owned, rose-award-winning park is situated between the attractions of Scarborough and the tranquillity of Filey. Full facilities. Holidays and short breaks for families and couples.

payment Credit/debit cards, cash/cheques

General P ☼ Leisure TV

SCARBOROUGH, North Yorkshire Map ref 6D3

★★★★★
HOLIDAY, TOURING & CAMPING PARK
ROSE AWARD

(220) £13.50–£18.50
(30) £13.50–£18.50
(50) £11.00–£18.50
(20) £190.00–£450.00
300 touring pitches

Flower of May Holiday Parks Ltd

Lebberston, Scarborough YO11 3NU **t** (01723) 584311 **f** (01723) 581361 **e** info@flowerofmay.com
w flowerofmay.com

payment Credit/debit cards, cash/cheques

Excellent facilities on family-run park. Luxury indoor pool, adventure playground, golf course. Ideal for coast and country. Prices based per pitch, per night for four people with car. Open April to October.

⊕ *From A64 take the A165 Scarborough/Filey coast road. Well signposted at Lebberston.*

♥ *Early-booking discount: £25 off full week's hire. 10% discount off full week's pitch fees, booked by post in advance.*

General P ☼ Leisure TV

SCARBOROUGH, North Yorkshire Map ref 6D3

★★★★★
TOURING PARK

(125) £12.50–£15.00
(40) £12.50–£15.00
125 touring pitches

Lebberston Touring Park

Lebberston, Scarborough YO11 3PE **t** (01723) 585723 **e** info@lebberstontouring.co.uk
w lebberstontouring.co.uk

Quiet country location. Well-spaced pitches. Extensive south-facing views. Ideal park for a peaceful, relaxing break. Fully modernised amenity blocks. Dogs on lead. Open March to October.

payment Credit/debit cards, cash/cheques

General P WP ☼

SLINGSBY, North Yorkshire Map ref 6C3

★★★★★
HOLIDAY, TOURING
& CAMPING PARK
ROSE AWARD

🚐(32) £10.00–£18.00
🚏(32) £10.00–£18.00
⛺ (32) £10.00–£18.00
🏠(20) £140.00–£455.00
32 touring pitches

Robin Hood Caravan & Camping Park

Green Dyke Lane, Slingsby, York YO62 4AP t (01653) 628391 f (01653) 628392
e info@robinhoodcaravanpark.co.uk w robinhoodcaravanpark.co.uk

A privately owned park set in the heart of picturesque Ryedale. Peaceful and tranquil, but within easy reach of York, North Yorkshire Moors, FlamingoLand and the coast.

payment Credit/debit cards, cash/cheques

General 🚐 P ⊕ ☐ 🍴 🤳 📶 🗒 🐾 ☀ Leisure ⚠ ∪ ✈

SNAINTON, North Yorkshire Map ref 6D3

★★★★★
HOLIDAY, TOURING
& CAMPING PARK

🚐(74) £12.50–£18.00
🚏(74) £12.50–£18.00
⛺ (20) £10.50–£18.00
🏠(1) £190.00–£330.00
94 touring pitches

Jasmine Park

Cross Lane, Snainton, Scarborough YO13 9BE t (01723) 859240 f (01723) 859240
e info@jasminepark.co.uk w jasminepark.co.uk

payment Credit/debit cards, cash/cheques

Picturesque and peaceful park between Pickering and Scarborough. Winner of Yorkshire Caravan Park of the Year and Yorkshire in Bloom. National Silver winner of Excellence in England Caravan Park of the Year. Gold David Bellamy Conservation Award. Storage available. Open March to December.

⊕ Turn south off the A170 in Snainton opposite the junior school at traffic lights. Signposted.

General 🚐 P ⊕ ☐ 🍴 🚐 🤳 ⊙ 📶 🗒 🐾 ☀ Leisure ∪ ▶ 🚲

SNEATON, North Yorkshire Map ref 6D3

★★★★
TOURING PARK

🚐(93) £8.50–£19.60
🚏(93) £8.50–£19.60
93 touring pitches

See Ad on inside back cover

Low Moor Caravan Club Site

Sneaton, Whitby YO22 5JE t (01947) 810505 w caravanclub.co.uk

payment Credit/debit cards, cash/cheques

Grassy, level, moorland site, sheltered by fir trees. Beautiful views over moorland. Ideal site for dog owners and a paradise for walkers. Open March to November.

⊕ Turn left off A171 (Scarborough-Whitby). In 13.5 miles turn onto B1416. In 1.75 miles turn left through red gates. Site on right.

♥ Special member rates mean you can save your membership subscription in less than a week. Visit our website to find out more.

General P ⊕ ☐ 🚐 🐾

STAINFORTH, North Yorkshire Map ref 6B3

★★★★
HOLIDAY, TOURING
& CAMPING PARK

🚐(50) £12.00–£14.00
🚏   £12.00–£14.00
⛺ (50) £12.00–£14.00
100 touring pitches

Knight Stainforth Hall Caravan and Camping Park

Little Stainforth, Settle BD24 0DP t (01729) 822200 e info@knightstainforth.co.uk
w knightstainforth.co.uk

In the Yorkshire Dales on the banks of the River Ribble, close to waterfalls and the National Trust Pack Horse Bridge. Open March to October.

payment Credit/debit cards, cash/cheques

General 🚐 🚐 P ⊕ ☐ 🍴 🤳 ⊙ 📶 🗒 🐾 🕭 ☀ Leisure 📺 ♦ ⚠ ✈ ▶ 🏊

THIRSK, North Yorkshire Map ref 6C3

★★
TOURING & CAMPING PARK

(60)	£9.35–£19.60
(60)	£9.35–£19.60
	on application

60 touring pitches

See Ad on inside back cover

Thirsk Racecourse Caravan Club Site

Station Road, Thirsk YO7 1QL **t** (01845) 525266 **w** caravanclub.co.uk

payment Credit/debit cards, cash/cheques

Pitches are within sight of the racecourse main stand, looking over the famous turf, surrounded by Herriot Country and the Dales. Open March to October.

Site on left of A61 (Thirsk-South Kilvington).

Special member rates mean you can save your membership subscription in less than a week. Visit our website to find out more.

General P Leisure

THIRSK, North Yorkshire Map ref 6C3

★★★★
HOLIDAY, TOURING & CAMPING PARK

(20)	£11.00–£13.50
	£11.00–£13.50
(12)	£9.00–£18.50

32 touring pitches

York House Caravan Park

Balk YO7 2AQ **t** (01845) 597495 **e** yorkhouse@yhlparks.co.uk **w** yhlparks.co.uk

At the foot of the Hambleton Hills, horse-riding, rambling, golf, swimming and sports all in the area. Nearest town is Thirsk. Open March to November.

payment Credit/debit cards, cash/cheques

General P Leisure

WHITBY, North Yorkshire Map ref 6D3

★★★★
HOLIDAY PARK
ROSE AWARD

(10) £200.00–£380.00

Flask Holiday Home Park

Robin Hood's Bay, Fylingdales, Whitby YO22 4QH **t** (01947) 880592 **f** (01947) 880592
e flaskinn@aol.com **w** flaskinn.com

payment Cash/cheques

Small, family-run site between Whitby and Scarborough, in the North York Moors. All super-luxury caravans have central heating and double glazing. Rose Award.

Situated on the A171, 7 miles to Whitby and 12 miles to Scarborough.

General P Leisure

WHITBY, North Yorkshire Map ref 6D3

★★★★★
TOURING & CAMPING PARK

	£13.50–£16.50
(6)	£13.50–£16.50
(4)	£11.80–£14.80

100 touring pitches

Ladycross Plantation Caravan Park

Whitby YO21 1UA **t** (01947) 895502 **e** enquiries@ladycrossplantation.co.uk
w ladycrossplantation.co.uk

Natural woodland site in the National Park. Caravans are pitched in groups of about ten within clearings in the trees. Central amenity block and five service points. Open 23 March to 21 October.

payment Credit/debit cards, cash/cheques

General P

WHITBY, North Yorkshire Map ref 6D3

★★★★★
**HOLIDAY, TOURING
& CAMPING PARK**
ROSE AWARD

🚐 (20) £10.00–£15.50
🚐 (20) £10.00–£15.50
⚠ (80) £8.00–£15.50
🏠 (30) £150.00–£565.00
100 touring pitches

Middlewood Farm Holiday Park

Middlewood Lane, Fylingthorpe, Robin Hood's Bay, Whitby YO22 4UF t (01947) 880414
f (01947) 880871 e info@middlewoodfarm.fsnet.co.uk w middlewoodfarm.com

payment Credit/debit cards, cash/cheques

Small, peaceful, award-winning family park. A walker's paradise with magnificent, panoramic coastal and moorland views! Level sheltered hardstandings, luxury heated facilities, private bathrooms, children's playground. Ten minutes' walk to pub/shops/beach. Superb caravans for hire. 'Twixt Whitby and Scarborough. Open: 1 March to 4 January. A friendly welcome awaits!

⊕ Follow A171 Scarborough to Whitby road signposted from Fylingthorpe junction. In Fylingthorpe turn onto Middlewood Lane. Park is 500yds. Follow brown tourist signs.

General P 🔌 🖰 🍴 🖵 🜕 ⊙ 🗐 🐾 🛗. Leisure 🏔 ∪ 🎣 🐾

WHITBY, North Yorkshire Map ref 6D3

★★★
HOLIDAY PARK

🏠 (6) £180.00–£280.00

Partridge Nest Farm Holiday Caravans

Eskdaleside, Whitby YO22 5ES t (01947) 810450 f (01947) 811413
e barbara@partridgenestfarm.com w partridgenestfarm.com

Partridge Nest Farm is a beautiful, secluded site with all its static caravans set away from the road, with fabulous views. Ideal for country lovers and bird-watchers. Open April to October.

payment Cash/cheques

General P 🜕 🐾

WITHERNSEA, East Riding of Yorkshire Map ref 5D1

★★★★
**HOLIDAY, TOURING
& CAMPING PARK**

🚐 (20) £14.00–£16.00
🚐 (10) £14.00–£16.00
🏠 (1) £150.00–£350.00
30 touring pitches

Willows Holiday Park

Hollym Road, Withernsea HU19 2PN t (01964) 612233 f (01964) 612957
e info@highfield.caravans.co.uk w highfield-caravans.co.uk

Set in attractive countryside, located within easy reach of the sea and town centre. Licensed club with family room, fishing lake, children's play area, mini-golf and laundry. Tesco supermarket nearby, ten-minute walk to beach.

open All year except Christmas and New Year
payment Cash/cheques

General 🔌 🖰 🍴 🜕 ⊙ 🗐 🐾 ☼ Leisure 🍷 🏔 🎣 ►

YORK, North Yorkshire Map ref 5C1

★★★★★
**TOURING &
CAMPING PARK**

🚐 £11.00–£12.50
🚐 £11.00–£12.50
40 touring pitches

Alders Caravan Park

Home Farm, Monk Green, Alne, York YO61 1RY t (01347) 838722 f (01347) 838722
e enquiries@homefarmalne.co.uk w alderscaravanpark.co.uk

On a working farm in historic parkland where visitors may enjoy peace and tranquillity. York (on bus route), moors, dales and coast nearby. Open March to October inclusive.

payment Cash/cheques

General 🔳 🚐 P 🔌 🖰 🍴 🜕 ⊙ 🖵 🐾 🛗.☼ Leisure 🎣 ►

visitBritain.com

Big city buzz or peaceful panoramas? Take a fresh look at Britain and you may be surprised at what's right on your doorstep. Explore the diversity online at visitbritain.com.

YORK, North Yorkshire Map ref 5C1

★★★★
HOLIDAY, TOURING & CAMPING PARK
ROSE AWARD

🚐 (20) £12.00–£14.00
🚙 (20) £12.00–£14.00
⛺ (20) £12.00–£14.00
🏠 (5) £207.00–£665.00
20 touring pitches

Allerton Park Caravan Park

Allerton Park, Knaresborough HG5 0SE **t** (01423) 330569 **f** (01759) 371377
e enquiries@yorkshireholidayparks.co.uk **w** yorkshireholidayparks.co.uk

A peaceful camping and caravan park 0.5 miles east of the A1 leading from the A59 York to Harrogate road. An ideal touring base for the York area. Overnight halts for A1 travellers.

payment Cash/cheques

General P 🚗 🗑 👤 🐾 ☺ 📼 🖥 🛒 ☼ Leisure ∪

YORK, North Yorkshire Map ref 5C1

★★★
HOLIDAY, TOURING & CAMPING PARK

🚐 (30) £14.00–£16.00
🚙 £14.00–£16.00
⛺ (30) £11.00–£13.00

Castle Howard Lakeside Holiday Park

Coneysthorpe YO60 7DD **t** (01653) 648316 **e** lakeside@castlehoward.co.uk **w** castlehoward.co.uk

This peaceful lakeside site has views of Castle Howard which is within walking distance. Pitches available for touring caravans and tents with electrical hook-up. Open March to October.

payment Credit/debit cards, cash/cheques

General P 🚗 👤 🐾 ☺ 🖥 🛒 Leisure ⚓

YORK, North Yorkshire Map ref 5C1

★★★★
HOLIDAY & TOURING PARK
ROSE AWARD

🚐 £12.00–£14.00
🚙 £12.00–£14.00
🏠 (8) £210.00–£475.00
20 touring pitches

Weir Caravan Park

Buttercrambe Road, Stamford Bridge, York YO41 1AN **t** (01759) 371377 **f** (01759) 371377
e enquiries@yorkshireholidayparks.co.uk **w** yorkshireholidayparks.co.uk

On level grassland seven miles east of York on the A166. Near the river where fishing is available. Village, pubs, restaurants etc are within a five-minute walk.

payment Cash/cheques

General P 🚗 🗑 👤 🐾 ☺ 🖥 🛒 ☼ Leisure ∪ ⚓

YORK, North Yorkshire Map ref 5C1

★★★★
TOURING & CAMPING PARK

🚐 (20) £10.00–£18.50
🚙 (20) £10.00–£18.50
⛺ (10) £10.00–£18.50
40 touring pitches

York Touring Caravan Site

Towthorpe Lane, Towthorpe, York YO32 9ST **t** (01904) 499275 **f** (01904) 499271
e info@yorkcaravansite.co.uk **w** yorkcaravansite.co.uk

open All year
payment Credit/debit cards, cash/cheques

Small, family-run, secluded park in an idyllic countryside setting, only five miles from York centre. Spacious pitches and superior facilities. New shower and toilet facilities. Bar open Friday and Saturday nights.

✦ *Travelling on the A64 towards Scarborough/Malton take the turn-off to the left signposted Strensall/Haxby. We are 1 mile down that road on the left.*

❤ *Book 7 nights in advance and only pay for 6 (excl Bank Holidays).*

General P 🚗 👤 📼 🐾 ☺ 📼 🖥 🛒 ☼ Leisure 📺 🍴 ⛰ ∪ ⚓ 🏹 🚲

Place index

If you know where you want to stay the index at the back of the guide will give you the page number which lists parks in or near your chosen town, city or village. Check out the other useful indexes too.

Heart of England

Birmingham › Black Country › Coventry & Warwickshire
Herefordshire & the Wye Valley › Shakespeare Country
Shropshire & the Welsh Borders › Staffordshire & the Peak District
Stoke & The Potteries › Worcestershire

gritstone heights, colourful canals, pioneering heritage

Main Sweeping views of the River Wye and The Forest of Dean from Symonds Yat
Left Shop until you drop at Birmingham's Bullring; take up the challenge at The Roaches, Staffordshire; alongside the Grand Union Canal, Hatton; impressive birds of prey at Warwick Castle

Cruise the inland waterways, discover rich industrial heritage and explore ruined castles. Home of the country's second biggest city, one of the world's leading theme parks and inspiring Shakespeare country, **the Heart of England is action packed.**

Explore
Heart of England

A Tale of Two Cities

You'll find yourself in shopping heaven in Birmingham's Bullring. With hundreds of outlets covering the space of 26 football pitches, this shoppers' paradise will satisfy your every retail need! Party 'til dawn in this City of Entertainment, with lively chatter in canal-side cafes and non-stop nightlife. Indulge in a visit to Cadbury World, learn the history of the nation's favourite treat and, if you're lucky, sample steaming liquid chocolate straight from the vat. Marvel at ruffled Pufferfish and explore AmaZonia at the Sea Life Centre.

Get in gear for a visit to Coventry Transport Museum where the fantastic collection of motor vehicles rivals any in the country. Tread softly around the awe-inspiring cathedral – a remarkable modern structure built upon ruins from World War II. Hop on a boat and cruise down the Canal Art Trail, or wander around Millennium Place where the stunning glass bridge and use of public space for artistic purposes will leave you speechless.

Historic times

Test your literary knowledge with a trip to the black-and-white town of Stratford-upon-Avon. Visit the birthplace of its most famous inhabitant – William Shakespeare – and gain an insight into the Tudor world in which the bard lived. Discover the horrors of the oubliette at Warwick Castle and learn the grizzly past of the historic fortress. Get your mind racing at the Ironbridge Gorge Museums and interactive technology centre in Shropshire – stroll amongst working Victorians at Blists Hill or let your imagination run wild at Enginuity.

Discover the story of Stoke-on-Trent's people, industry, products and landscapes at The Potteries – the world's finest collection of Staffordshire ceramics. Or explore the remarkable ruins of Witley Court, a once great Jacobean manor-house, near Worcester. Take a picnic and spend a day in the picturesque and historic Shropshire market town of Ludlow: peer from the ruins of the cliff-top castle or stroll the banks of the sleepy River Teme.

Rolling hills

Gaze out from Worcestershire Beacon across the undulating Malvern Hills for spectacular views of the Cotswolds. Admire differing landscapes and explore geological variety and patchwork fields. Follow the Wye Valley through breathtaking scenery, and take time to enjoy the outstanding views from Symonds Yat and spot peregrines.

Step up the pace and head out on foot across the Shropshire Hills. Challenge yourself to a section of the hundreds of miles of footpaths leading you along ancient trackways, through river valleys and down sunken lanes.

Goblins and grassland

Hold on tight and feel your senses spin at the ever-popular Alton Towers theme park. Or go on a journey across Middle-earth (Birmingham) on the Tolkien Trail and explore the local landmarks that inspired the many settings for The Lord of the Rings.

Tee off in the glorious setting of Trentham Park in Staffordshire, or wander into the National Forest, relax amongst the trees and spot abundant wildlife.

Places to **visit**

0 ——————— 50 miles
0 ——————— 75 kms

PEAK
DISTRICT

Stoke-on-Trent

OFFA'S DYKE
PATH

Stafford

The National
Forest

Shrewsbury

Cannock
Chase

5

54

Ironbridge

Dudley •

Birmingham

Shropshire
Hills

• Solihull

Coventry

OFFA'S DYKE
PATH

5

Rugby •

• Ludlow

Warwick •

Worcester

Stratford-upon-Avon

Kington

Malvern
Hills

Hay-on-Wye •

Broadway

Hereford

Wye
Valley

Cotswolds

OFFA'S DYKE
PATH

Ross-
on-Wye •

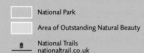

National Park

Area of Outstanding Natural Beauty

National Trails
nationaltrail.co.uk

Sections of the
National Cycle Network
nationalcyclenetwork.org.uk

Alton Towers Theme Park
Stoke-on-Trent, Staffordshire
0870 520 4060
altontowers.com
Britain's number one theme park

**Black Country Living
Museum**
Dudley, West Midlands
(0121) 557 9643
bclm.co.uk
*Twenty-six acres of fascinating
living history*

Bullring
Birmingham, West Midlands
(0121) 632 1500
bullring.co.uk
*Hundreds of outlets – a
shopper's paradise*

Cadbury World
Birmingham,
West Midlands
0845 450 3599
cadburyworld.co.uk
*Chocolate-making
demonstrations and samples*

Sea Life Centre
Birmingham, West Midlands
(0121) 643 6777
sealife.co.uk
Marine life at your fingertips

Shakespeare's Birthplace
Stratford-upon-Avon,
Warwickshire
(01789) 201822
shakespeare.org.uk
The bard's inspiring dwelling place

Tolkien Trail
Birmingham, West Midlands
(0121) 777 6612
bmag.org.uk/sarehole_mill
Journey through Middle-earth

Canal Art Trail
Coventry, West Midlands
(024) 7678 5507
covcanalsoc.org.uk
Cruise through five miles of inspiring work

Cider Museum and King Offa Distillery
Hereford
(01432) 354207
cidermuseum.co.uk
Be sure to sample a free tasting of distillery products

Coventry Cathedral
Coventry, West Midlands
(024) 7652 1200
coventrycathedral.org
Glorious and unique 20th-century arcitecture to both inspire and enthrall

Coventry Transport Museum
Coventry, West Midlands
(024) 7623 4270
transport-museum.com
Fascinating and immense collection of vehicles spanning the ages

Hawkstone Hall and Gardens
Shrewsbury, Shropshire
(01630) 685242
hawkstone-hall.com
Beautiful Georgian mansion in spacious parkland with outstanding rose gardens and a stunning lilly pool

Ironbridge Gorge Museums
Shropshire
(01952) 435900
ironbridge.org.uk
Revolutionary inventions in inspiring museums

Millennium Place
Coventry, West Midlands
(024) 7622 7264
coventryinspires.com
Stunning public art space

National Motorcycle Museum
Solihull, West Midlands
(01675) 443311
nationalmotorcyclemuseum.co.uk
Largest of its kind in the world

The Potteries
Stoke-on-Trent,
Staffordshire
(01782) 236000
visitstoke.co.uk
Finest collection of Staffordshire ceramics

Trentham Leisure
Stoke-on-Trent,
Staffordshire
(01782) 657341
trenthamleisure.co.uk
Incredibly scenic, outstanding leisure complex

Warwick Castle
0870 442 2000
warwick-castle.co.uk
Historic fortress with grizzly past

West Midland Safari and Leisure Park
Bewdley, Worcestershire
(01299) 402114
wmsp.co.uk
Observe rare white lions

Witley Court
Worcestershire
0870 333 1181
english-heritage.co.uk
Country house with stunning grounds

Tourist information centres

When you arrive at your destination, visit a tourist information centre for help with accommodation and information about local attractions and events, or email your request before you go.

Bewdley	Load Street	(01299) 404740	bewdleytic@btconnect.com
Birmingham (NEC)	The Atrium	(0121) 202 5099	atrium@marketingbirmingham.com
Birmingham (NEC)	The Piazza	(0121) 202 5099	piazza@marketingbirmingham.com
Birmingham Rotunda	150 New Street	(0121) 202 5099	ticketshop@marketingbirmingham.com
Bridgnorth	Listley Street	(01746) 763257	bridgnorth.tourism@shropshire-cc.gov.uk
Bromsgrove	26 Birmingham Road	(01527) 831809	
Bromyard	Cruxwell Street	(01432) 260280	tic-bromyard@herefordshire.gov.uk
Burton upon Trent	Horninglow Street	(01283) 508111	tic@eaststaffsbc.gov.uk
Church Stretton	Church Street	(01694) 723133	churchstretton.tourism@shropshire-cc.gov.uk
Coventry	4 Priory Row	(024) 7622 7264	tic@cvone.co.uk
Droitwich Spa	Victoria Square	(01905) 774312	heritage@droitwichspa.gov.uk
Dudley	St James's Road	(01384) 812830	information.centre@dudley.gov.uk
Ellesmere, Shropshire*	Mereside	(01691) 622981	ellesmere.tourism@shropshire-cc.gov.uk
Evesham	Abbey Gate	(01386) 446944	tic@almonry.ndo.co.uk
Hereford	1 King Street	(01432) 268430	tic-hereford@herefordshire.gov.uk
Ironbridge	Ironbridge Gorge Museum Trust	(01952) 884391	tic@ironbridge.org.uk
Kenilworth	11 Smalley Place	(01926) 748900	kenilworthlibrary@warwickshire.gov.uk
Leamington Spa	The Parade	(01926) 742762	leamington@shakespeare-country.co.uk
Ledbury	3 The Homend	(01531) 636147	tic-ledbury@herefordshire.gov.uk
Leek	Stockwell Street	(01538) 483741	tourism.services@staffsmoorlands.gov.uk
Leominster	1 Corn Square	(01568) 616460	
Lichfield	Bore Street	(01543) 308209	info@visitlichfield.com
Ludlow	Castle Street	(01584) 875053	ludlow.tourism@shropshire-cc.gov.uk
Malvern	21 Church Street	(01684) 892289	malvern.tic@malvernhills.gov.uk
Market Drayton	49 Cheshire Street	(01630) 653114	marketdrayton.tourism@shropshire-cc.gov.uk
Merry Hill	Merry Hill	(01384) 487900	
Much Wenlock*	High Street	(01952) 727679	muchwenlock.tourism@shropshire-cc.gov.uk
Newcastle-under-Lyme	Ironmarket	(01782) 297313	tic.newcastle@staffordshire.gov.uk
Nuneaton	Church Street	(024) 7634 7006	nuneatonlibrary@warwickshire.gov.uk
Oswestry (Mile End)	Mile End	(01691) 662488	tic@oswestry-bc.gov.uk
Oswestry Town (Heritage Centre)	2 Church Terrace	(01691) 662753	ot@oswestry-welshborders.org.uk
Queenswood*	Dinmore Hill	(01568) 797842	
Redditch	Alcester Street	(01527) 60806	info.centre@redditchbc.gov.uk
Ross-on-Wye	Edde Cross Street	(01989) 562768	tic-ross@herefordshire.gov.uk
Rugby	Little Elborow Street	(01788) 534970	visitor.centre@rugby.gov.uk
Shrewsbury	The Square	(01743) 281200	tic@shrewsburytourism.co.uk

Solihull	Homer Road	(0121) 704 6130	ckelly@solihull.gov.uk
Stafford	Market Street	(01785) 619619	tic@staffordbc.gov.uk
Stoke-on-Trent	Bagnall Street	(01782) 236000	stoke.tic@stoke.gov.uk
Stratford-upon-Avon	Bridgefoot	0870 160 7930	stratfordtic@shakespeare-country.co.uk
Tamworth	29 Market Street	(01827) 709581	tic@tamworth.gov.uk
Telford	The Telford Centre	(01952) 238008	tourist-info@telfordshopping.co.uk
Upton-upon-Severn	4 High Street	(01684) 594200	upton.tic@malvernhills.gov.uk
Walsall	St Pauls Street	(01922) 625540	walsalltt&i@travelwm.co.uk
Warwick	Jury Street	(01926) 492212	touristinfo@warwick-uk.co.uk
Whitchurch (Shropshire)	12 St Mary's Street	(01948) 664577	whitchurch.heritage@ukonline.co.uk
Wolverhampton	18 Queen Square	(01902) 556110	wolverhampton.tic@dial.pipex.com
Worcester	High Street	(01905) 726311	touristinfo@cityofworcester.gov.uk

* seasonal opening

Alternatively, you can text **TIC LOCATE** to **64118** to find your nearest tourist information centre

Find out **more**

The following publications are available from Heart of England Tourism by logging on to **visitheartofengland.com** or calling **(01905) 761100**:

Bed & Breakfast Touring Map including Camping and Caravan Parks 2007

Visit the Heart of England 2007
Attractions in the Heart of England.

Gardens of the Heart
Details of over 100 from around the region, from small cottage gardens to grand formal affairs.

Heart of England in Bloom Floral Trail
A guide to cities, towns and villages involved in the regional Britain in Bloom competition.

Touring the Heart
Ideas for driving, cycling, boating and walking.

Heroes of the Heart
Attractions associated with some of the famous people from the region.

Heritage of the Heart
Detailed information on the historic properties in the Heart of England.

Family Fun in the Heart
A guide to family friendly attractions.

Travel **info**

By road:
Britain's main motorways (M1/M6/M5) meet in the Heart of England; the M40 links with the M42 south of Birmingham while the M4 provides fast access from London to the south of the region. These road links ensure that the Heart of England is more accessible by road than any other region in the UK.

By rail:
The Heart of England is served by an excellent rail network. InterCity rail services are fast and frequent from London and other major cities into the region. Trains run from Euston to Birmingham, Coventry and Rugby; from Paddington to the Cotswolds, Stratford-upon-Avon and Worcester; and from Marylebone to Birmingham and Stourbridge. From the main stations a network of regional routes take you around the Heart of England.

By air:
Fly into Birmingham, Coventry or Nottingham East Midlands.

where to stay in
Heart of England

All place names in the blue bands are shown on the maps at the front of this guide.

A complete listing of all VisitBritain assessed parks in England appears at the back.

Accommodation symbols

Symbols give useful information about services and facilities. Inside the back-cover flap you can find a key to these symbols. Keep it open for easy reference.

ASTON CANTLOW, Warwickshire Map ref 3B1

★★★
HOLIDAY, TOURING
& CAMPING PARK

🚐 (24)	£16.00
🚍 (24)	£16.00
▲ (10)	£13.00
🏠 (5)	£295.00–£395.00

24 touring pitches

Island Meadow Caravan Park

The Mill House, Aston Cantlow B95 6JP t (01789) 488273 f (01789) 488273
e holiday@islandmeadowcaravanpark.co.uk w islandmeadowcaravanpark.co.uk

A quiet, peaceful riverside park just outside the historic village of Aston Cantlow and within six miles of Stratford. An ideal centre for Warwick, Evesham, Birmingham and the Cotswolds. Open March to October.

payment Cash/cheques, euros

General P 🚐 🕭 🚿 🛐 🖵 🖭 ☺ 🗐 🖸 🧺 ♀ ♠ ☼ Leisure ♪

BIRMINGHAM, West Midlands Map ref 5B3

★★★★★
TOURING PARK

🚐 (99)	£12.50–£25.10
🚍 (99)	£12.50–£25.10

99 touring pitches

See Ad on inside back cover

Chapel Lane Caravan Club Site

Chapel Lane, Wythall, Birmingham B47 6JX t (01564) 826483 w caravanclub.co.uk

open All year
payment Credit/debit cards, cash/cheques

Wythall is a quiet, rural area yet convenient for Birmingham (nine miles) and the NEC (13 miles). Visit Cadbury's World or explore the surrounding countryside and local canals.

⊕ *From M1 jct 23a, jct 3 off M42 then A435 to Birmingham. After 1 mile at roundabout take 1st exit, Middle Lane. Turn right at church then immediately right into site.*

♥ *Special member rates mean you can save your membership subscription in less than a week. Visit our website to find out more.*

General 🖵 P 🚐 🕭 🚿 🛐 🖭 ☺ 🗐 🖸 ♀ ☼ Leisure ⚠ ♪ ▶

BIRMINGHAM INTERNATIONAL AIRPORT

See under Birmingham, Meriden

Check it out

Information on parks listed in this guide has been supplied by proprietors. As changes may occur you should remember to check all relevant details at the time of booking.

BRIDGNORTH, Shropshire Map ref 5A3

Park Grange Holidays

★★★★
HOLIDAY PARK
🚐(5)　£5.00–£12.00
🚍　£5.00–£12.00
🛏(4) £161.00–£336.00

Park Grange, Morville, Bridgnorth WV16 4RN　t (01746) 714285　f (01746) 714145
e info@parkgrangeholidays.co.uk　w parkgrangeholidays.co.uk

Holiday caravans set in 24 acres of glorious
Shropshire countryside. Small, secluded and safe
family park with goats, pony, wildlife and fishing
ponds. Caravan Club members only on touring
site.

open All year
payment Cash/cheques, euros

General 🖵 🚗 P 🍴 📶 ☼　Leisure 🏔 ∪ ♪ ↟ 🚴

BROMYARD, Herefordshire Map ref 3B1

Bromyard Downs Caravan Club Site

★★★★
HOLIDAY &
CAMPING PARK
🚐(40)　£7.90–£17.10
🚍(40)　£7.90–£17.10
40 touring pitches

See Ad on inside back cover

Brockhampton, Bringsty, Worcester WR6 5TE　t (01885) 482607　w caravanclub.co.uk

payment Credit/debit cards, cash/cheques

Secluded woodland site set in beautiful countryside
between the cathedral cities of Hereford and
Worcester, with many lovely walks nearby. Open
March to October.

⊕ *Site on left of A44 (Worcester-Bromyard) about 0.25 miles
past Brockhampton (National Trust) entrance.*

♥ *Special member rates mean you can save your membership
subscription in less than a week. Visit our website to find
out more.*

General P 🚗 ➍ 🐾

ELLESMERE, Shropshire Map ref 5A2

Fernwood Caravan Park

★★★★★
HOLIDAY &
TOURING PARK
🚐　£15.50–£19.50
🚍　£15.50–£19.50
🛏(1) £280.00–£410.00
60 touring pitches

Lyneal, Ellesmere SY12 0QF　t (01948) 710221　f (01948) 710324　e enquiries@fernwoodpark.co.uk
w fernwoodpark.co.uk

Picturesque, 25-acre country park for static
holiday homes, tourers and motor homes. Forty
acres' adjacent woodland and lake for coarse
fishing. Shop and launderette. Pets welcome.

payment Credit/debit cards, cash/cheques

General 🖵 P 🚗 ➍ 🍴 🚗 ⌂ ☉ 📶📶 🐾 ☼　Leisure 🏔 ♪

EVESHAM, Worcestershire Map ref 3B1

The Ranch Caravan Park

★★★★★
HOLIDAY &
TOURING PARK
🚐　£16.50–£21.50
🚍　£16.50–£21.50
🛏(4) £290.00–£420.00
120 touring pitches

Station Road, Honeybourne, Evesham WR11 7PR　t (01386) 830744　f (01386) 833503
e enquiries@ranch.co.uk　w ranch.co.uk

An established family-run holiday park located in
Honeybourne, six miles from Evesham. Level
pitches in a landscaped setting. Well situated for
visiting the Cotswolds and Shakespeare Country.
Open March to November.

payment Credit/debit cards, cash/cheques

General 🖵 P 🚗 ➍ 🍴 🚗 ⌂ ☉ 📶📶 🐾 ✕ 🐾 ☼　Leisure ➰ 📺 🍴 ♪ 🔦 🏔

HEREFORD, Herefordshire Map ref 3A1

★★★★★
**HOLIDAY &
TOURING PARK**
ROSE AWARD

🚐 (80) £11.00–£12.00
🚚 (80) £11.00–£12.00
⛺ (40) £6.50–£12.00
🏠 (2) £170.00–£300.00
80 touring pitches

Lucksall Caravan and Camping Park

Mordiford, Hereford HR1 4LP **t** (01432) 870213 **f** (01432) 870213 **e** enquiries@lucksallpark.co.uk
w lucksallpark.co.uk

Peacefully situated on the banks of the River Wye. Seventeen acres of level ground, 16-amp hook-up. Excellent for walking, canoeing, fishing. Disabled facilities, shop, canoe hire. Open 1 March to 30 November.

payment Credit/debit cards

General 🔌🖥️🚐P🔥🍴🚿🚰☕🌂☉🍳🔒🛒🐾🐶⛽☼ Leisure 🏔️ 🏊 🚴

LITTLE TARRINGTON, Herefordshire Map ref 3A1

★★★★★
**TOURING &
CAMPING PARK**

🚐 (40) £13.00–£16.00
🚚 (40) £13.00–£16.00
⛺ (15) £11.50–£16.00
55 touring pitches

The Millpond

Little Tarrington, Hereford HR1 4JA **t** (01432) 890243 **f** (01432) 890243 **e** enquiries@millpond.co.uk

The Millpond is a coarse-fishing lake with touring caravan and camping facilities, set in a rural landscape, surrounded by woodland planting. Open March to October.

payment Cash/cheques

General 🖥️P🔥🍴☕🌂☉🍳🐾🐶☼ Leisure 🏊

MERIDEN, West Midlands Map ref 5B3

★★★★★
TOURING PARK

🚐 (48) £17.00
🚚 (48) £17.00
48 touring pitches

Somers Wood Caravan Park

Somers Road, Meriden CV7 7PL **t** (01676) 522978 **f** (01676) 522978
e enquiries@somerswood.co.uk **w** somerswood.co.uk

A quality touring park, set in woodland, exclusively for adults. Adjacent golf course, club house and coarse fishery. Three miles from the National Exhibition Centre. Open 1 February to 15 December.

payment Credit/debit cards, cash/cheques

General P🔥🍴🚿🌂☉🍳🐾 Leisure ⛳🏊▶

RUGELEY, Staffordshire Map ref 5B3

★★★★
HOLIDAY PARK
ROSE AWARD

🏠 (9) £259.00–£440.00

Silver Trees Caravan Park

Stafford Brook Road, Penkridge Bank, Rugeley WS15 2TX **t** (01889) 582185 **f** (01889) 582373
e enquiries@silvertreescaravanpark.co.uk **w** silvertreescaravanpark.co.uk

Rose Award holiday homes to hire in quiet woodland park, suitable for couples and families enjoying wildlife, walks and cycling on Cannock Chase. Area of Outstanding Natural Beauty. View deer from your caravan! Open March to Christmas.

payment Credit/debit cards, cash/cheques

General P🌂🍳🔒 Leisure 🎣🏊⛳🚴

Our quality rating schemes

For a detailed explanation of the quality and facilities represented by the stars please refer to the back of this guide.

STOKE-ON-TRENT, Staffordshire Map ref 5B2

★★★★★
**HOLIDAY, TOURING
& CAMPING PARK**
ROSE AWARD

⚐ (60) £12.00–£14.00
🚐 (30) £12.00–£14.00
Å (30) £12.00–£14.00
⛺ (9) £280.00–£400.00
120 touring pitches

The Star Caravan and Camping Park

Star Road, Cotton, Stoke-on-Trent ST10 3DW **t** (01538) 702219 **f** (01538) 703704
w starcaravanpark.co.uk

payment Cash/cheques

The closest touring park to Alton Towers. Strict 11pm-all-quiet rule on site. No single-sex groups allowed. Families and mixed couples always welcomed. Set in stunning countryside surrounded by mature trees and hedgerows. Ten miles from four market towns, and only four miles from the Peak District National Park. Open March to October.

⊕ *From M6 jct 16 or M1 jct 23a follow signs for Alton Towers. Go past and follow the road (Beelow Lane) for 0.75 miles to crossroad. Turn right up hill. Site on right after 400m.*

♥ *Early-season discounts on caravan holidays homes. Free 2nd-day admission to Alton Towers for 2 persons (ring for information).*

General 🖵 P ⚐ ⌂ 🐾 ⟲ 🄑🔟 🐾 ⚓ ☼ Leisure 🛆 ∪ 🕹 🚲

STRATFORD-UPON-AVON, Warwickshire Map ref 3B1

★★★
**TOURING &
CAMPING PARK**
⚐ (50) £14.00–£16.00
🚐 (50) £14.00–£16.00
Å (50) £12.50–£14.50
50 touring pitches

Dodwell Park

Evesham Rd, Stratford-upon-Avon CV37 9SR **t** (01789) 204957 **f** (01926) 620199
e enquiries@dodwellpark.co.uk **w** dodwellpark.co.uk

Small, family-run touring park two miles south west of Stratford-upon-Avon on the B439. Country walks to River Avon and Luddington village. Ideal for visiting Warwick Castle, Shakespeare's birthplace and the Cotswolds.

open All year
payment Credit/debit cards, cash/cheques

General 🖵 P ⚐ ⌂ 🐾 ⟲ 🄑🔟 🐾 ⚓ ☼ Leisure 🕹 🚲

UTTOXETER, Staffordshire Map ref 5B2

★★
TOURING PARK
⚐ (76) £8.50–£19.60
🚐 (76) £8.50–£19.60
Å on application
76 touring pitches

See Ad on inside back cover

Uttoxeter Racecourse Caravan Club Site

Wood Lane, Uttoxeter ST14 8BD **t** (01889) 564172 **w** caravanclub.co.uk

payment Credit/debit cards, cash/cheques

Popular site with families, for its proximity to Alton Towers, and dog owners, for its 60 acres of exercise space. Good for golfers and racing enthusiasts. Open March to November.

⊕ *Turn off A50 at roundabout onto A518. Site entrance on left.*

♥ *Special member rates mean you can save your membership subscription in less than a week. Visit our website to find out more.*

General P ⚐ ⌂ ⚐ 🄑 🄑🔟 🐾 Leisure ⚑

WYE VALLEY

See under Hereford

Check the maps

Colour maps at the front pinpoint all the places you will find accommodation entries in the regional sections. Pick your location and then refer to the place index at the back to find the page number.

East Midlands

Derbyshire & the Peak District › Leicestershire & Rutland
Lincolnshire › Northamptonshire › Nottinghamshire

On target at Sherwood Forest Country Park

England's East Midlands
enjoyeastmidlands.com
Leicester Shire Promotions
0906 294 1113
goleicestershire.com
Lincolnshire Tourism
(01522) 526450
visitlincolnshire.com

Explore Northamptonshire
(01604) 838800
explorenorthamptonshire.co.uk
Experience Nottinghamshire
(0115) 962 8300
visitnottingham.com
Peak District and Derbyshire
0870 444 7275
derbyshirethepeakdistrict.com
visitpeakdistrict.com

Pleasurable peaks, forest adventure, vibrant cities

Main Live the high life in the Peak District **Left** There's always time for adventure at Rockingham Castle, Market Harborough; celebrate Diwali in style in Leicester; cruising along the Grand Union Canal; time for lift-off at the National Space Centre, Leicester

From the adventurous trails of the Peak District and the gentle waters of the Leicestershire canals to the vibrant, cosmopolitan buzz of the cities – **the East Midlands may surprise you.**

Explore
East Midlands

Picture the scene

Take up the challenge and scale the face of a weathered crag in the Peak District, or find your feet on a section of the Pennine Way where spectacular scenery will spur you on. Disappear underground and try potholing, or get those bicycle wheels spinning and head out across Derwent Valley past historic reservoirs and enchanting woodland.

The National Forest is crying out for a visit: take to the water and sail across one of its beautiful lakes, or don your green fingers and plant a tree, and become involved in the future of the forest. Let the kids go nuts for Conkers at the heart of the forest for unforgettable outdoor experiences.

Lose yourself in legend in Sherwood Forest, home of the notorious Robin Hood, try your hand at a spot of archery and hunt for the Major Oak. Explore the rich heritage and natural beauty of the fens, and keep your eyes peeled for the vast array of wildlife at Rutland Water Nature Reserve.

City diversity

Let your senses guide you down Belgrave Road in Leicester to sample the vast range of curried delights. Explore the city's historic quarter, and drop in on the National Space Centre for an experience, quite literally, out of this world! Travel through centuries of crime and punishment at Nottingham's Galleries of Justice, or slip on some headphones for an audio tour in the preserved workhouse in Southwell and listen to the forgotten inhabitants.

Indulge in a treat as you stroll around the unique shopping areas of Lincoln and gaze up in awe from the base of the hilltop cathedral. Unravel 250,000 years of history at The Collection – the city's museum of art and archaeology – where the exhibitions are continually growing, or head 'downhill' – as the locals call it – for the vibrant nightlife and cafe culture.

Fun for all the family

Watch your knuckles turn white on the Boomerang at Pleasure Island in Cleethorpes, or observe seals and penguins playfully scrambling for fish at Natureland on the 'Fun Coast' in Skegness.

Rifle your way through one of the oldest markets in the region in Bakewell and sample one of the local tarts. Catch a glimpse of the traditional and decorative well dressing, on display throughout Derbyshire. Watch the sun sparkle off the jets from the beautiful fountains at Chatsworth House, or take a step back in time at delightful medieval manor-house, Haddon Hall.

Sights to behold

Pull your boots on and follow the enthralling five-mile Bamford Touchstones Sculpture Trail in Derbyshire, or roll out a picnic rug in the beautiful gardens of Althorp in Northamptonshire – home of the Spencer family for over 500 years. Wander through the grounds of the remarkable Rockingham Castle, built on the instruction of William the Conqueror, and fill your lungs with the sweet scent of the stunning 19th-century rose garden.

Places to **visit**

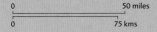

0   50 miles
0   75 kms

Barton-upon-Humber

Burton upon Stather

Scunthorpe   **Grimsby**   Cleethorpes

PENNINE WAY

Derwent Reservoir
Ladybower Reservoir

Edale

Lincolnshire Wolds

Buxton

PEAK DISTRICT

Bakewell

[67]

[6]

Lincoln   **Skegness**

PENNINE BRIDLEWAY

Matlock
Carsington Water

[1]

Nottingham

Boston

[68]

Derby

Ashby-de-la-Zouch
The National Forest

Melton Mowbray **[12]**

Oakham

Leicester

Rutland Water

[6]

[70]

Northampton

Althorp
Northampton
(01604) 770107
althorp.com
Spencer family home since 1508

Bamford Touchstones Sculpture Trail
Derbyshire
bamfordvillage.co.uk
Encompassing all the natural elements

Bradgate Country Park
Newtown Linford, Leicestershire
(0116) 236 2713
nationalforest.org
Historic heather-covered parkland

Buxton Opera House
Buxton, Derbyshire
0845 127 2190
buxton-opera.co.uk
Beautifully restored Edwardian theatre

National Park

Area of Outstanding Natural Beauty

National Trails
nationaltrail.co.uk

Sections of the
National Cycle Network
nationalcyclenetwork.org.uk

[70] Regional Route

Chatsworth House, Garden, Farmyard & Adventure Playground
Bakewell, Derbyshire
(01246) 582204
chatsworth.org
Beautiful house and fountains

The Collection
Lincoln
(01522) 550990
thecollection.lincoln.museum
Museum of art and archaeology

Conkers
near Ashby-de-la-Zouch, Derbyshire
(01283) 216633
visitconkers.com
Interactive exhibits and woodland trails in The National Forest

Creswell Crags Museum and Education Centre, Picnic Site, Caves & Gorge
Worksop, Derbyshire
(01909) 720378
creswell-crags.org.uk
Limestone gorge, caves and lake

Crich Tramway Village
Matlock, Derbyshire
0870 758 7267
tramway.co.uk
Street scenes, rides and exhibits in a charming setting

Derwent Valley Visitor Centre
Belper, Derbyshire
(01773) 880474
belpernorthmill.org.uk
Industrial exhibits, models and machinery

The Galleries of Justice
Nottingham
(0115) 952 0555
galleriesofjustice.org.uk
Delve into the history of crime and punishment throughout the ages

Gibraltar Point National Nature Reserve and Visitor Centre
Skegness, Lincolnshire
(01754) 762677
lincstrust.org.uk
1,500 acres of glorious sand dunes, salt marsh and muddy shores

Haddon Hall
Bakewell, Derbyshire
(01629) 812855
haddonhall.co.uk
Medieval and Tudor manor-house

National Space Centre
Leicester
0870 607 7223
spacecentre.co.uk
The UK's largest space attraction

Natureland
Skegness, Lincolnshire
(01754) 764345
skegnessnatureland.co.uk
Watch seals and penguins feeding

Pleasure Island Family Theme Park
Cleethorpes, Lincolnshire
(01472) 211511
pleasure-island.co.uk
Featuring rides for all ages

Rockingham Castle
Market Harborough, Northamptonshire
(01536) 770240
rockinghamcastle.com
Rose gardens and exquisite art

Rutland Water
Oakham
(01572) 653026
rutlandwater.net
Vast, stunning man-made lake

Sherwood Forest Country Park
Mansfield, Nottinghamshire
(01623) 821327
sherwood-forest.org.uk
Native woodland packed with adventure

The Workhouse
Nottingham
(01636) 817250
nationaltrust.org.uk
Fascinating 19th-century preserved workhouse

Tourist information centres

When you arrive at your destination, visit a tourist information centre for help with accommodation and information about local attractions and events, or email your request before you go.

Ashbourne	13 Market Place	(01335) 343666	ashbourneinfo@derbyshiredales.gov.uk
Ashby-de-la-Zouch	North Street	(01530) 411767	ashby.tic@nwleices.gov.uk
Bakewell	Bridge Street	(01629) 816558	bakewell@peakdistrict-npa.gov.uk
Boston	Market Place	(01205) 356656	ticboston@boston.gov.uk
Brackley	2 Bridge Street	(01280) 700111	tic@southnorthants.gov.uk
Buxton	The Crescent	(01298) 25106	tourism@highpeak.gov.uk
Chesterfield	Rykneld Square	(01246) 345777	tourism@chesterfield.gov.uk
Corby	George Street	(01536) 407507	tic@corby.gov.uk
Derby City	Market Place	(01332) 255802	tourism@derby.gov.uk
Glossop	Victoria Street	(01457) 855920	info@glossoptouristcentre.co.uk
Grantham	St Peter's Hill	(01476) 406166	granthamtic@southkesteven.gov.uk
Hinckley	Lancaster Road	(01455) 635106	hinckleytic@leics.gov.uk
Horncastle	14 Bull Ring	(01507) 526636	horncastleinfo@e-lindsey.gov.uk
Kettering	Sheep Street	(01536) 410266	tic@kettering.gov.uk
Leicester City	7/9 Every Street	0906 294 1113**	info@goleicestershire.com
Lincoln Castle Hill	9 Castle Hill	(01522) 873213	tourism@lincoln.gov.uk
Lincoln Corn Hill	21 Cornhill	(01522) 873256	tourism@lincoln.gov.uk
Loughborough	Market Place	(01509) 218113	tic@charnwoodbc.gov.uk
Louth	The Market Hall	(01507) 609289	louthinfo@e-lindsey.gov.uk
Mablethorpe	The Dunes Centre	(01507) 474939	mablethorpeinfo@e-lindsey.gov.uk
Market Harborough	Adam & Eve Street	(01858) 828282	customer.services@harborough.gov.uk
Matlock	Crown Square	(01629) 583388	matlockinfo@derbyshiredales.gov.uk
Matlock Bath*	The Pavillion	(01629) 55082	matlockbathinfo@derbyshiredales.gov.uk
Melton Mowbray	7 King Street	(01664) 480992	tic@melton.gov.uk
Newark	Castlegate	(01636) 655765	gilstrap@nsdc.info
Northampton	St Giles Street	(01604) 838800	northampton.tic@ explorenorthamptonshire.co.uk
Nottingham	1-4 Smithy Row	0844 477 5678	tourist.information@nottinghamcity.gov.uk
Oakham	39 High Street	(01572) 758441	oakhamtic@biz-dial.co.uk
Ollerton	Sherwood Heath	(01623) 824545	sherwoodheath@nsdc.info
Oundle	14 West Street	(01832) 274333	oundle@east-northamptonshire.gov.uk
Retford	40 Grove Street	(01777) 860780	retford.tourist@bassetlaw.gov.uk
Ripley	Market Place	(01773) 841488	touristinformation@ambervalley.gov.uk
Rutland Water*	Sykes Lane	(01572) 653026	tic@anglianwater.co.uk
Skegness	Grand Parade	(01754) 899887	skegnessinfo@e-lindsey.gov.uk
Sleaford	Carre Street	(01529) 414294	tic@n-kesteven.gov.uk
Spalding	Market Place	(01775) 725468	tic@sholland.gov.uk
Stamford	27 St Mary's Street	(01780) 755611	stamfordtic@southkesteven.gov.uk
Woodhall Spa*	Iddesleigh Road	(01526) 353775	woodhallspainfo@e-lindsey.gov.uk
Worksop	Memorial Avenue	(01909) 501148	worksop.tourist@bassetlaw.gov.uk

*seasonal opening ** calls to this number are charged at premium rate*

Alternatively, you can text **TIC LOCATE** to **64118** to find your nearest tourist information centre

Find out **more**

Further publications are available from the following organisations:

Experience Nottinghamshire
w visitnotts.com
> **Nottinghamshire Essential Guide**
> **Nottinghamshire Where to Stay Guide**
> **Nottinghamshire Stay Somewhere Different**
> **Nottinghamshire City Breaks**
> **Nottinghamshire Attractions – A Family Day Out**

Peak District and Derbyshire
w derbyshirethepeakdistrict.com or
  visitpeakdistrict.com
> **Peak District Visitor Guide**
> **Savour the Flavour of the Peak District**
> **Derbyshire – the Peak District Visitor Guide**
> **Derbyshire – the Peak District Attractions Guide**
> **Camping and Caravanning Guide**
> **What's on Guide**

Lincolnshire
w visitlincolnshire.com
> **Visit Lincolnshire – Destination Guide**
> **Visit Lincolnshire – Great days out**
> **Visit Lincolnshire – Gardens & Nurseries**
> **Visit Lincolnshire – Aviation Heritage**
> **Tastes of Lincolnshire – Good Taste**

Explore Northamptonshire
w explorenorthamptonshire.co.uk
> **Explore Northamptonshire Visitor Guide**
> **Explore Northamptonshire County Map**
> **Explore Northamptonshire Food and Drink**

Leicestershire and Rutland
w goleicestershire.com
> **Rutland Visitor Guide**
> **Market Harborough & Lutterworth Guide**
> **Leicester City Guide**
> **Ashby de la Zouch and The National Forest Guide**
> **Belgrave Guide**
> **Melton Mowbray and the Vale of Belvoir**
> **Hinkley and Market Bosworth Guide**
> **Loughborough and Charnwood Forest**

Travel **info**

The central location of the East Midlands makes it easily accessible from all parts of the UK.

By road:
From the north and south, the M1 bisects the East Midlands with access to the region from junctions 14 through to 31. The A1 offers better access to the eastern part of the region, particularly Lincolnshire and Rutland. From the west, the M69, M/A42 and A50 provide easy access.

By rail:
The region is well served by three main line operators – GNER, Midland Mainline and Virgin Trains, each offering direct services from London and the north of England and Scotland to the East Midlands' major cities and towns. East/west links are provided by Central Trains, offering not only access to the region but also travel within it.

By air:
Nottingham East Midlands airport is located centrally in the region, with scheduled domestic flights from Aberdeen, Belfast, Edinburgh, Glasgow, Isle of Man and the Channel Islands. Manchester, Birmingham, Luton, Stansted and Humberside airports also offer domestic scheduled routes, with easy access to the region by road and rail.

where to stay in
East Midlands

All place names in the blue bands are shown on the maps at the front of this guide.

A complete listing of all VisitBritain assessed parks in England appears at the back.

Accommodation symbols
Symbols give useful information about services and facilities. Inside the back-cover flap you can find a key to these symbols. Keep it open for easy reference.

ALSOP-EN-LE-DALE, Derbyshire Map ref 5B2

★★★★
HOLIDAY, TOURING
& CAMPING PARK

⌖(81) £9.50–£17.20
⌖(81) £9.50–£17.20
Å (30) £9.50–£17.20
111 touring pitches

Rivendale Caravan and Leisure Park

Buxton Road, Alsop en le Dale, Ashbourne DE6 1QU t (01335) 310311 f (01332) 842311
e greg@rivendalecaravanpark.co.uk w rivendalecaravanpark.co.uk

payment Credit/debit cards, cash/cheques
Surrounded by spectacular Peak District scenery, convenient for Alton Towers, Chatsworth, Dove Dale and Carsington Water. Ideal for cyclists and ramblers with a network of footpaths and trails accessible directly from site. Choice of all-grass, hardstanding or 50/50 pitches. Closed 7 January to 1 February.

⊕ From A515, Rivendale is situated 6.5 miles north of Ashbourne, directly off the A515 Buxton road on the right-hand side, travelling north.

♥ Receive £15 discount for every 7-night stay (includes multiples of 7-night stays).

General ▦P♨☞☎⌧⋒☉▥▦▧✕⛏♞⚘☼ Leisure ▨▮♣⌂∪⌿♣

BOSTON, Lincolnshire Map ref 4A1

★★★
HOLIDAY, TOURING
& CAMPING PARK

⌖ £12.00–£14.00
⌖ £12.00–£14.00
Å £6.00–£14.00
⌖(4) £190.00–£230.00
87 touring pitches

Orchard Caravan Park

Frampton Lane, Hubberts Bridge, Boston PE20 3QU t (01205) 290328 f (01205) 290247
e DavidMay@orchardholidaypark.fsnet.co.uk w orchardpark.co.uk

Just a five-minute riverside walk takes you to the village, station and pub serving meals all day. Coarse fishing available. Situated between the Forty Foot River and the B1192. No children.

open All year
payment Cash/cheques

General ▦P♨☞☎⋒☉▥▦▧✕♞☼ Leisure ▨▮♫♣⌂∪⌿♪

BUXTON, Derbyshire Map ref 5B2

★★★
TOURING &
CAMPING PARK

⌖(30) Min £10.00
⌖(30) Min £10.00
Å (30) Min £8.00
30 touring pitches

Cottage Farm Caravan Park

Beech Croft, Blackwell, Buxton SK17 9TQ t (01298) 85330 e mail@cottagefarmsite.co.uk
w cottagefarmsite.co.uk

We are a family-run site, southerly facing with easy access from the A6. We can boast a beautiful walk along the River Wye at nearby Cheedale.

payment Cash/cheques

General P♨☞☎⋒☉▥▦♞

BUXTON, Derbyshire Map ref 5B2

★★★★
HOLIDAY, TOURING & CAMPING PARK
ROSE AWARD

(65) £16.00–£18.00
(15) £16.00–£18.00
(70) £13.00–£15.00
(12) £180.00–£440.00
65 touring pitches

Lime Tree Park

Dukes Drive, Buxton SK17 9RP **t** (01298) 22988 **f** (01298) 22988 **e** info@limetreeparkbuxton.co.uk **w** limetreeparkbuxton.co.uk

A convenient site in a gently sloping valley on the southern outskirts of Buxton. Facilities for touring and camping. From the town centre, travel south for 0.75 miles on A515, then turn left after Buxton hospital.

payment Credit/debit cards, cash/cheques

General Leisure

BUXTON, Derbyshire Map ref 5B2

★★★★
HOLIDAY, TOURING & CAMPING PARK

(47) £15.50–£17.00
(47) £15.50–£17.00
(47) £13.50–£15.50
(3) £210.00–£290.00
47 touring pitches

Longnor Wood Caravan Park

Longnor, Buxton SK17 0NG **t** (01298) 83648 **f** (01298) 83648 **e** enquiries@longnorwood.co.uk **w** longnorwood.co.uk

A small, select park just for adults. A warm welcome awaits all our visitors who will find peace and tranquillity in the heart of the Peak District National Park.

open All year
payment Credit/debit cards, cash/cheques

General

BUXTON, Derbyshire Map ref 5B2

★★★
HOLIDAY, TOURING & CAMPING PARK

(95) £9.50–£10.75
(4) £9.50–£10.75
(30) £9.50–£10.75
125 touring pitches

Newhaven Caravan and Camping Park

Newhaven, Nr Buxton SK17 0DT **t** (01298) 84300 **f** (01332) 726027 **w** newhavencaravanpark.co.uk

Halfway between Ashbourne and Buxton in the Peak National Park. Well-established park with modern facilities, close to the Tessington and High Peak trails, historic houses and Derbyshire Dales. Open March to October

payment Credit/debit cards, cash/cheques

General Leisure

CASTLETON, Derbyshire Map ref 5B2

★★★★★
TOURING & CAMPING PARK

(78) £12.50–£25.10
(78) £12.50–£25.10
on application
78 touring pitches

See Ad on inside back cover

Losehill Caravan Club Site

Castleton, Hope Valley S33 8WB **t** (01433) 620636 **w** caravanclub.co.uk

open All year
payment Credit/debit cards, cash/cheques

This popular site, set in the north of the Peak District National Park, is an excellent base for outdoor activities, including rock-climbing, potholing, biking and horse-riding.

⊕ *From Hathersage on the B6001. In about 2.5 miles, turn left onto the A6187 (signposted Castleton). Site on right in 5 miles.*

❤ *Special member rates mean you can save your membership subscription in less than a week. Visit our website to find out more.*

THE CARAVAN CLUB

General Leisure

DERBY, Derbyshire Map ref 5B2

★★★
TOURING PARK
(44) £8.50–£19.60
(44) £8.50–£19.60
on application
44 touring pitches

See Ad on inside back cover

Elvaston Castle Caravan Club Site

Elvaston Castle Country Park, Borrowash Road, Derby DE72 3EP **t** (01332) 573735
w caravanclub.co.uk

payment Credit/debit cards, cash/cheques

Site within 280-acre country park where squirrels and rabbits roam freely. Many walks to choose from. Open March to October.

Leave A50, turn right onto B5010. Continue left on B5010, in about 1 mile turn left into country park. Site on left.

Special member rates mean you can save your membership subscription in less than a week. Visit our website to find out more.

General P Leisure

HORNCASTLE, Lincolnshire Map ref 5D2

★★★★
HOLIDAY, TOURING & CAMPING PARK
(70) £11.00–£19.50
(10) £11.00–£19.50
(10) £11.00–£14.50
90 touring pitches

Ashby Park

Horncastle, West Ashby LN9 5PP **t** (01507) 527966 **e** ashsbyparklakes@aol.com
w ukparks.co.uk/ashby

open All year except Christmas and New Year
payment Credit/debit cards, cash/cheques

David Bellamy Gold Conservation Award park offering a friendly and informal atmosphere, peace and tranquillity, good walks, seven fishing lakes and a diversity of wildlife. Set in 70 acres of unspoilt countryside.

1.5 miles north of Horncastle between the A153 and the A158.

General P Leisure

LINCOLN, Lincolnshire Map ref 5C2

★★★
TOURING PARK
£9.80–£19.20
£9.80–£19.20
(14) £6.00–£13.80
32 touring pitches

Hartsholme Country Park

Skellingthorpe Road, Lincoln LN6 0EY **t** (01522) 873578 **e** hartsholmecp@lincoln.gov.uk
w lincoln.gov.uk

Flat/level grassy site set in mature wooded park. Ideal for a relaxing family holiday or when visiting friends and relatives. Easy access to city centre and tourist sites. Open March to October.

payment Credit/debit cards, cash/cheques

General P Leisure

PEAK DISTRICT

See under Alsop-en-le-Dale, Buxton, Castleton

Check it out

Information on parks listed in this guide has been supplied by proprietors. As changes may occur you should remember to check all relevant details at the time of booking.

RIPLEY, Derbyshire Map ref 5B2

Golden Valley Caravan & Camping

★★★
TOURING &
CAMPING PARK

🚐 £15.00–£20.00
🚐 £15.00–£20.00
⚠ £7.50–£10.00
24 touring pitches

The Tanyard, Coach Road, Golden Valley, Ripley DE5 3QU t (01773) 513881 & 07971 283643
e enquiries@goldenvalleycaravanpark.co.uk w goldenvalleycaravanpark.co.uk

payment Cash/cheques

Secluded woodland hideaway. All-weather children's play facilities. Electric hook-ups on individual landscaped sites. Jacuzzi, gymnasium, cafe and takeaway. Fishing on site. Next to Butterley Railway. Function room. Open March to October.

⊕ A610 to Codnor. Follow signs to Alfreton. Bottom of hill, site on left.

General 🚐 P 🔌 🕭 🍴 🛒 ⋒ ⊙ 🚻 🖵 🐾 🐕 🕭 Leisure 🍷 🎵 🔍 ⋔ 🚵 🏇 🏊

SCUNTHORPE, Lincolnshire Map ref 5C1

Brookside Caravan Park

★★★★★
TOURING PARK

🚐 (15) £12.50
🚐 (15) £12.50
⚠ (5) £10.00
35 touring pitches

Stather Road, Burton upon Stather, Scunthorpe DN15 9DH t (01724) 721369 e brookside@aol.com
w brooksidecaravanpark.co.uk

Quiet, family-run park that will meet all your requirements, with views over the River Trent and woodland.

open All year
payment Cash/cheques

General 🖵 🚐 P 🔌 🍴 🛒 ⋒ ⊙ 🚻 🖵 🐕 🕭 ☼ Leisure ⋔ ∪ 🚵 🏊

SKEGNESS, Lincolnshire Map ref 5D2

Richmond Holiday Centre

★★★
HOLIDAY &
TOURING PARK

🚐 (89) £12.00–£19.00
🚐 (89) £12.00–£19.00
🏠 (121) £180.00–
£460.00
89 touring pitches

Richmond Drive, Skegness PE25 3TQ t (01754) 762097 f (01754) 765631
e sales@richmondholidays.com w richmondholidays.com

The ideal holiday base, a gentle stroll from the bustling resort of Skegness with its funfairs, sandy beaches and donkey rides. Nightly entertainment during the peak weeks. Open March to October.

payment Credit/debit cards, cash/cheques

General P 🔌 🕭 🍴 ⋒ ⊙ 🚻 🖵 🐾 ✕ 🐕 ☼ Leisure 🎣 🍷 🎵 🔍 ⋔

SKEGNESS, Lincolnshire Map ref 5D2

Skegness Water Leisure Park

★★★
HOLIDAY, TOURING
& CAMPING PARK

🚐 £13.50
🚐 £14.50–£18.00
⚠ £13.50
250 touring pitches

Walls Lane, Ingoldmells, Skegness PE25 1JF t (01754) 899400 f (01754) 897867
e enquiries@skegnesswaterleisurepark.co.uk

Family-orientated caravan and camping site 'where the coast meets the countryside'. Ten-minute walk to award-winning beaches with scenic, rural views. Open March to November.

payment Credit/debit cards, cash/cheques, euros

General 🔌 P 🔌 🕭 🍴 🛒 ⋒ 🚻 🖵 🐾 ✕ 🐕 Leisure 🍷 🎵 🚵

Check the maps

Colour maps at the front pinpoint all the places you will find accommodation entries in the regional sections. Pick your location and then refer to the place index at the back to find the page number.

TANSLEY, Derbyshire Map ref 5B2

★★★★
HOLIDAY &
TOURING PARK

🚐 (80)   £14.50–£20.00
🚙 (80)   £14.50–£20.00

Lickpenny Caravan Park

Lickpenny Lane, Tansley, Matlock DE4 5GF **t** (01629) 583040 **f** (01629) 583040
e lickpenny@btinternet.com **w** lickpennycaravanpark.co.uk

Peaceful countryside location within easy reach of Matlock Bath, Bakewell and Chatsworth. All pitches are hardstanding with 16-amp electric hook-up. Each pitch is separated by its own boundary, with ample room for caravan, car and awning.

open All year
payment Credit/debit cards, cash/cheques

General 🖼 🚮 P 🎡 🌡 🐾 🗺 🌀 ☺ 🍴 ★ 🛠 ☼   Leisure ⚠ ∪ ⚓ ►

Walkers and cyclists
welcome

Look out for quality-assessed accommodation displaying the Walkers Welcome and Cyclists Welcome signs.

Participants in this scheme actively encourage and support walking and cycling. In addition to special meal arrangements and helpful information, they'll provide a water supply to wash off the mud, an area for drying wet clothing and footwear, maps and books to look up cycling and walking routes and even an emergency puncture-repair kit! Bikes can also be locked up securely undercover.

The standards for the scheme have been developed in partnership with the tourist boards in Northern Ireland, Scotland and Wales, so wherever you're travelling in the UK you'll receive the same welcome.

CYCLISTS WELCOME

WALKERS WELCOME

enjoyEngland ™

official tourist board publications

Hotels
Guide to quality-assured accommodation in England
2007

Hotels, including
country house and
town house hotels,
metro and budget
hotels in England 2007

£10.99

Bed & Breakfast
Guide to quality-assured accommodation in England
2007

Guest accommodation,
B&Bs, guest houses,
farmhouses, inns,
restaurants with rooms,
campus and hostel
accommodation in
England 2007

£11.99

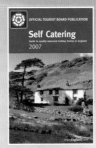
Self Catering
Guide to quality-assessed holiday homes in England
2007

Self-catering holiday
homes, including
serviced apartments and
approved caravan
holiday homes, boat
accommodation and
holiday cottage agencies
in England 2007

£11.99

Britain's Camping & Caravan Parks
Guide to quality-assessed sites
2007

Touring parks, camping
parks and holiday
parks and villages in
Britain 2007

£8.99

informative, easy to use and great value for money

Pets Come Too!
Guide to quality-assured pet-friendly hotels, B&Bs, and self-catering accommodation in England
2007

Pet-friendly hotels,
B&Bs and self-catering
accommodation in
England 2007

£9.99

Days Out For All
Great ideas for places to visit, eat and stay in England

Great ideas for places
to visit and stay
in England

£12.99

Places to Stay and Visit
South West England

Places to stay and visit
in South West England

£9.99

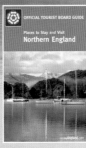
Places to Stay and Visit
Northern England

Places to stay and visit
in Northern England

£7.99

Britain's
accessible
2006

Accessible places
to stay in Britain

£9.99

From good bookshops, online at **visitbritaindirect.com**
or by mail order from:

VisitBritain Fulfilment Centre
t **0870 606 7204**   e **fulfilment@visitbritain.org**

East of England

Bedfordshire › Cambridgeshire › Essex
Hertfordshire › Norfolk › Suffolk

The stunning Scallop sculpture at Aldeburgh

East of England Tourist Board
Toppesfield Hall, Hadleigh
Suffolk IP7 5DN
0870 225 4800
visiteastofengland.com

timeless pleasures, unspoilt coastline, treetop action

Main Spot spiralling birdlife at Minsmere Nature Reserve, Suffolk **Left** Enjoy the beautiful gardens at Audley End House, Essex; admire the breathtaking cathedral at Ely; revel in the excitement of an air show at the Imperial War Museum Duxford; stroll through the evening glow of cornfields on the Norfolk Broads

Rich in heritage, and scattered with market towns, fishing villages and seaside resorts, the East of England makes **a great escape for a quintessential English break.**

Explore
East of England

Coasting along

Traverse the shingle beaches of the tranquil town of Felixstowe, relax in the award-winning gardens and stroll along the promenade staring wistfully out to sea. Admire the contours of the Scallop sculpture in Aldeburgh, explore the wide, Georgian high street and watch the fishermen arrive with their daily catch. If you're here in June, sample the delights of the Aldeburgh Festival – a concoction of art, literature and classical music to both tantalise and entertain.

Amble past brightly coloured beach huts in Southwold and sup a pint of the local brew, climb the lighthouse for fantastic views and try your luck on the vintage arcade machines on the pier. For an action-packed break, head to the popular resort of Great Yarmouth, enjoy the buzz of the nightlife and take your chances on the towering Sky-Drop at the Pleasure Beach.

Two legs, two wheels

Get your spokes spinning and feel the country air fill your lungs on one of the many cycling routes. Explore the vast, flat landscape of The Fens Cycle Way and imagine the Romans cultivating the land, or admire the re-created 19th-century Swiss village surroundings of the Old Warden cycle route in Bedfordshire. Pull on your boots and spot lizards and crabs along the Peddars Way National Trail on the Norfolk Coast Path from Knettishall to Cromer.

Breathe deeply at Norfolk Lavender farm and be enthralled by the dramatic, sweeping purple landscape. Relax on a chequered rug in the gardens of Audley End House and enjoy an excerpt from the Music on a Summer Evening concert programme.

Experience stunning sunsets across glowing Norfolk cornfields and fantastic panoramas throughout the Norfolk Broads. Explore the Broads (the country's largest wetland), meander between restored windmills, medieval churches and magnificent gardens, or hire a boat and discover the 125 miles of rivers snaking their way through the lush green countryside.

Unforgettable experiences

Feel the harmony between the extraordinary sculptures and glorious landscapes at the Henry Moore Foundation at Perry Green. Take time to explore the fruitful heritage of the region and visit the royal Anglo-Saxon burial ground of Sutton Hoo. Find yourself transfixed by the elegant beauty of the Cathedral and Abbey Church of St Alban, or settle down for an outstanding performance from one of the most famous choirs in the world at King's College Chapel in Cambridge.

Out and about

Shadow a ranger for a day at the Woburn Safari Park, or explore the extensive leisure area and meet the animals in residence. Allow the Nene Valley Railway in Peterborough to whisk you back in time as you steam along the tracks in a preserved locomotive. Descend into an excavation shaft at Grimes Graves Neolithic flint mine in Norfolk, or snap up a prize at The British Open Crabbing Championships in the charming coastal village of Walberswick in Suffolk.

Places to **visit**

0 ————— 50 miles
0 ————— 75 kms

Cromer
Hunstanton
Norfolk Coast

King's Lynn
PEDDARS WAY & NORFOLK COAST PATH
1
1
Norwich
13
Great Yarmouth
63
THE BROADS
Peterborough
Welney
Lowestoft
Ely
Thetford
Suffolk Coast & Heaths
Southwold
Newmarket
1
Bedford
Bury St Edmunds
Aldeburgh
Cambridge
Lavenham
Ipswich
51
Saffron Walden
Dedham Vale
Royston
51
Colchester
Harwich
Stevenage
Coggeshall
Dunstable
Hertford
Brightlingsea
Clacton-on-Sea
St Albans
Chelmsford
6
Epping

Southend-on-Sea

Audley End House and Gardens
Saffron Walden, Essex
(01799) 522842
english-heritage.org.uk
One of England's grandest stately homes
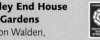

Bodyflight Bedford
Clapham, Bedfordshire
0845 200 2960
bodyflight.co.uk
Learn to sky dive indoors

Cathedral and Abbey Church of St Alban
St Albans, Hertfordshire
(01727) 864511
stalbans.gov.uk/tourism
Witness the stunning medieval architecture
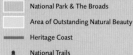

Colchester Castle
Essex
(01206) 282939
colchestermuseums.org.uk
Spectacular displays of Colchester history

National Park & The Broads
Area of Outstanding Natural Beauty
Heritage Coast
National Trails
nationaltrail.co.uk
Sections of the National Cycle Network
nationalcyclenetwork.org.uk

Colchester Zoo
Essex
(01206) 331292
colchester-zoo.com
Impressive specimens, plus gardens and lakes

Grimes Graves
near Thetford, Norfolk
0870 333 1181
english-heritage.org.uk
Climb into the flint mine and explore

New Pleasurewood Hills Leisure Park
Lowestoft, Suffolk
(01502) 586000
pleasurewoodhills.com
An abundance of rides for all

Norfolk Lavender
near King's Lynn, Norfolk
(01485) 570384
norfolk-lavender.co.uk
Learn about lavender in a beautiful location

Shuttleworth Collection
near Bedford
(01767) 627927
shuttleworth.org
A unique and historical collection of aircraft out on display

Sutton Hoo Burial Site
Woodbridge, Suffolk
(01394) 389700
suttonhoo.org
Grassy mounds overlooking River Deben, and fascinating exhibition hall

The Henry Moore Foundation
Perry Green, Hertfordshire
(01279) 843333
henry-moore-fdn.co.uk
Provocative artworks in beautiful setting

King's College Chapel
Cambridge
0906 58602526
visitcambridge.org
Listen to the famous choir

Knebworth House, Gardens and Park
Hertfordshire
(01438) 812661
knebworthhouse.com
View exhibits and explore parkland

Nene Valley Railway
Peterborough, Cambridgeshire
(01780) 784444
nvr.org.uk/thomas
Ride in a preserved locomotive

Oliver Cromwell's House
Ely, Cambridgeshire
(01353) 662062
ely.org.uk/tic
Step into his haunted bedroom

Pleasure Beach
Great Yarmouth, Norfolk
(01493) 844585
pleasure-beach.co.uk
A classic coastal fun park

RSPB Minsmere Nature Reserve
Saxmundham, Suffolk
(01728) 648281
rspb.org.uk
Bird-watching hides and trails

Sainsbury Centre for Visual Arts
Norwich, Norfolk
(01603) 593199
scva.org.uk
Featuring works by Picasso and Henry Moore

West Stow Anglo-Saxon Village
Bury St Edmunds, Suffolk
(01284) 728718
stedmundsbury.gov.uk
A fascinating reconstructed piece of history, bringing the past to life

Woburn Safari Park
Bedfordshire
(01525) 290407
discoverwoburn.co.uk
Observe and interact with an impressive selection of animals in a natural setting

Tourist information centres

When you arrive at your destination, visit a tourist information centre for help with accommodation and information about local attractions and events, or email your request before you go.

Aldeburgh	152 High Street	(01728) 453637	atic@suffolkcoastal.gov.uk
Aylsham	Norwich Road	(01263) 733903	aylsham.tic@broadland.gov.uk
Beccles*	Fen Lane	(01502) 713196	becclesinfo@broads-authority.gov.uk
Bedford	St Pauls Square	(01234) 215226	TouristInfo@bedford.gov.uk
Birchanger Green	Welcome Break Service Area	(01279) 508656	
Bishop's Stortford	Windhill	(01279) 655831	tic@bishopsstortford.org
Braintree	Market Place	(01376) 550066	tic@braintree.gov.uk
Brentwood	44 High Street	(01277) 200300	michelle.constable@brentwood.gov.uk
Burnham Deepdale	Deepdale Farm	(01485) 210256	info@deepdalefarm.co.uk
Bury St Edmunds	6 Angel Hill	(01284) 764667	tic@stedsbc.gov.uk
Cambridge	Wheeler Street	0871 226 8006	tourism@cambridge.gov.uk
Clacton-on-Sea	Station Road	(01255) 423400	emorgan@tendringdc.gov.uk
Colchester	1 Queen Street	(01206) 282920	vic@colchester.gov.uk
Cromer	Prince of Wales Road	0871 200 3071	cromertic@north-norfolk.gov.uk
Diss	Mere Street	(01379) 650523	dtic@s-norfolk.gov.uk
Downham Market	78 Priory Road	(01366) 383287	downham-market.tic@west-norfolk.gov.uk
Ely	29 St Mary's Street	(01353) 662062	tic@eastcambs.gov.uk
Felixstowe	91 Undercliff Road West	(01394) 276770	ftic@suffolkcoastal.gov.uk
Flatford	Flatford Lane	(01206) 299460	flatfordvic@babergh.gov.uk
Great Yarmouth	25 Marine Parade	(01493) 846345	tourism@great-yarmouth.gov.uk
Harwich Connexions	Iconfield Park	(01255) 506139	tic@harwichticconnexions.co.uk
Hemel Hempstead	Marlowes	(01442) 234222	stephanie.canadas@dacorum.gov.uk
Hertford	10 Market Place	(01992) 584322	tic@hertford.gov.uk
Holt*	3 Pound House	0871 200 3071	holttic@north-norfolk.gov.uk
Hoveton*	Station Road	(01603) 782281	hovetoninfo@broads-authority.gov.uk
Hunstanton	The Green	(01485) 532610	hunstanton.tic@west-norfolk.gov.uk
Huntingdon	Princes Street	(01480) 388588	hunts.tic@huntsdc.gov.uk
Ipswich	St Stephens Lane	(01473) 258070	tourist@ipswich.gov.uk
King's Lynn	Purfleet Quay	(01553) 763044	kings-lynn.tic@west-norfolk.gov.uk
Lavenham*	Lady Street	(01787) 248207	lavenhamtic@babergh.gov.uk
Letchworth Garden City	33-35 Station Road	(01462) 487868	tic@letchworth.com
Lowestoft	Royal Plain	(01502) 533600	touristinfo@waveney.gov.uk
Luton	St George's Square	(01582) 401579	tourist.information@luton.gov.uk
Maldon	Coach Lane	(01621) 856503	tic@maldon.gov.uk
Newmarket	Palace Street	(01638) 667200	tic.newmarket@forest-heath.gov.uk
Norwich	Millennium Plain	(01603) 727927	tourism@norwich.gov.uk

Peterborough	3-5 Minster Precincts	(01733) 452336	tic@peterborough.gov.uk
Saffron Walden	1 Market Place	(01799) 510444	tourism@uttlesford.gov.uk
Sandy	5 Shannon Court	(01767) 682728	tourism@sandytowncouncil.gov.uk
Sheringham*	Station Approach	0871 200 3071	sheringhamtic@north-norfolk.gov.uk
Southend-on-Sea	Western Esplanade	(01702) 215620	vic@southend.gov.uk
Southwold	69 High Street	(01502) 724729	southwold.tic@waveney.gov.uk
St Albans	Market Place	(01727) 864511	tic@stalbans.gov.uk
St Neots	8 New Street	(01480) 388788	stneots.tic@huntsdc.gov.uk
Stowmarket	Museum of East Anglican Life	(01449) 676800	tic@midsuffolk.gov.uk
Sudbury	Market Hill	(01787) 881320	sudburytic@babergh.gov.uk
Swaffham*	Market Place	(01760) 722255	swaffham@eetb.info
Thetford	4 White Hart Street	(01842) 820689	info@thetfordtourism.co.uk
Waltham Abbey	2-4 Highbridge Street	(01992) 652295	tic@walthamabbey.org.uk
Wells-next-the-Sea*	Staithe Street	0871 200 3071	wellstic@north-norfolk.gov.uk
Wisbech	2-3 Bridge Street	(01945) 583263	tourism@fenland.gov.uk
Woodbridge	Station Buildings	(01394) 382240	wtic@suffolkcoastal.gov.uk
Wymondham	Market Place	(01953) 604721	wymondhamtic@btconnect.com

* seasonal opening

Alternatively, you can text **TIC LOCATE** to **64118** to find your nearest tourist information centre

Find out **more**

The following publications are available from East of England by logging on to **visiteastofengland.com** or calling **0870 225 4800**:

> ### East of England 2007
A great flavour of what the East of England has to offer – vibrant cities, coastal escapes, seaside fun and so much more. This free publication is a gateway for holiday ideas, promoting a wide range of more detailed printed matter and websites.

> ### Let's Go East of England 2007
A region so diverse, right on London's doorstep – the East of England has so much to offer for short breaks and day trips. A free A5 publication packed full of great ideas, linking to a fine array of special offers. Suggestions for trips by rail are included, but this is also one you'll want to keep in your glove box!

> ### East of England – Cycling
The East of England offers perfect cycling country, from quiet country lanes to ancient trackways. This free publication promotes the many Cycling Discovery Maps that are available, as well as providing useful information for anyone planning a cycling tour of the region.

> ### East of England – Gardens
The East of England has English country gardens to inspire. This free publication is more than a just directory for gardens to visit – its features, behind-the-scenes insights and masterclass tips make it a gardening inspiration in itself.

Travel **info**

By road:
The region is easily accessible: from London and the South via the A1(M), M11, M25, A10, M1 and A12; from the North via the A1(M), A17, A15, A5, M1 and A6; from the West via the A14, A47, A421, A428, A418, A41, A422 and A427.

By rail:
Regular fast and frequent trains run to all major cities and towns. London stations which serve the region are Liverpool Street, King's Cross, Fenchurch Street, Marylebone and Euston. Bedford, Luton and St Albans are on the Thameslink line which runs to King's Cross and on to London Gatwick Airport. There is also a direct link between London Stansted Airport and Liverpool Street. Through the Channel Tunnel, there are trains direct from Paris and Brussels to Waterloo Station, London. A short journey on the Underground will bring passengers to those stations operating services into the East of England. Further information on rail journeys in the East of England can be obtained on 0845 748 4950.

By air:
Fly into London Luton, London Stansted or Norwich International.

Striking sculptures at The Henry Moore Foundation, Perry Green

where to stay in
East of England

All place names in the blue bands are shown on the maps at the front of this guide.

A complete listing of all VisitBritain assessed parks in England appears at the back.

Accommodation symbols
Symbols give useful information about services and facilities. Inside the back-cover flap you can find a key to these symbols. Keep it open for easy reference.

BAWBURGH, Norfolk Map ref 4B1

★★★★
TOURING PARK

🚐 (60)   £10.35–£21.40
🚑 (60)   £10.35–£21.40
60 touring pitches

See Ad on inside back cover

Norfolk Showground Caravan Club Site

Royal Norfolk Showground, Long Lane, Bawburgh, Norwich NR9 3LX   t (01603) 742708
w caravanclub.co.uk

payment Credit/debit cards, cash/cheques

A charming and secluded site set adjacent to the Norfolk Showground, this is an ideal escape. Golf course and well-stocked fishing lakes nearby. Open March to October.

⊕ Turn off A47 Norwich southern bypass at Longwater intersection (Bawburgh). Follow signpost Bawburgh, site entrance on right 0.25 miles.

♥ Special member rates mean you can save your membership subscription in less than a week. Visit our website to find out more.

General 🖵 P 🔌 🕗 🍴 🚐 🎢 ☉ 🚻🗑 🐴 ☼   Leisure 🏊 ▶

BURNHAM DEEPDALE, Norfolk Map ref 4B1

★★★★
CAMPING PARK

🚑 (22)   £6.00–£13.00
⛺ (22)   £6.00–£13.00

Deepdale Camping

Deepdale Farms, Burnham Deepdale, King's Lynn PE31 8DD   t (01485) 210256   f (01485) 210158
e info@deepdalefarm.co.uk   w deepdalefarm.co.uk

A quiet, family-friendly campsite, with two well-kept paddocks, in the heart of the beautiful village of Burnham Deepdale.

open All year
payment Credit/debit cards, cash/cheques

General ♿ P 🕗 🎢 ☉ 🚻🗑 🛒 ✕ 🐴 🗙 ☼   Leisure ⚸ ∪ 🏊 ▶ 🚲 🛶

visitBritain.com

Get in the know – log on for a wealth of information and inspiration. All the latest news on places to visit, events and quality-assessed accommodation is literally at your fingertips. Explore all that Britain has to offer!

CAMBRIDGE, Cambridgeshire Map ref 3D1

★★★★★
TOURING &
CAMPING PARK

🚐 (60)   £9.75–£13.50
🚚 (60)   £9.75–£13.50
⛺ (60)   £9.25–£13.25
120 touring pitches

Highfield Farm Touring Park

Long Road, Comberton, Cambridge CB3 7DG t (01223) 262308 f (01223) 262308
e enquiries@highfieldfarmtouringpark.co.uk w highfieldfarmtouringpark.co.uk

payment Cash/cheques, euros

A popular, family-run park with excellent facilities close to the university city of Cambridge, Imperial War Museum, Duxford. Ideally situated for touring East Anglia. Open April to October. Please view our website for further information.

⊕ *From Cambridge, A428 to Bedford. After 3 miles, left at roundabout, follow sign to Comberton. From M11 jct 12, A603 to Sandy (0.5 miles). Then B1046 to Comberton.*

♥ *Low-season rate for Senior Citizens – 10% discount for stay of 3 nights or longer.*

General 📺 P 🔌 🚻 🚿 🆿 ⏱ ☉ 📶 🖥 ⚡ 🐕 🕅   Leisure 🎢 ∪ 🏊 🚴

CROMER, Norfolk Map ref 4C1

Rating Applied For
TOURING &
CAMPING PARK

🚐 (100)   £9.50–£21.40
🚚 (100)   £9.50–£21.40
100 touring pitches

See Ad on inside back cover

Seacroft Caravan Club Site

Runton Road, Cromer NR27 9NH t (01263) 514938 w caravanclub.co.uk

payment Credit/debit cards, cash/cheques

An ideal site for a family holiday. Within walking distance of the beach. Heated swimming pool, communal barbecue, bar, restaurant, takeaway and a separate field for recreational use. Open May to October.

⊕ *Turn left off A149 (Cromer-Sheringham). Site entrance on left in 1 mile.*

♥ *Special member rates mean you can save your membership subscription in less than a week. Visit our website to find out more.*

General 📺 P 🔌 🚻 🚿 🆿 🖥 ⚡ ✕ 🕅   Leisure ⚡ 📺 ⚡ 🎵 ◑ ∪

FAKENHAM, Norfolk Map ref 4B1

★★★
TOURING PARK

🚐 (120)   £12.00–£25.00
🚚 (30)   £12.00–£25.00
⛺ (30)   £7.00–£25.00
120 touring pitches

Fakenham Racecourse

The Racecourse, Fakenham NR21 7NY t (01328) 862388 e caravan@fakenhamracecourse.co.uk
w fakenhamracecourse.co.uk

open All year
payment Credit/debit cards, cash/cheques

Fakenham Racecourse is the ideal base for caravanning and camping holidays in Norfolk. Just ten miles from a magnificent coastline and on the edge of the market town of Fakenham, the site is set in beautiful countryside and sheltered by conifers. The grounds and modern facilities are excellently maintained.

⊕ *On all major approach routes to Fakenham follow brown signs stating 'Racecourse' and showing 'caravan and tent' symbols. Site entrance on Hempton Road.*

♥ *Open to all but with discounts for Caravan Club members. Special rates for rally groups. Check website for events.*

General 🚐 P 🔌 🚻 🚿 🆿 🆿 ☉ 📶 🖥 ⚡ ✕ 🐕 🕅 ☼   Leisure ⚡ 🎣 🚶 ⚡

GREAT YARMOUTH, Norfolk Map ref 4C1

★★★★
HOLIDAY PARK
🛏 (72) £159.00–£629.00

Cherry Tree Holiday Park

Burgh Castle, Great Yarmouth NR31 9QR t 0870 420 2997 f (0191) 268 5986
e enquiries@parkdeanholidays.co.uk w parkdeanholidays.co.uk

payment Credit/debit cards, cash/cheques

With the picturesque Norfolk Broads on your doorstep, and popular Great Yarmouth just two miles away, Cherry Tree has the best location for a traditional family holiday! There's lots to do without even leaving the park! Facilities include outdoor and indoor pools, kids' clubs and The Orchard family entertainment venue. Open March to October.

⊕ A47 to Great Yarmouth. Take 3rd exit at 1st roundabout across bridge. At next roundabout take 3rd exit, 3rd exit again, then turn left at t-junction.

♥ Short breaks available.

General P 🏠 ⬚ 🖵 🅰 ✕ 🐾   Leisure 🎿 🐾 🍴 🎵 ◕ 🎢 🏃 🚲

GREAT YARMOUTH, Norfolk Map ref 4C1

★★★
TOURING PARK
🚐 (40) £10.00–£14.00
🚙 (6) £10.00–£14.00
🛏 (10) £100.00–£350.00
46 touring pitches

Grasmere Caravan Park

Bultitudes Loke, Yarmouth Road, Caister-on-Sea, Great Yarmouth NR30 5DH t (01493) 720382
f (01493) 377573 w grasmere-wentworth.co.uk

Small family park with no on-site entertainment. Approach Caister on A149, then follow brown tourist signs. Open April to October.

payment Credit/debit cards, cash/cheques

General 🚗 🚐 P 🔌 🗑 🏠 ◕ ⬚ 🅰 ☼

GREAT YARMOUTH, Norfolk Map ref 4C1

★★★★
HOLIDAY PARK
🚐 (115) £11.00–£24.00
🚙 (115) £11.00–£24.00
115 touring pitches

See Ad on inside back cover

Great Yarmouth Caravan Club Site

Great Yarmouth Racecourse, Jellicoe Road, Great Yarmouth NR30 4AU t (01493) 855223
w caravanclub.co.uk

payment Credit/debit cards, cash/cheques

Spacious, level site in a very popular family resort offering wide, sandy beaches, countless seaside attractions and fishing, golf, sailboarding, ballroom dancing and bowls. Open March to November.

⊕ Travel north on A149, left at lights (within 1 mile past 40mph sign on southern outskirts of Caister) into Jellicoe Road. Within 0.25 miles, left into racecourse entrance.

♥ Special member rates mean you can save your membership subscription in less than a week. Visit our website to find out more.

General P 🔌 🗑 🏠 🚗 🏠 ◕ ⬚ 🅰 ☼   Leisure 🎢 ♪ 🏃

The great outdoors

Discover Britain's green heart with this easy-to-use guide. Featuring a selection of the most stunning gardens in the country, The Gardens Explorer is complete with a handy fold-out map and illustrated guide. You can purchase the Explorer series from good bookshops and online at visitbritaindirect.com.

HEMEL HEMPSTEAD, Hertfordshire Map ref 3D1

Rating Applied For
TOURING PARK
🚐 (54) £8.50–£19.60
🚃 (54) £8.50–£19.60
⛺ on application
54 touring pitches

See Ad on inside back cover

Breakspear Way Caravan Club Site

Buncefield Lane, Breakspear Way, Hemel Hempstead HP2 4TZ t (01442) 268466
w caravanclub.co.uk

payment Credit/debit cards, cash/cheques

The site is a green oasis screened from the surrounding countryside by trees, yet within a mile of the M1. Ideally situated to explore London. Open March to November.

⊕ M1 jct 8, onto A414 (Hemel Hempstead). At 2nd roundabout turn and return on A414 towards M1. Within 0.5 miles, left immediately past petrol station into Buncefield Lane.

♥ Special member rates mean you can save your membership subscription in less than a week. Visit our website to find out more.

THE CARAVAN CLUB

General P 🅿 🛈 🍴 🚐 🎤 ☉ 📷 ✕ 🐴 Leisure ⛰ ⤵ ▶

HEMINGFORD ABBOTS, Cambridgeshire Map ref 4A2

★★★★
HOLIDAY, TOURING
& CAMPING PARK
🚐 (20) £12.00–£15.00
🚃 (20) £12.00–£15.00
⛺ (20) £12.00–£15.00
🚏 (9) £235.00–£355.00
20 touring pitches

Quiet Waters Caravan Park

Hemingford Abbots, Huntingdon PE28 9AJ t (01480) 463405 f (01480) 463405
e quietwaters.park@btopenworld.com w quietwaterscaravanpark.co.uk

A quiet riverside park situated in centre of picturesque village. Many local walks and cycle routes. Ideal for fishing from own banks. Family run. Open April to October.

payment Credit/debit cards, cash/cheques

General P 🅿 🛈 🍴 🎤 ☉ 📷 🐴 ☼ Leisure ∪ ⤵

HODDESDON, Hertfordshire Map ref 3D1

★★★★
TOURING &
CAMPING PARK
🚐 (50) £12.40–£15.00
🚃 £12.40–£15.00
⛺ (50) £12.40
100 touring pitches

Lee Valley Caravan Park

Essex Road, Hoddesdon EN11 0AS t (01992) 462090 f (01992) 462090

In a delightful riverside setting, with many leisure activities nearby. Local shops within easy reach. Shop on site, fishing on site. Open 1 March to last Sunday in November.

payment Credit/debit cards, cash/cheques

General P 🅿 🛈 🍴 🚐 🎤 📷 🐴 Leisure ⤵

HUNSTANTON, Norfolk Map ref 4B1

★★★★★
HOLIDAY, TOURING
& CAMPING PARK
ROSE AWARD
🚐 (157) £11.00–£33.00
🚃 (50) £11.00–£33.00
⛺ (125) £10.00–£32.00
🚏 (156) £189.00–£1,188.00
332 touring pitches

Searles Leisure Resort

South Beach Road, Hunstanton PE36 5BB t (01485) 534211 f (01485) 533815
e bookings@searles.co.uk w searles.co.uk

payment Credit/debit cards, cash/cheques

The quality family holiday centre. Family run, and established for fifty years, Searles has something for everyone: excellent pitches and hook-ups, bars, restaurants, entertainment, swimming pools, nine-hole golf-course, fishing lake and more – all 200yds from a sandy beach. The ideal base for exploring the Norfolk coast.

⊕ From King's Lynn take the A149 to Hunstanton. Upon entering Hunstanton follow B1161 to South Beach.

♥ Superb themed breaks every autumn. Kids' breaks, music weekends, Turkey and Tinsel breaks. Please check website for more details.

General 🎪 🖥 ♿ P 🅿 🛈 🍴 🚐 🎤 ☉ 📷 🛒 ✕ ☼ Leisure 🎣 ⚡ 📺 🍴 🎵 🎮 ⛰ 🔍 ∪ ⤵ ▶ 🚴

LITTLE CORNARD, Suffolk Map ref 4B2

★★★
TOURING &
CAMPING PARK

🚐(15) £10.00–£11.00
🚐(15) £10.00–£11.00
🛆 (15) £8.00–£11.00
35 touring pitches

Willowmere Caravan Park

Bures Road, Little Cornard, Sudbury CO10 0NN t (01787) 375559 f (01787) 375559

A small, quiet site surrounded by trees and meadows. Situated on the B1508 Sudbury to Bures road on the Essex/Suffolk border in the River Stour valley. Open Easter to October.

payment Cash/cheques

General P 🔌 🕁 🛉 🐾 ⊙ 📮🖥 🐕 Leisure 🏊

MILDENHALL, Suffolk Map ref 4B2

★★★★
HOLIDAY PARK

🚐(95) £6.00–£13.00
🚐(95) £6.00–£13.00
95 touring pitches

See Ad on inside back cover

THE
CARAVAN
CLUB

Round Plantation Caravan Club Site

Brandon Road, Mildenhall, Bury St Edmunds IP28 7JE t (01638) 713089 w caravanclub.co.uk

payment Credit/debit cards, cash/cheques

A landscaped site set in Forestry Commission woodland. Open pitching areas within the woodland, and quiet walks from the site. Good for bird-watchers. Open April to October.

⊕ From A1101 turn into Brandon Road at Half Moon Public House. Site on right in 0.6 miles.

♥ Special member rates mean you can save your membership subscription in less than a week. Visit our website to find out more.

General P 🔌 🕁 🐕 🐾

MUNDESLEY, Norfolk Map ref 4C1

★★★
HOLIDAY &
TOURING PARK

🚐(40) £8.00–£18.00
🚐(40) £8.00–£18.00
🏠(2) £200.00–£360.00
40 touring pitches

Sandy Gulls Cliff Top Touring Park

Cromer Road, Mundesley, Norwich NR11 8DF t (01263) 720513

payment Cash/cheques

The area's only cliff-top touring park. Located just south of Cromer. All pitches have panoramic sea views, electric/TV hook-ups. Free access to superb shower facilities. Miles of clean, sandy beaches and rural footpaths. Managed by the owning family for forty years. We don't cater for children or teenagers.

⊕ From Cromer drive south along coast road for 5 miles.

General P 🔌 🕁 🛉 🐾 ⊙ 📮🖥 🐕 🐾 Leisure ∪ 🏊 ►

NORFOLK BROADS

See under Great Yarmouth

Check the maps

Colour maps at the front pinpoint all the cities, towns and villages where you will find accommodation entries in the regional sections. Pick your location and then refer to the place index at the back to find the page number.

PETERBOROUGH, Cambridgeshire Map ref 4A1

★★★★★
HOLIDAY PARK
🚐 (254) £11.00–£24.00
🚐 (254) £11.00–£24.00
254 touring pitches

See Ad on inside back cover

WALKERS ■ □ CYCLISTS □
WELCOME   WELCOME
□ WALKERS ■ □ CYCLISTS ■

THE
CARAVAN
CLUB
2005

Ferry Meadows Caravan Club Site

Ham Lane, Peterborough PE2 5UU **t** (01733) 233526 **f** (01733) 239880 **w** caravanclub.co.uk

open All year
payment Credit/debit cards, cash/cheques

Set in 500-acre Nene Country Park. Plenty of activities including canoeing, windsurfing and sailing. Also nature trails, two golf courses, pitch and putt and bird sanctuary.

⊕ *From any direction, on approaching Peterborough, follow the brown signs to Nene Park and Ferry Meadows.*

♥ *Special member rates mean you can save your membership subscription in less than a week. Visit our website to find out more.*

General 📶 P 🔌 🜀 🜂 🍴 🜆 🜇 ☉ 🜈🜉 ☂ ☀   Leisure ⚠ ♪ ▶

SCRATBY, Norfolk Map ref 4C1

★★★★
TOURING &
CAMPING PARK
🚐   £5.75–£14.00
🚐   £5.75–£14.00
Å   £5.75–£14.00
108 touring pitches

Scratby Hall Caravan Park

Thoroughfare Lane, Scratby, Great Yarmouth NR29 3PH **t** (01493) 730283

payment Cash/cheques

Secluded, rural setting, approximately five miles north of Great Yarmouth and 0.5 miles from the beach. Free showers, shop, launderette, children's playground, disabled facilities. Open Easter to early October.

⊕ *From A149 Great Yarmouth to Caister. Onto B1159 Scratby, site signed.*

General P 🔌 🜀 🍴 🜆 ☉ 🜈🜉 🜊 ☂ ☀   Leisure ⚓ ♣ ⚠ ∪ ♪

STANHOE, Norfolk Map ref 4B1

★★★★
TOURING PARK
🚐   £9.00–£11.00
🚐   £9.00–£11.00
Å   £9.00–£11.00
30 touring pitches

The Rickels Caravan and Camping Park

Bircham Road, Stanhoe, King's Lynn PE31 8PU **t** (01485) 518671

From King's Lynn take A148 to Hillington, turn left onto B1153 to Great Bircham. Fork right onto B1155, to crossroads, straight over. Site 100yds on left. Open April to October. Adults only.

payment Cash/cheques

General 🜋 P 🔌 🜀 🍴 🜆 🜇 ☉ 🜈 ☂ 🜍 ☀   Leisure ♪ 🚲

Get on the road

Take yourself on a journey through England's historic towns and villages, past stunning coastlines and beautiful countryside with VisitBritain's series of inspirational touring guides. You can purchase the guides from good bookshops and online at visitbritaindirect.com.

SWAFFHAM, Norfolk Map ref 4B1

★★★★
TOURING PARK
🚐 (103) £7.00–£17.10
🚍 (103) £7.00–£17.10
103 touring pitches

See Ad on inside back cover

The Covert Caravan Club Site

High Ash, Hilborough, Thetford IP26 5BZ t (01842) 878356 w caravanclub.co.uk

payment Credit/debit cards, cash/cheques

Secluded site in beautiful wooded countryside owned by the Forestry Commission. Ideal for the wildlife observer and good for walkers. Own sanitation required. Open March to October.

⊕ Site entrance from A1065, 2 miles north of Mundford and 2.7 miles south of Hilborough.

♥ Special member rates mean you can save your membership subscription in less than a week. Visit our website to find out more.

General P 🚐 🕒 🆚 🐾 🛱.

WYTON, Cambridgeshire Map ref 4A2

★★★★
HOLIDAY PARK
🚐 (40) Min £13.50
🚍 (10) Min £13.50
▲ (10) Min £10.00
40 touring pitches

Wyton Lakes Holiday Park

Banks End, Wyton, Huntingdon PE28 2AA t (01480) 412715 e loupeter@supanet.com
w wytonlakes.com

payment Cash/cheques

Adults-only park. Some pitches beside the on-site carp and coarse-fishing lakes. River frontage. Close to local amenities. Open April to October.

⊕ Exit 23 off A14. Follow signs A141 March. Go past 4 roundabouts. At 4th roundabout take A1123 to St Ives. Park approx 1 mile on right.

♥ 10% discount on all bookings 7 nights or over paid in full on arrival. 7 days' fishing for the price of 6.

General P 🚐 🕒 🎁 🐾 ☉ 🛱 ☼ Leisure 🎣

David Bellamy Conservation Awards

Want to experience wrap-around nature? Simply head for a park that's achieved the David Bellamy Conservation Award. Launched in 1996 under the auspices of the British Holiday and Home Parks Association and the Conservation Foundation, the awards recognise, among 16 tough criteria, high standards of wildlife conservation, waste recycling, resource management and visitor involvement. More than 500 parks are now members of the scheme, in a Gold, Silver or Bronze category. More information about the award scheme can be found at the back of the guide.

GOLD

Finding a park

is as easy as 1 2 3 4

Britain's Camping and Caravan Parks guide makes it quick and easy to find a place to stay. There are several ways to use this guide.

1 PARK INDEX

If you know the name of the site you wish to book, turn to the park index at the back where the relevant page number is shown.

2 PLACE INDEX

The place index at the back lists all locations with parks featured in the regional sections. A page number is shown where you can find full accommodation and contact details.

3 COLOUR MAPS

All the place names in black on the colour maps at the front have an entry in the regional sections. Refer to the place index for the page number where you will find one or more parks in your chosen town or village.

4 ALL ASSESSED ACCOMMODATION

Contact details for all British Graded Holiday Parks Scheme participants throughout England, together with their quality rating, are given in the back section of this guide. Parks with a full entry in the regional sections are shown in bold. Look in the park index for the page number where their full entry appears.

London

Including Greater London

Visit London
6th Floor, 2 More London Riverside
London SE1 2RR
(020) 7234 5800
visitlondon.com

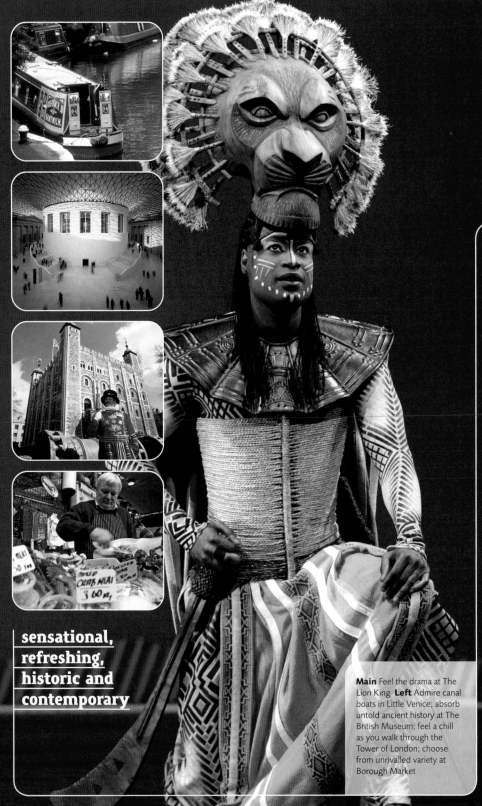

**sensational,
refreshing,
historic and
contemporary**

Main Feel the drama at The
Lion King **Left** Admire canal
boats in Little Venice; absorb
untold ancient history at The
British Museum; feel a chill
as you walk through the
Tower of London; choose
from unrivalled variety at
Borough Market

Enjoy the culture, the sights and the entertainment of one of the most lively and cosmopolitan cities in the world, **or take the chance to explore its greener corners.**

Explore London

History in the making

Take a ferry along the Thames and race to the centre of the maze at the magnificent red-bricked Hampton Court Palace. Marvel at the Crown Jewels and feel a chill run down your spine as you walk the grounds of the Tower of London. Many a nobleman suffered at the hands of the high executioner – can you still hear their screams?

Head to the Museum in Docklands and absorb 2,000 years of the city's remarkable history, sign up for a guided tour of the docks and hear echoes of the past when the Thames was alive with bustling trade. Take a ride above the city on the British Airways London Eye for a capital view and pick out your favourite landmarks, then step into the London Aquarium and witness divers hand-feeding rays and sharks amid the colourful marine life.

Markets and museums

Discover the many markets London has to offer and get a feel for the diversity of the city. At Borough Market your taste buds will tingle at the sight of the eclectic selection of foods from all corners of the globe. Snap up a bargain at the world's largest antiques market on Portobello Road, or have your palm read at Camden Lock and browse the colourful stalls at the Stables Market. A trip to London wouldn't be complete without venturing into the Harrods Food Hall and seeing the delectable and flavoursome wares, or wandering through the bustling crowds on Oxford Street.

Enjoy a calming day out discovering museums at your leisure. Allow yourself to be swept off your feet at Tate Modern, where the passionate embrace of The Kiss by Rodin is enough to make the coolest of hearts flutter. Try the Science Museum and keep the kids amused at Launch Pad and head to the Natural History Museum to inspect the impressive dinosaurs.

The grass is greener

Relax with a picnic in one of London's many parks. Spot the roaming deer in Richmond Park, don your swimmers and take a dip in the pond at Hampstead Heath, or take in a play at the Open Air Theatre, Regents Park.

Give the kids a treat and visit London Wetland Centre in Barnes to admire the spectacular and rare breeds of bird life wandering the grounds. Make a day of it at London Zoo where you can discover far-off climates at the new exhibit Into Africa and be dazzled by the flitting colours throughout Butterfly Paradise.

The main event

Seek out one of the many theatres in the nearby West End, or enjoy a play at Shakespeare's Globe – described as 'the beating heart of theatrical London'. With no end of variety, from musicals to Chekhov, and the famous to the little known, there is something to entertain everyone.

Places to **visit**

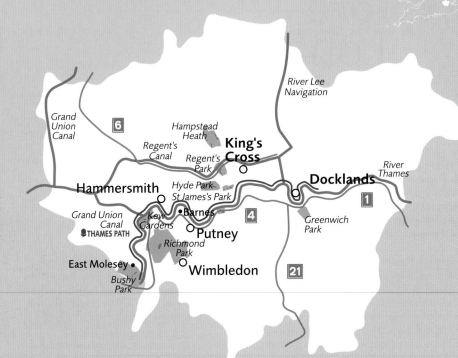

**British Airways
London Eye**
0870 500 0600
ba-londoneye.com
View the capital from above

The British Museum
London
(020) 7323 8299
thebritishmuseum.ac.uk
Outstanding and famous exhibits

Buckingham Palace
London
(020) 7766 7300
royalcollection.org.uk
*The Queen's official
London residence*

**Cabinet War
Rooms and
Churchill Museum**
London
(020) 7930 6961
iwm.org.uk
*Preserved rooms and
fascinating exhibition
detailing the former Prime
Minister's term*

Cutty Sark Clipper Ship
London
(020) 8858 3445
cuttysark.org.uk
*Climb aboard the world's last
and most famous tea-clipper
ever built*

National Trails
nationaltrail.co.uk

Sections of the National
Cycle Network
nationalcyclenetwork.org.uk

Hampton Court Palace

East Molesey,
Greater London
0870 752 7777
hrp.org.uk
Outstanding Tudor palace with famous maze

Kew Gardens (Royal Botanic Gardens)

Greater London
(020) 8332 5655
kew.org
Stunning vistas and magnificent glasshouses

London Aquarium

(020) 7967 8000
londonaquarium.co.uk
Come face to face with zebra sharks

The London Dungeon

(020) 7403 7221
thedungeons.com
Gruesome British events re-enacted

London Wetland Centre

Barnes, Greater London
(020) 8409 4400
wwt.org.uk
Observe wildlife in recreated natural habitats

London Zoo

(020) 7722 3333
londonzoo.co.uk
Walk-through enclosures and beautiful gardens

Madame Tussauds and the London Planetarium

0870 400 3000
madame-tussauds.com
Spot many a famous face

Museum in Docklands

London
0870 444 3857
museumindocklands.org.uk
Learn the history of London

Natural History Museum

London
(020) 7942 5000
nhm.ac.uk
Highlighting the earth's natural treasures

Royal Observatory Greenwich

London
(020) 8858 4422
nmm.ac.uk
Treat yourself to a guided tour and explore the history of astronomy and time

Science Museum

London
0870 870 4868
sciencemuseum.org.uk
With fantastic interactive features at Launch Pad

Shakespeare's Globe Exhibition and Tour

London
(020) 7902 1500
shakespeares-globe.org
A fascinating introduction to William Shakespeare's London

St Paul's Cathedral

London
(020) 7246 8357
stpauls.co.uk
Sir Christopher Wren's stunning masterpiece

Tate Modern

London
(020) 7887 8008
tate.org.uk
The UK's largest modern art gallery

Tower of London

0870 756 6060
hrp.org.uk
Resting place of the Crown Jewels, with a tortured history

Tourist information centres

When you arrive at your destination, visit a tourist information centre for help with accommodation and information about local attractions and events, or email your request before you go.

Bexley (Hall Place)	Bourne Road	(01322) 558676	hallplaceshoptic@tiscali.co.uk
Britain & London Visitor Centre	1 Regent Street		blvcinfo@visitbritain.org
Croydon	Katharine Street	(020) 8253 1009	tic@croydon.gov.uk
Greenwich	2 Cutty Sark Gardens	0870 608 2000	tic@greenwich.gov.uk
Harrow	Station Road	(020) 8424 1102	info@harrow.gov.uk
Hillingdon	14-15 High Street	(01895) 250706	libraryinfoteam@hillingdongrid.org
Hounslow	High Street	0845 456 2929	tic@cip.org.uk
Kingston	Market Place	(020) 8547 5592	tourist.information@rbk.kingston.gov.uk
Lewisham	199-201 Lewisham High Street	(020) 8297 8317	tic@lewisham.gov.uk
Richmond	Whittaker Avenue	(020) 8940 9125	info@visitrichmond.co.uk
Southwark	1 Bank End	(020) 7357 9168	tourisminfo@southwark.gov.uk
Swanley	London Road	(01322) 614660	touristinfo@swanley.org.uk
Twickenham	44 York Street	(020) 8891 7272	info@visitrichmond.co.uk
Waterloo International	Arrivals Hall	(020) 7620 1550	london.visitorcentre@iceplc.com

Alternatively, you can text **TIC LOCATE** to **64118** to find your nearest tourist information centre

Find out more

By logging on to **visitlondon.com** or calling **0870 1 LONDON** for the following:

> **A London tourist information pack**

> **Tourist information on London**
Speak to an expert for information and advice on museums, galleries, attractions, riverboat trips, sightseeing tours, theatre, shopping, eating out and much more! Or simply visit www.visitlondon.com.

> **Accommodation reservations**

Or visit one of London's tourist information centres listed above.

Which part of London?

The majority of tourist accommodation is situated in the central parts of London and is therefore very convenient for most of the city's attractions and nightlife.

However, there are many establishments in Outer London which provide other advantages, such as easier parking. In the accommodation pages which follow, you will find establishments listed under INNER LONDON (covering the E1 to W14 London Postal Area) and OUTER LONDON (covering the remainder of Greater London). Colour maps 6 and 7 at the front of the guide show place names and London postal area codes and will help you to locate accommodation in your chosen area.

Glitz and glamour at the Notting Hill Carnival

Travel **info**

By road:
Major trunk roads into London include: A1, M1, A5, A10, A11, M11, A13, A2, M2, A23, A3, M3, A4, M4, A40, M40, A41, M25 (London orbital).

Transport for London is responsible for running London's bus services, the underground rail network and the DLR (Docklands Light Railway) and river services. (020) 7222 1234 (24-hour telephone service; calls answered in rotation).

By rail:
Main rail terminals: Victoria/Waterloo/ Charing Cross – serving the South/South East; King's Cross – serving the North East; Euston – serving the North West/Midlands; Liverpool Street – serving the East; Paddington – serving the Thames Valley/West.

By air:
Fly into London City, London Gatwick, London Heathrow, London Luton and London Stansted.

where to stay in
London

All place names in the blue bands are shown on the maps at the front of this guide.

A complete listing of all VisitBritain assessed parks in England appears at the back.

Accommodation symbols
Symbols give useful information about services and facilities. Inside the back-cover flap you can find a key to these symbols. Keep it open for easy reference.

INNER LONDON
LONDON N9

★★★★
TOURING &
CAMPING PARK

⏚ (100)   Min £12.60
🚐 (100)   Min £12.60
▲ (60)   Min £12.60
160 touring pitches

Lee Valley Leisure Centre Camping and Caravan Park
Picketts Lock Lane, London N9 0AS   t (020) 8803 6900   f (020) 8884 4975
e leisurecentre@leevalleypark.org.uk   w leevalleypark.com

open All year except Christmas and New Year
payment Credit/debit cards, cash/cheques

A peaceful site within easy reach of central London and the Lee Valley Regional Park. Riding and ice centres close by. The West End, Trafalgar Square, Piccadilly Circus and Buckingham Palace are a short journey away. Also nearby are Epping Forest, the River Lee Country Park and historic Waltham Abbey.

⊕ *M25 jct 25, follow signs for City. 1st set of lights, left (signposted Freezywater – A1055). Continue for approx 6 miles. Follow signs for Lee Valley Leisure Complex.*

General ▦ P 🔌 🕆 ⛺ 🚽 ⟨⟩ ⊙ ⧈ ▨ ▩ ✕ 🐾 ☼   Leisure 📺 ⚴ ९ ∪ ⌥ ▶

LONDON SE2

★★★★★
TOURING &
CAMPING PARK

⏚ (220)   £13.10–£27.00
🚐 (220)   £13.10–£27.00
220 touring pitches

See Ad on inside back cover

Abbey Wood Caravan Club Site
Federation Road, Abbey Wood, London SE2 0LS   t (020) 8311 7708   w caravanclub.co.uk

open All year
payment Credit/debit cards, cash/cheques

Redeveloped to the highest standards, this site is the ideal base for exploring the capital. A green, gently sloping site with mature trees screening its spacious grounds.

⊕ *On M2 turn off at A221. Then turn right into McLeod Road, right into Knee Hill and the site is the 2nd turning on the right.*

♥ *Special member rates mean you can save your membership subscription in less than a week. Visit our website to find out more.*

General ▦ P 🔌 🕆 ⛺ 🚽 ⟨⟩ ⊙ ⧈ ▨ 🐾 ☼   Leisure ⚴ ▶

LONDON SE19

★★★★★
TOURING &
CAMPING PARK

🚐 (126) £13.10–£27.00
🚐 (126) £13.10–£27.00
126 touring pitches

See Ad on inside back cover

Crystal Palace Caravan Club Site

Crystal Palace Parade, London SE19 1UF **t** (020) 8778 7155 **f** (020) 8676 0980 **w** caravanclub.co.uk

open All year
payment Credit/debit cards, cash/cheques

Popular with European families in the summer, a friendly site on the edge of a pleasant park, in close proximity to all of London's attractions.

⊕ *Turn off the A205, South Circular road at West Dulwich into Croxted Road. The site is adjacent to the BBC television mast.*

♥ *Special member rates mean you can save your membership subscription in less than a week. Visit our website to find out more.*

General 🖃 P 🚐 🕁 🏕 🚐 🛉 ☺ 🏕🖃 🐾 ☼ Leisure ⚠ ⚑

Bank holiday
dates for your diary

holiday	2007	2008
January Bank Holiday (Scotland)	2 January	2 January
New Year's Day (England & Wales)	1 January	1 January
New Year's Day (Scotland)	1 January	1 January
Good Friday	6 April	21 March
Easter Monday (England & Wales)	9 April	24 March
Early May Bank Holiday	7 May	5 May
Spring Bank Holiday	28 May	26 May
Summer Bank Holiday (Scotland)	6 August	4 August
Summer Bank Holiday (England & Wales)	27 August	25 August
Christmas Day	25 December	25 December
Boxing Day	26 December	26 December

Tales of the city

Allow The London Explorer to guide you through the streets of the capital leaving no stone unturned. All you need for the perfect day out is in this handy package – featuring an easy-to-use fold-out map and illustrated guide. You can purchase the Explorer series from good bookshops and online at enjoyenglanddirect.com.

South East England

Berkshire › Buckinghamshire › East Sussex › Hampshire
Isle of Wight › Kent › Oxfordshire › Surrey › West Sussex

Step back in time at Dinosaur Isle, Isle of Wight

Tourism South East
40 Chamberlayne Road,
Eastleigh, Hampshire SO50 5JH
(023) 8062 5400
visitsoutheastengland.com

classic sites,
glorious
gardens,
retail
therapy

Main Speeding through the grounds of Hever Castle, Kent **Left** Dizzy heights at the Spinnaker Tower, Portsmouth; take part in the history at Bodiam Castle, East Sussex; take a walk with the Surrey Hills Llamas, near Guildford; awe-inspiring architecture at Winchester Cathedral, Hampshire

Stroll around a true English country garden, set sail on one of the many splendid waters, wander by spectacular coastlines and **soak up the rich history the South East has to offer.**

Explore
South East England

On the coast

Take a day trip to the seaside – wander around vibrant Brighton & Hove, delve into the unique shops in The Lanes, stop by The Royal Pavilion and marvel at the intricate Chinese furnishings, or tuck into a bag of fish and chips on the pier.

Head to Portsmouth and tentatively ascend the elegant Spinnaker Tower for views stretching over 23 miles on a clear day. Then explore the historic dockyard: climb aboard Nelson's HMS Victory and be amazed by the remarkable shipwreck, and Henry VIII's favourite vessel, The Mary Rose. For a breath of fresh salty air, stroll along the chalky white cliffs of Dover and wonder if bluebirds ever gracefully flew over their jagged edges.

For all the family

Treat the kids and revisit your youth with a trip to the enchanting Ashdown Forest, within the stunning High Weald. Allow A A Milne's creations to come to life – enjoy a game of Poohsticks and step into Pooh Corner. Continuing the storybook theme, lose yourself in a world of extraordinary fairytales at The Roald Dahl Museum and Story Centre in Buckinghamshire. Or get the adrenalin pumping as you prepare for a white-knuckle ride and defy gravity aboard Nemesis Inferno at Tussauds Thorpe Park.

Historical times

Visit the historic cities and towns of Windsor, Oxford and Canterbury. Discover elegant cathedrals and sturdy castles and relax in one of the many charming pavement cafes. Explore 5,000 sweeping acres of Windsor Great Park and marvel at the mysterious Uffington White Horse, chalked into an Oxfordshire hillside.

Take time to stride around Leeds and Hever castles in Kent and explore their outstanding gardens and grounds, or head to the impressive 11th-century Carisbrooke Castle on the Isle of Wight. Be sure to catch a boat around the mighty Needles at Alum Bay, where the multi-coloured cliffs prove a worthy spectacle.

English country gardens

The South East is blessed with outstanding gardens and scenery. Follow in the footsteps of poet John Keats through Winchester's Water Meadows, or wander through the calming Royal Botanic Gardens, Wakehurst Place in West Sussex. Feel inspired by the changing of the seasons and the natural beauty to be found in each one.

Escape on horseback into the New Forest, past blankets of heather, grazing deer and foraging pigs, or hike past glorious landscapes peppered with colour and spot scurrying wildlife. And take a trip to the stunning Blenheim Palace in Oxfordshire to achieve what Sir Winston Churchill's mother described as 'the finest view in England'.

Places to **visit**

0   50 miles

0   75 kms

Blenheim Palace
Woodstock, Oxfordshire
(01993) 811091
blenheimpalace.com
*Beautiful palace surrounded
by parkland*

Carisbrooke Castle
Newport, Isle of Wight
(01983) 522107
english-heritage.org.uk
Splendid Norman castle

Dinosaur Isle
Sandown, Isle of Wight
(01983) 404344
dinosaurisle.com
Walk back through fossilized time

**Go Ape! High Ropes
Forest Adventure**
near Bracknell, Berkshire
0870 444 5562
goape.co.uk
Swing through the forest trees

Hever Castle
Kent
(01732) 865224
hever-castle.co.uk
*Anne Boleyn's beautiful
childhood home*

**Leeds Castle
and Gardens**
Maidstone, Kent
(01622) 765400
leeds-castle.com
*Ninth-century, lovingly
restored castle*

Legoland Windsor
Berkshire
0870 504 0404
legoland.co.uk
*Witness Lego creations
come to life*

	National Park
	South Downs National Park (designated but not yet confirmed)
	Area of Outstanding Natural Beauty
	Heritage Coast
	National Trails nationaltrail.co.uk
3	Sections of the National Cycle Network nationalcyclenetwork.org.uk
67	Regional route
	Ferry routes

Banbury
Buckingham **5**
Milton Keynes
Cotswolds
51
THAMES PATH
Oxford
Chilterns
THAMES PATH
RIDGEWAY
Henley-on-Thames
Windsor
4
4
Bracknell
North Wessex Downs
Basingstoke
Guildford
Farnham
Surrey Hills
23
SOUTH DOWNS
Winchester
East Hampshire
Midhurst
Southampton
SOUTH DOWNS WAY
Steyning
Lyndhurst
Chichester Harbour
Sussex Downs
THE NEW FOREST
Lymington
Chichester
Portsmouth
Cowes
Yarmouth
Isle of Wight
22
67

Marwell Zoological Park
Winchester, Hampshire
(01962) 777407
marwell.org.uk
Observe many endangered species

The Needles Park
Totland Bay, Isle of Wight
0870 458 0022
theneedles.co.uk
Catch a chairlift over Alum Bay

Portsmouth Historic Dockyard
Hampshire
(023) 9283 9766
historicdockyard.co.uk
Home of historically important warships

The Roald Dahl Museum and Story Centre
Great Missenden,
Buckinghamshire
(01494) 892192
roalddahlmuseum.org
Step inside his imaginative world

Royal Pavilion
Brighton, East Sussex
(01273) 290900
royalpavilion.org.uk
Magnificent former royal seaside residence

Royal Botanic Gardens, Wakehurst Place
near Haywards Heath, West Sussex
(01444) 894000
rbgkew.org.uk
Beautiful gardens throughout the seasons

The Savill Garden, Windsor Great Park
Berkshire
(01753) 847518
savillgarden.co.uk
Beautiful gardens with royal connections

Spinnaker Tower
Portsmouth, Hampshire
(023) 9285 7520
spinnakertower.co.uk
Striking viewing tower with three platforms

Smugglers Adventure
Hastings, East Sussex
(01424) 422964
discoverhastings.co.uk
Dramatic interactive adventure and exhibition

Tussauds Thorpe Park
Chertsey, Surrey
0870 444 4466
thorpepark.co.uk
Thrilling rides for the whole family

Uffington White Horse
Oxfordshire
0870 333 1181
wiltshirewhitehorses.org.uk
Mysterious chalk markings in the hillside

Water Meadows
Winchester, Hampshire
(01962) 840500
visitwinchester.co.uk
Meander along the Keats Walk

Winchester Cathedral
Hampshire
(01962) 857225
winchester-cathedral.org.uk
Magnificent cathedral, and Jane Austen's tomb

Tourist information centres

When you arrive at your destination, visit a tourist information centre for help with accommodation and information about local attractions and events, or email your request before you go.

Aldershot	39 High Street	(01252) 320968	mail@rushmoorvic.com
Alton	7 Cross and Pillory Lane	(01420) 88448	altoninfo@btconnect.com
Andover	6 Church Close	(01264) 324320	andovertic@testvalley.gov.uk
Arundel	61 High Street	(01903) 882268	arundel.vic@arun.gov.uk
Ashford	18 The Churchyard	(01233) 629165	tourism@ashford.gov.uk
Aylesbury	Kings Head Passage	(01296) 330559	tic@aylesburyvaledc.gov.uk
Banbury	Spiceball Park Road	(01295) 259855	banbury.tic@cherwell-dc.gov.uk
Basingstoke	Market Place	(01256) 817618	basingstoket.i.c@btconnect.com
Battle	High Street	(01424) 773721	battletic@rother.gov.uk
Bicester	Bicester Village	(01869) 369055	bicester.vc@cherwell-dc.gov.uk
Bognor Regis	Belmont Street	(01243) 823140	bognorregis.vic@arun.gov.uk
Bracknell	Nine Mile Ride	(01344) 354409	TheLookOut@bracknell-forest.gov.uk
Brighton	10 Bartholomew Square	0906 711 2255**	brighton-tourism@brighton-hove.gov.uk
Broadstairs	2 Victoria Parade	0870 2646111	
Buckingham	Market Hill	(01280) 823020	buckingham.t.i.c@btconnect.com
Burford	Sheep Street	(01993) 823558	burford.vic@westoxon.gov.uk
Burgess Hill	96 Church Walk	(01444) 238202	touristinformation@burgesshill.gov.uk
Canterbury	12/13 Sun Street	(01227) 378100	canterburyinformation@canterbury.gov.uk
Chichester	29a South Street	(01243) 775888	chitic@chichester.gov.uk
Cowes	9 The Arcade	(01983) 813818	info@islandbreaks.co.uk
Crawley	County Mall	(01293) 846968	vip@countymall.co.uk
Deal	129 High Street	(01304) 369576	tic@doveruk.com
Didcot	118 Broadway	(01235) 813243	didcottic@tourismse.com
Dover	Biggin	(01304) 205108	tic@doveruk.com
Eastbourne	Cornfield Road	0906 711 2212**	tic@eastbourne.gov.uk
Fareham	West Street	(01329) 221342	touristinfo@fareham.gov.uk
Faringdon	5 Market Place	(01367) 242191	tourism@faringdontowncouncil.org.uk
Faversham	13 Preston Street	(01795) 534542	fata@visitfaversham.com
Fleet	236 Fleet Road	(01252) 811151	
Folkestone	Harbour Street	(01303) 258594	
Fordingbridge*	Salisbury Street	(01425) 654560	fordingbridgetic@tourismse.com
Gosport	South Street	(023) 9252 2944	tourism@gosport.gov.uk
Gravesend	18a St George's Square	(01474) 337600	info@towncentric.co.uk
Guildford	14 Tunsgate	(01483) 444333	tic@guildford.gov.uk
Hastings (Old Town)*	The Stade	(01424) 781111	hic@hastings.gov.uk
Hastings	Queens Square	(01424) 781111	hic@hastings.gov.uk
Havant	1 Park Road South	(023) 9248 0024	tourism@havant.gov.uk
Hayling Island*	Seafront	(023) 9246 7111	tourism@havant.gov.uk
Henley-on-Thames	Kings Road	(01491) 578034	henleytic@hotmail.com
Herne Bay	Central Parade	(01227) 361911	hernebayinformation@canterbury.gov.uk
High Wycombe	Paul's Row	(01494) 421892	tourism_enquiries@wycombe.gov.uk

Horsham	9 The Causeway	(01403) 211661	tourist.information@horsham.gov.uk
Hythe	Scanlons Bridge Road	(01303) 266421	
Lewes	187 High Street	(01273) 483448	lewes.tic@lewes.gov.uk
Littlehampton	63-65 Surrey Street	(01903) 721866	littlehampton.vic@arun.gov.uk
Lymington	New Street	(01590) 689000	information@nfdc.gov.uk
Lyndhurst & New Forest	Main Car Park	(023) 8028 2269	information@nfdc.gov.uk
Maidenhead	St Ives Road	(01628) 796502	maidenhead.tic@rbwm.gov.uk
Maidstone	High Street	(01622) 602169	tourism@maidstone.gov.uk
Margate	12-13 The Parade	0870 264 6111	margate.tic@visitor-centre.net
Marlow	31 High Street	(01628) 483597	tourism_enquiries@wycombe.gov.uk
Midhurst	North Street	(01730) 817322	midtic@chichester.gov.uk
New Romney	New Romney Station	(01797) 362353	
Newbury	The Wharf	(01635) 30267	tourism@westberks.gov.uk
Newport	High Street	(01983) 813818	info@islandbreaks.co.uk
Oxford	15/16 Broad Street	(01865) 726871	tic@oxford.gov.uk
Petersfield	27 The Square	(01730) 268829	petersfieldinfo@btconnect.com
Petworth*	The Old Bakery	(01798) 343523	
Portsmouth	Clarence Esplanade	(023) 9282 6722	vis@portsmouthcc.gov.uk
Portsmouth	The Hard	(023) 9282 6722	vis@portsmouthcc.gov.uk
Ramsgate	17 Albert Court	0870 2646111	ramsgate.tic@visitor-centre.net
Reading	Chain Street	(0118) 956 6226	touristinfo@reading.gov.uk
Ringwood	The Furlong	(01425) 470896	information@nfdc.gov.uk
Rochester	95 High Street	(01634) 843666	visitor.centre@medway.gov.uk
Romsey	13 Church Street	(01794) 512987	romseytic@testvalley.gov.uk
Royal Tunbridge Wells	The Pantiles	(01892) 515675	touristinformationcentre@tunbridgewells.gov.uk
Ryde	81-83 Union Street	(01983) 813818	info@islandbreaks.co.uk
Rye	Strand Quay	(01797) 226696	ryetic@rother.gov.uk
Sandown	8 High Street	(01983) 813818	info@islandbreaks.co.uk
Sandwich*	Cattle Market	(01304) 613565	info@ticsandwich.wanadoo.co.uk
Seaford	25 Clinton Place	(01323) 897426	seaford.tic@lewes.gov.uk
Sevenoaks	Buckhurst Lane	(01732) 450305	tic@sevenoakstown.gov.uk
Shanklin	67 High Street	(01983) 813818	info@islandbreaks.co.uk
Southampton	9 Civic Centre Road	(023) 8083 3333	tourist.information@southampton.gov.uk
Southsea	Clarence Esplanade	(023) 9282 6722	vis@portsmouthcc.gov.uk
Tenterden*	High Street	(01580) 763572	tentic@ashford.gov.uk
Tonbridge	Castle Street	(01732) 770929	tonbridge.castle@tmbc.gov.uk
Wendover	High Street	(01296) 696759	tourism@wendover-pc.gov.uk
Whitstable	7 Oxford Street	(01227) 275482	whitstableinformation@canterbury.gov.uk
Winchester	High Street	(01962) 840500	tourism@winchester.gov.uk
Windsor	24 High Street	(01753) 743900	windsor.tic@rbwm.gov.uk
Witney	26a Market Square	(01993) 775802	witney.vic@westoxon.gov.uk
Woodstock	Park Street	(01993) 813276	woodstock.vic@westoxon.gov.uk
Worthing	Chapel Road	(01903) 221307	tic@worthing.gov.uk
Worthing*	Marine Parade	(01903) 221307	tic@worthing.gov.uk
Yarmouth	The Quay	(01983) 813818	info@islandbreaks.co.uk

*seasonal opening ** calls to this number are charged at premium rate

Alternatively, you can text **TIC LOCATE** to **64118** to find your nearest tourist information centre

Find out **more**

The following publications are available from Tourism South East by logging on to **visitsouthernengland.com** or calling **(023) 8062 5400**:

> **Escape into the Countryside**
> **Cities**
> **Favourite Gardens and Garden Stays**
> **Great Days Out in Berkshire, Buckinghamshire and Oxfordshire**
> **Distinctive Country Inns**
> **We Know Just the Place**

Travel **info**

By road:
From the North East – M1 & M25;
the North West – M6, M40 & M25;
the West and Wales – M4 & M25;
the East – M25;
the South West – M5, M4 & M25;
London – M25, M2, M20, M23, M3, M4 or M40.

By rail:
Regular services from London's Charing Cross, Victoria, Waterloo and Waterloo East stations to all parts of the South East. Further information on rail journeys in the South East can be obtained on 0845 748 4950.

By air:
Fly into London City, London Heathrow, London Gatwick, London Southend, Southampton or Shoreham (Brighton City).

Relaxing on the River Thames at Cookham Dean, Berkshire

where to stay in
South East England

All place names in the blue bands are shown on the maps at the front of this guide.

A complete listing of all VisitBritain assessed parks in England appears at the back.

Accommodation symbols
Symbols give useful information about services and facilities. Inside the back-cover flap you can find a key to these symbols. Keep it open for easy reference.

ANDOVER, Hampshire Map ref 3C2

★★★
TOURING &
CAMPING PARK

🚐 £14.00–£20.00
🚎 £14.00–£20.00
⛺ £14.00–£20.00
69 touring pitches

Wyke Down Touring Caravan & Camping Park
Picket Piece, Andover SP11 6LX **t** (01264) 352048 **f** (01264) 324661
e wykedown@wykedown.co.uk **w** wykedown.co.uk

Level, sheltered site with public house and restaurant. Also recreation room, play area and golf driving range. Follow caravan and camping park signs from A303.

open All year
payment Credit/debit cards, cash/cheques

General 🖭 📶 P 🔌 🚲 🍴 🗄 ☉ 🕮✕ 🐕   Leisure ⚡ ▼ ⋔ ∪ ♫

ASHFORD, Kent Map ref 4B4

★★★★★
HOLIDAY, TOURING
& CAMPING PARK

🚐 £12.00–£18.00
🚎 £12.00–£18.00
⛺ £12.00–£15.00
🏠 (5) £220.00–£450.00
70 touring pitches

Broadhembury Caravan & Camping Park
Steeds Lane, Kingsnorth, Ashford TN26 1NQ **t** (01233) 620859 **f** (01233) 620918
e holidays@broadhembury.co.uk **w** broadhembury.co.uk

For walking, cycling, visiting castles and gardens or just relaxing, Broadhembury, in quiet Kentish countryside, is a park for all seasons. Convenient for Channel crossings and Canterbury.

open All year
payment Credit/debit cards, cash/cheques, euros

General 🖭 📶 P 🔌 🗄 🍴 🗄 🗄 ☉ 🕮🗄 🖳 🐕 🐾.☼   Leisure 📺 🔍 ⋔ ∪ ♫ ▶

BATTLE, East Sussex Map ref 4B4

★★★★★
HOLIDAY PARK
ROSE AWARD

🏠 (54) £275.00–£950.00

Crowhurst Park
Telham Lane, Battle TN33 0SL **t** (01424) 773344 **f** (01424) 775727
e enquiries@crowhurstpark.co.uk **w** crowhurstpark.co.uk

payment Credit/debit cards, cash/cheques

Quality development of luxury Scandinavian-style pine lodges within the grounds of a 17thC country estate. Facilities include leisure club with indoor swimming pool, bar, restaurant and children's playground. Open 3 March to 5 January.

⊕ *Two miles south of Battle on A2100.*

♥ *Christmas and New Year breaks available.*

General 🔊 P 🗄 🕮🗄 🖳 ✕ ☼   Leisure 🗄 📺 ▼ ♫ 🔍 ⋔ 🔍 🗄 🚲

Best of both worlds

South Coast, Country & New Forest Locations

All five of our holiday parks are set in peaceful, unspoilt parkland in the beautiful South Coast area.

There are comprehensive leisure facilities available and great entertainment for the whole family.

Pamper yourself in our new 'Reflections' Day Spa at Shorefield Country Park or explore Britain's latest National Park - the New Forest.

For full details, ask for our brochure or browse on-line.

For a really memorable family holiday

BATTLE, East Sussex Map ref 4B4

★★★★★
TOURING PARK
🚐(150) £11.00–£24.00
🚏(150) £11.00–£24.00
150 touring pitches

See Ad on inside back cover

Normanhurst Court Caravan Club Site
Stevens Crouch, Battle TN33 9LR t (01424) 773808 w caravanclub.co.uk

payment Credit/debit cards, cash/cheques

An elegant site, set in the heart of 1066 Country. Visit historic Battle Abbey or picturesque Rye, littered with antique shops and tea rooms. Open March to October.

⊕ From Battle, turn left onto A271. Site is 3 miles on left.

♥ Special member rates mean you can save your membership subscription in less than a week. Visit our website to find out more.

General 🔲 P 🔌 🕭 🛉 🏧 🅵 ☉ 🔟 🐕 ☼   Leisure ⚠ 🎵 ﹢

BEACONSFIELD, Buckinghamshire Map ref 3C2

★★★★
TOURING &
CAMPING PARK
🚐(60) £15.00–£20.00
🚏(60) £15.00–£20.00
Å (35) £10.00–£12.00
95 touring pitches

Highclere Farm Country Touring Park
Newbarn Lane, Seer Green, Beaconsfield HP9 2QZ t (01494) 874505 f (01494) 875238
e highclerepark@aol.com w highclerepark.co.uk

Quiet meadowland park, low-cost Tube prices to London (25 minutes). Eleven miles Legoland. Launderette, showers, superb toilet block, play area. Open March to January inclusive.

payment Credit/debit cards, cash/cheques

General 🔲 P 🔌 🕭 🛉 🏧 🅵 ☉ 🔟 🐾 🐕 ☼   Leisure ⚠ ∪ 🚲

BEMBRIDGE, Isle of Wight Map ref 3C3

★★★★
HOLIDAY PARK
🚐(400) £12.00–£19.00
🚏(400) £12.00–£19.00
Å (400) £12.00–£19.00
🏠(230) £70.00–£720.00
400 touring pitches

Whitecliff Bay Holiday Park
Hillway Road, Bembridge PO35 5PL t (01983) 872671 f (01983) 872941
e holiday@whitecliff-bay.com w whitecliff-bay.com

payment Credit/debit cards, cash/cheques, euros

Situated in an Area of Outstanding Natural Beauty, the park offers great-value family holidays. There are facilities on site for all ages. Open March to October.

⊕ From A3055 turn onto B3395 at Brading and follow signposts.

♥ Special offers are available from time to time – please visit our website for full details.

General 🔋 🔲 P 🔌 🕭 🛉 🏧 🅵 ☉ 🔟 🐾 ✕ ☼   Leisure 📶 📶 🍹 🎵 ☕ ⚠ 🎵 ﹢

BEXHILL-ON-SEA, East Sussex Map ref 4B4

★★★★
HOLIDAY, TOURING
& CAMPING PARK
🚐(55) £7.00–£7.80
🚏(55) £6.80–£7.60
Å (55) £7.00–£7.80
🏠(2) £110.00–£280.00
55 touring pitches

Cobbs Hill Farm Caravan & Camping Park
Watermill Lane, Sidley, Bexhill-on-Sea TN39 5JA t (01424) 213460 e cobbshillfarmuk@hotmail.com
w cobbshillfarm.co.uk

Quiet site in countryside with selection of farm animals. Touring and hire vans, level pitches, tent and rally fields. Near Hastings, Battle and Eastbourne.

payment Cash/cheques

General 🔲 P 🔌 🕭 🛉 🅵 ☉ 🔟 🐾 🐕 🏠 ☼   Leisure ☕ ⚠

BEXHILL-ON-SEA, East Sussex Map ref 4B4

★★★★★
TOURING &
CAMPING PARK

Max £16.00
Max £16.00
£12.50–£25.00
50 touring pitches

Kloofs Caravan Park

Sandhurst Lane, Bexhill-on-Sea TN39 4RG t (01424) 842839 f (01424) 845669
e camping@kloofs.com

Freedom all year round, whatever the weather! Fully serviced, hard, extra-large pitches. Modern facilities, private washing, central heating. In a quiet, rural setting.

open All year
payment Credit/debit cards, cash/cheques

General ▢ P ▣ ◻ ♀ 🔲 ⌂ ☺ ▣▣ ▣ ☂ ⚡ ☼ Leisure ⟁ ∪ ♪ ►

BIRCHINGTON, Kent Map ref 4C3

★★★★★
HOLIDAY, TOURING
& CAMPING PARK

(100) £12.00–£20.00
(100) £12.00–£20.00
(100) £12.00–£20.00
300 touring pitches

Two Chimneys Holiday Park

Shottendane Road, Birchington CT7 0HD t (01843) 841068 f (01843) 848099
e info@twochimneys.co.uk w twochimneys.co.uk

payment Credit/debit cards, cash/cheques

A friendly, family-run country site near sandy beaches. Spacious, level pitches. Modern wc/shower and laundry facilities including disabled. Children's play and ball-games areas. Open Easter to 31 October.

⊕ A2 then A28 to Birchington. Turn right into Park Lane, bear left into Manston Road, left at crossroads (B2049), site on right.

General ▢ P ▣ ◻ ♀ 🔲 ⌂ ☺ ▣▣ ▣ ☂ ☼ Leisure ≷ ▌ ◆ ⟁ ⚲ ∪ ♪

BOGNOR REGIS, West Sussex Map ref 3C3

★★★
TOURING PARK

(25) £10.00–£14.00
(25) £10.00–£14.00
(16) £10.00–£14.00
(8) £199.00–£340.00
49 touring pitches

The Lillies Caravan Park

Yapton Road, Barnham, Bognor Regis PO22 0AY t (01243) 552081 f (01243) 552081
e thelillies@hotmail.com w lilliescaravanpark.co.uk

Secluded caravan park set in three acres of quiet countryside, within easy reach of beaches, towns, swimming, golf, sailing, theatre, Goodwood horse and car racing, Arundel and South Downs.

open All year
payment Credit/debit cards, cash/cheques

General P ▣ ◻ ♀ 🔲 ⌂ ☺ ▣▣ ▣ ☂ ☼ Leisure ⟁ ∪

BRIGHTON & HOVE, East Sussex Map ref 3D3

★★★★★
TOURING &
CAMPING PARK

(169) £13.10–£27.00
(169) £13.10–£27.00
169 touring pitches

See Ad on inside back cover

Sheepcote Valley Caravan Club Site

East Brighton Park, Brighton BN2 5TS t (01273) 626546 w caravanclub.co.uk

open All year
payment Credit/debit cards, cash/cheques

Located on the South Downs, just two miles from Brighton. Visit the Marina, with its shops, pubs, restaurants and cinema, and take a tour of the exotic Royal Pavilion.

⊕ M23/A23, join A27 (Lewes). B2123 (Falmer/Rottingdean). Right, onto B2123 (Woodingdean). In 2 miles, at traffic lights, right (Warren Road). In 1 mile, left (Wilson Avenue).

♥ Special member rates mean you can save your membership subscription in less than a week. Visit our website to find out more.

General ▢ P ▣ ◻ ♀ 🔲 ⌂ ☺ ▣▣ ▣ ☂ ☼ Leisure ⟁ ►

BROOK, Isle of Wight Map ref 3C3

★★
HOLIDAY PARK
🚐 £12.00–£13.00
🅰 (28) £12.00–£13.00
🚚 (12) £260.00–£440.00

Compton Farm

Military Road, Brook, Newport, Isle of Wight PO30 4HF **t** (01983) 740215 **f** (01983) 740215

Working farm with single-suckler beef herd, hens and geese. Families welcome. A small site with huge field to fly kites or ride bikes. Steam engines, vintage machinery. Sandy beach.

payment Cash/cheques

General P 🏡 ⊙ 📲📺 🐾 ☼ Leisure ∪ ♪ ▶

BURFORD, Oxfordshire Map ref 3B1

★★★★★
TOURING PARK
🚐 (120) £11.00–£24.00
🚚 (120) £11.00–£24.00
120 touring pitches

See Ad on inside back cover

🏵 THE
CARAVAN
CLUB

Burford Caravan Club Site

Bradwell Grove, Burford OX18 4JJ **t** (01993) 823080 **w** caravanclub.co.uk

payment Credit/debit cards, cash/cheques

Attractive, spacious site opposite Cotswold Wildlife Park. Burford has superb Tudor houses, a museum and historic inns. A great base from which to explore the Cotswolds. Open March to October.

⊕ From roundabout at A40/A361 junction in Burford, take A361 signposted Lechlade. Site on right after 2.5 miles. Site signposted from roundabout.

♥ Special member rates mean you can save your membership subscription in less than a week. Visit our website to find out more.

General 🔲 P 🚗 🗘 🍴 🚐 🏡 ⊙ 📲📺 🐾 ☼ Leisure ⚠ ♪ ▶

CANTERBURY, Kent Map ref 4B3

★★★★
HOLIDAY, TOURING
& CAMPING PARK
🚐 (15) £13.00–£18.50
🚚 (5) £13.00–£18.50
🅰 (25) £11.00–£16.50
🚚 (7) £175.00–£405.00
45 touring pitches

Yew Tree Park

Stone Street, Petham, Canterbury CT4 5PL **t** (01227) 700306 **f** (01227) 700306
e info@yewtreepark.com **w** yewtreepark.com

payment Credit/debit cards, cash/cheques

Picturesque country park close to Canterbury, centrally located for exploring Kent. Naturally landscaped touring and camping facilities. Self-catering (not assessed) apartments and holiday units. Outdoor pool.

⊕ On B2068, 4 miles south of Canterbury, 9 miles north of M20, jct 11.

General 🔲 P 🚗 🗘 🍴 🏡 ⊙ 📲📺 ☼ Leisure ⌐ ⚠

CHICHESTER, West Sussex Map ref 3C3

★
HOLIDAY &
TOURING PARK
🚐 (15) Max £13.00
🚚 (15) Max £13.00

Bell Caravan Park

Bell Lane, Birdham, Chichester PO20 7HY **t** (01243) 512264

From Chichester take the main road to East and West Wittering. At village of Birdham turn left into Bell Lane. Park is a few hundred yards on the left. Open March to October.

payment Cash/cheques

General 🏡 P 🚗 🗘 🍴 🏡 📲 🐾 ☼ Leisure ∪ ♪ 🚲

COTSWOLDS

See under Burford, Standlake
See also Cotswolds in South West England section

EASTBOURNE, East Sussex Map ref 4B4

★★★★
TOURING &
CAMPING PARK
🚐 (60) £11.00–£16.00
🚏 (60) £11.00–£16.00
🛖 (60) £11.00–£16.00
60 touring pitches

Fairfields Farm Caravan & Camping Park

Eastbourne Road, Westham, Pevensey BN24 5NG t (01323) 763165 f (01323) 469175
e enquiries@fairfieldsfarm.com w fairfieldsfarm.com

payment Credit/debit cards, cash/cheques

A quiet country touring site on a working farm. Close to the beautiful seaside resort of Eastbourne, and a good base from which to explore the diverse scenery and attractions of south east England. Open April to October.

⊕ Signposted off A27 Pevensey roundabout. Straight through Pevensey and Westham villages towards castle. Then B2191 (left) to Eastbourne east, over level crossing on the left.

♥ Special low season, mid-week offer: 3 nights for the price of 2. Contact us for more details.

General 🏕 P 🚿 🛒 🍴 ⛺ ☉ 🗑 🛒 🐴 ⚡ ☼ Leisure 🚴 ⛳

FOLKESTONE, Kent Map ref 4B4

★★★★★
TOURING &
CAMPING PARK
🚐 (140) £11.00–£24.00
🚏 (140) £11.00–£24.00
140 touring pitches

See Ad on inside back cover

Black Horse Farm Caravan Club Site

385 Canterbury Road, Densole, Folkestone CT18 7BG t (01303) 892665 w caravanclub.co.uk

open All year
payment Credit/debit cards, cash/cheques

Landscaped, peaceful, rural site set on the Downs. Folkestone four miles, Dover eight miles, Canterbury 11 miles. Why not stop here en route to Europe?

⊕ From M20 jct 13 on A260 to Canterbury, 2 miles from junction with A20, site on left 200yds past Black Horse inn.

♥ Special member rates mean you can save your membership subscription in less than a week. Visit our website to find out more.

General 🖥 P 🚿 🛒 🍴 🔌 🗑 🍴 🐴 ☼ Leisure 🎯 🚴 ⚓

FORDINGBRIDGE, Hampshire Map ref 3B3

unwind
just drift away

Hi

We're enjoying a stay at Sandy Balls Holiday Centre in the New Forest National Park.

Visit www.sandy-balls.co.uk to discover the ways you can unwind and drift away or call us on 01425 653 042

New Forest
Sandy Balls

Luxury Lodges • Holiday Homes • Touring • Camping

GATWICK AIRPORT

See under Horsham, Redhill

HAILSHAM, East Sussex Map ref 3D3

★★★★
HOLIDAY, TOURING
& CAMPING PARK

🚐(14) £11.00–£15.00
🚐(2) £11.00–£15.00
🅰 (4) £5.00–£17.00
🏠(3) £170.00–£210.00
20 touring pitches

Peel House Farm Caravan Park

Sayerland Lane, Polegate BN26 6QX t (01323) 845629 f (01323) 845629 e peelhocp@tesco.net

payment Cash/cheques

Friendly, peaceful, rural site with resident proprietors. Views to South Downs. Good walking and cycling. Access to Cuckoo Trail. Free hot water and showers. Garden produce in season. Eastbourne five miles. Many attractions in area. Open April to October inclusive.

⊕ From A22 take A295 to Hailsham then sharp right at mini-roundabout signed Pevensey (Ersham Road). Park is 1.25 miles on right.

General 🖼 🚲 P 🔌 🖰 🍴 ☏ ☺ 🗐 🗄 🐂 🐕 ☼ Leisure 🎣 ⛰ ∪ 🏊 🚲

HORAM, East Sussex Map ref 3D3

★★★★
TOURING &
CAMPING PARK

🚐(40) £14.50
🚐(10) £14.50
🅰 (40) £14.50
90 touring pitches

Horam Manor Touring Park

Horam, Heathfield TN21 0YD t (01435) 813662 e camp@horam-manor.co.uk w horam-manor.co.uk

An established park with modern facilities including free hot water and showers. A tranquil setting in an Area of Outstanding Natural Beauty. On the A267, ten miles north of Eastbourne. Open March to October.

payment Cash/cheques

General 🚲 P 🔌 🖰 🍴 ☏ ☺ 🗐 🗄 🐂 ☼ Leisure ⛰ ✎ ∪ 🏊 ► 🚲

HORSHAM, West Sussex Map ref 3D2

★★★★
HOLIDAY PARK

🚐(200) £15.00–£23.00
🚐(100) £15.00–£23.00
🅰 (80) £15.00–£19.00
200 touring pitches

Honeybridge Park

Honeybridge Lane, Dial Post, Nr Horsham RH13 8NX t (01403) 710923 f (01403) 712815
e enquiries@honeybridgepark.co.uk w honeybridgepark.co.uk

open All year
payment Credit/debit cards, cash/cheques, euros

Delightfully situated within an Area of Outstanding Natural Beauty. A rural retreat with relaxed atmosphere providing exclusive holiday lodges for sale. Highest standards maintained with spacious touring pitches, heated amenity blocks, licensed shop, takeaway, play area. Seasonal pitches and storage facilities. Ideal touring base. Convenient to coast, London and theme parks..

⊕ On A24 travelling south, turn left 1 mile past Dial Post turning. At Old Barn Nurseries continue for 300yds and site is on the right.

♥ 10% discount on pitch fees for Senior Citizens, foreign Camping Carnet holders and 7 nights or more. Mid-week special: £6 off (incl Tue).

General 🖼 P 🔌 🖰 🍴 🚗 🍴 ☏ ☺ 🗐 🗄 🐂 🐕 ☼ Leisure 🎣 ⛰ 🏊 ► 🚲

HORSHAM, West Sussex Map ref 3D2

★★★★
TOURING PARK

🚐(60) £14.50–£18.50
🚐(60) £14.50–£18.50
🅰 (30) £14.50–£18.50

Sumners Ponds Fishery & Campsite

Slaughterford Farm, Chapel Road, Barns Green, Horsham RH13 0PR t (01403) 732539
e sumnersponds@dsl.pipex.com w sumnersponds.co.uk

A very beautiful site set on a working farm amongst three lakes, woodland and pastures. Excellent facilities and a village pub and shop five minutes' walk away.

open All year
payment Credit/debit cards, cash/cheques

General P 🔌 🍴 🚗 ☏ ☺ 🗄 🐂 🐕 ☼ Leisure 🏊

HOVE

See under Brighton & Hove

HURLEY, Berkshire Map ref 3C2

★★★★
HOLIDAY PARK

🚐 (138) £9.50–£15.50
🚛 (138) £9.50–£15.50
⛺ (62) £8.25–£14.25
🚐 (10) £200.00–£450.00
200 touring pitches

Hurley Riverside Park

Hurley, Maidenhead SL6 5NE t (01628) 824493 f (01628) 825533 e info@hurleyriversidepark.co.uk
w hurleyriversidepark.co.uk

payment Credit/debit cards, cash/cheques

Our family-run park is situated in the picturesque Thames Valley, surrounded by farmland. Access to the Thames Path. Ideal location for visiting Windsor, Legoland, Oxford and London. Open March to October.

General 🏢 P 🔌 🚰 🍴 🚐 📶 ☉ 🏪 🔌 🛒 🐕 🚭 ☀ Leisure ⚓ 🏃

ISLE OF WIGHT

See under Bembridge, Brook, Ryde

LINGFIELD, Surrey Map ref 3D2

★★
TOURING PARK

🚐 (60) £12.50–£15.00
🚛 (60) £12.50–£15.00
⛺ (60) £12.50–£15.00
60 touring pitches

Long Acres Caravan & Camping Park

Newchapel Road, Lingfield RH7 6LE t (01342) 833205 f (01622) 739966
e longacrescamping@yahoo.co.uk w longacrescamping.co.uk

Family-run park, ideal to visit London by train, Sussex, Surrey and Kent. Many local attractions – Hever, Chartwell House and gardens, Ardingly.

open All year
payment Cash/cheques

General 🏢 P 🔌 🚰 🍴 🚐 📶 ☉ 🏪 🔌 🐕 🚭 Leisure ⚓ 🏃

MARDEN, Kent Map ref 4B4

★★★★★
TOURING &
CAMPING PARK

🚐 (100) £12.00–£18.00
🚛 (33) £12.00–£18.00
⛺ (20) £12.00–£18.00
100 touring pitches

Tanner Farm Touring Caravan & Camping Park

Goudhurst Road, Tonbridge TN12 9ND t (01622) 832399 f (01622) 832472
e enquiries@tannerfarmpark.co.uk w tannerfarmpark.co.uk

open All year
payment Credit/debit cards, cash/cheques

Immaculate, secluded park surrounded by beautiful countryside on family farm. Ideal touring base for the area. Gold David Bellamy Conservation Award. Bed and breakfast also available. Green Tourism Business Scheme silver.

⊕ *From A21 or A229 onto B2079; midway between Marden and Goudhurst.*

♥ *Caravan Club AS.*

General 🏢 P 🔌 🚰 🍴 🚐 📶 ☉ 🏪 🔌 🛒 🐕 🚭 ☀ Leisure 🎢 ⚓

Check it out

Information on parks listed in this guide has been supplied by proprietors. As changes may occur you should remember to check all relevant details at the time of booking.

MILFORD ON SEA, Hampshire Map ref 3C3

★★★★
HOLIDAY PARK
(23) £130.00–£520.00

Downton Holiday Park

Shorefield Road, Milford on Sea, Lymington SO41 0LH **t** (01425) 476131 & (01590) 642515
f (01590) 642515 **e** info@downtonholidaypark.co.uk

A small, peaceful park on the edge of the New Forest, within easy reach of picturesque villages. Near to coast. Pets welcome in some caravans.

payment Credit/debit cards, cash/cheques

General P Leisure

MOLLINGTON, Oxfordshire Map ref 3C1

★★★★
TOURING & CAMPING PARK
£11.50–£12.50
£10.00–£11.00
(15) £6.00–£10.00
£160.00–£795.00
36 touring pitches

Anita's Touring Caravan Park

Church Farm, Mollington, Banbury OX17 1AZ **t** (01295) 750731 **f** (01295) 750731
e anitagail@btopenworld.com

Family-run site on working farm. Quality toilet/shower facility. Central to many places of interest, the Cotswolds, National Trust properties, Blenheim, Oxford, Stratford. Rallies welcome. Three superb cottages for hire.

open All year
payment Cash/cheques

General P Leisure

NEW FOREST

See under Milford on Sea, Ringwood

PEVENSEY BAY, East Sussex Map ref 4B4

★★★
HOLIDAY, TOURING & CAMPING PARK
(40) £13.00–£16.00
(4) £13.00–£16.00
(50) £13.00
(8) £170.00–£550.00
94 touring pitches

Bay View Park

Old Martello Road, Pevensey Bay BN24 6DX **t** (01323) 768688 **f** (01323) 769637
e holidays@bay-view.co.uk **w** bay-view.co.uk

Family site on a private road next to the beach. Play area. Showers and laundry. Small, well-stocked shop. Ideal touring base. Open April to October.

payment Credit/debit cards, cash/cheques

General P Leisure

REDHILL, Surrey Map ref 3D2

★★★★
TOURING PARK
(79) £11.00–£24.00
(79) £11.00–£24.00
79 touring pitches

See Ad on inside back cover

Alderstead Heath Caravan Club Site

Dean Lane, Redhill RH1 3AH **t** (01737) 644629 **w** caravanclub.co.uk

open All year
payment Credit/debit cards, cash/cheques

Quiet site with views over rolling, wooded North Downs. Denbies Wine Estate nearby. For day trips try Chessington and Thorpe Park and the lively city of Brighton. Non-members welcome.

M25 jct 8, A217 towards Reigate, fork left after 300yds towards Merstham. 2.5 miles, left at T-junction onto A23. 0.5 miles turn right into Shepherds Hill (B2031). 1 mile, left into Dean Lane.

Special member rates mean you can save your membership subscription in less than a week. Visit our website to find out more.

General P Leisure

Check the maps

Colour maps at the front pinpoint all the places you will find accommodation entries in the regional sections. Pick your location and then refer to the place index at the back to find the page number.

RINGWOOD, Hampshire Map ref 3B3

ROMSEY, Hampshire Map ref 3C3

★★★★
HOLIDAY, TOURING & CAMPING PARK

🚐 (70) £16.00–£22.00
🚎 (70) £16.00–£22.00
⛺ (40) £12.00–£16.00
🏠 (6) £170.00–£400.00
70 touring pitches

Hill Farm Caravan Park

Branches Lane, Sherfield English, Romsey SO51 6FH **t** (01794) 340402 **f** (01794) 342358
e gib@hillfarmpark.com **w** hillfarmpark.com

Set in 11 acres of beautiful countryside on the edge of the New Forest, our family-run site provides an ideal base from which to visit the area. Touring pitches from March to October, holiday homes from February to January.

payment Cash/cheques

General ▢ ⛟ P ⚙ ◔ ☕ 🚿 🝆 ⊙ 🗑 🝊 ✕ 🐾 🏕. ☀ Leisure ⚠ ∪ ⌁ ⤢ 🛶

RYDE, Isle of Wight Map ref 3C3

★★★
TOURING & CAMPING PARK

🚐 (6) £10.50–£12.50
🚎 (6) £10.50–£12.50
⛺ (20) £9.00–£11.00
32 touring pitches

Roebeck Camping and Caravan Park

Gatehouse Road, Upton, Ryde PO33 4BP **t** (01522) 545088 **e** info@roebeck-farm.co.uk
w roebeck-farm.co.uk

A small campsite set in 10 acres of farmland on the outskirts of Ryde, with toilet, shower and laundry facilities. Also tipi hiring available. Open April to October.

payment Cash/cheques, euros

General ⛟ P ⚙ ◔ ☕ 🚿 🝆 ⊙ 🗑 🐾 🏕. ☀ Leisure ⚠ ⌁

ST HELENS, Isle of Wight Map ref 3C3

★★★
TOURING & CAMPING PARK

🚐 (70) £8.00–£10.00
🚎 (70) £8.00–£10.00
⛺ (70) £8.00–£10.00
70 touring pitches

Carpenters Farm Campsite

Carpenters Road, St Helens, Ryde PO33 1YL **t** (01983) 874557 **e** info@carpentersfarm.co.uk
w carpentersfarm.co.uk

Farm campsite with beautiful views in picturesque rural setting, adjacent to RSPB Reserve and SSSI. Close to beaches and attractions. Relaxed atmosphere on site. Families, groups and pets very welcome. Open 1 April to 1 October.

payment Cash/cheques

General ▢ P ⚙ ◔ ☕ 🝆 ⊙ 🗑 🐾 🏕. ☀ Leisure ⚠ ⌁

Country Code
Always follow the Country Code

- Be safe – plan ahead and follow any signs
- Leave gates and property as you find them
- Protect plants and animals, and take your litter home
- Keep dogs under close control
- Consider other people

ST HELENS, Isle of Wight Map ref 3C3

★★★★★
HOLIDAY PARK
ROSE AWARD

(35) £150.00–£730.00

Field Lane Holiday Park

Field Lane, St Helens, Ryde PO33 1UX **t** (01983) 872779 **f** (01983) 873000 **e** office@fieldlane.com
w fieldlane.com

payment Credit/debit cards, cash/cheques

A refreshingly peaceful park that is secluded but not isolated. For couples and families who appreciate peace and quiet in civilised surroundings. Centrally heated units for spring and autumn. Wheelchair-access caravan available. Prices include return car ferry crossing. Rose awards, high quality, the right choice! Open March to October.

A3055 Ryde-Sandown road. Turn left at lights onto B3330, St Helens. Field Lane is 1st left in village. Bus service from Ryde to St Helens.

Special offers are posted on our website. Look out for Easter and May specials.

General Leisure

ST NICHOLAS AT WADE, Kent Map ref 4C3

★★
TOURING &
CAMPING PARK

(15)	£12.00–£15.00
(5)	£12.00–£14.00
(55)	£9.00–£12.00

75 touring pitches

St Nicholas Camping Site

Court Road, St Nicholas at Wade, Birchington CT7 0NH **t** (01843) 847245

The site – flat, grassy and well-sheltered – is on the outskirts of the village, close to the village shop. The resort of Thanet is within easy reach. The site is signposted from the A299 and A28.

payment Cash/cheques

General P Leisure

SEASALTER, Kent Map ref 4B3

★★★★★
HOLIDAY, TOURING
& CAMPING PARK

(43)	£9.50–£19.00
(43)	£9.50–£19.00
(43)	£7.50–£19.00
(5)	£100.00–£300.00

43 touring pitches

Homing Leisure Park

Church Lane, Seasalter, Whitstable CT5 4BU **t** (01227) 771777 **f** (01227) 273512
e info@homingpark.co.uk **w** coastandcountryleisure.com

Overlooking Whitstable Bay and close to all local amenities. Facilities nearby for horse-riding, watersports and golf. Open early March to late October.

payment Credit/debit cards, cash/cheques

General P Leisure

SELSEY, West Sussex Map ref 3C3

★★★★★
TOURING PARK

(250)	£18.00–£31.00
(250)	£18.00–£31.00
(50)	£16.00–£29.00

250 touring pitches

Warner Farm Touring Park

Warners Lane, Selsey, Chichester PO20 9EL **t** (01243) 604499 & (01243) 606080 **f** (01243) 604095
e touring@bunnleisure.co.uk **w** bunnleisure.co.uk

The park is part of the Bunn Leisure complex. Ballrooms, restaurants and swimming pool are within a 15-minute walk. Open 1 March to 31 October.

payment Credit/debit cards, cash/cheques

General P Leisure

STANDLAKE, Oxfordshire Map ref 3C1

WASHINGTON, West Sussex Map ref 3D3

★★★★
TOURING & CAMPING PARK
(21) Max £15.00
(5) Max £15.00
(80) Max £15.00
21 touring pitches

Washington Caravan & Camping Park

London Road, Washington, Pulborough RH20 4AJ **t** (01903) 892869 **f** (01903) 893252
e washcamp@amserve.com **w** washcamp.com

The park is set in beautifully landscaped grounds beneath the South Downs affording the right atmosphere for an enjoyable stay. Well situated for visiting places of interest.

open All year
payment Credit/debit cards, cash/cheques

General P Leisure

WESTENHANGER, Kent Map ref 4B4

★★★
HOLIDAY & CAMPING PARK
(44) £9.35–£19.60
(44) £9.35–£19.60
44 touring pitches

See Ad on inside back cover

Folkestone Racecourse Caravan Club Site

Westenhanger, Hythe CT21 4HX **t** (01303) 261761 **w** caravanclub.co.uk

payment Credit/debit cards, cash/cheques

Ideal for an overnight stop on the way to the continent – situated on the outskirts of Hythe. Easy rail access to London. Pleasant walking nearby. Open March to September.

From M20 jct 11, follow signs Folkestone Racecourse (A261). At A20 roundabout follow signs Sellindge and Lympne. Turn right, site on left.

Special member rates mean you can save your membership subscription in less than a week. Visit our website to find out more.

General P Leisure

WORTHING, West Sussex Map ref 3D3

★★★★
TOURING PARK
(129) £9.50–£21.40
(129) £9.50–£21.40
129 touring pitches

See Ad on inside back cover

Northbrook Farm Caravan Club Site

Titnore Way, Worthing BN13 3RT **t** (01903) 502962 **w** caravanclub.co.uk

payment Credit/debit cards, cash/cheques

An attractive, grassy site in open countryside with good trees, and only two miles from the coast. Open March to October.

From A24 follow signs for Chichester/Littlehampton approx 4 miles on, far side of bridge, signposted Ferring and Goring. After 0.75 miles, left. Caravan site sign Titnore Way is on left.

Special member rates mean you can save your membership subscription in less than a week. Visit our website to find out more.

General P Leisure

Check the maps

Colour maps at the front pinpoint all the cities, towns and villages where you will find accommodation entries in the regional sections. Pick your location and then refer to the place index at the back to find the page number.

South West England

Bath & Bristol › **Cornwall & the Isles of Scilly** › **Devon** › **Dorset**
Gloucestershire & the Cotswolds › **Somerset** › **Wiltshire**

Surf's up at Polzeath, Cornwall

South West Tourism
Woodwater Park
Exeter EX2 5WT
0870 442 0800
visitsouthwest.co.uk

**sheltered
bays,
wild moors,
relaxing
resorts**

Main Find yourself inspired by The Forest of Dean Sculpture Trail
Left Venturing through the Eden Project, near St Austell; sweeping views across the Jurassic Coast World Heritage Site; breathtaking colours at the Balloon Festival, Bristol; free spirits at Glastonbury Festival

Ride on the crest of a wave, then relax on a beautiful sandy beach, feel inspired by sweeping moors and wooded valleys, and **enjoy the party atmosphere in the coastal resorts.**

Explore
South West England

Surf's up

It's hard to beat the dramatic stretching beaches and magnificent coastlines of the South West. Learn to surf, or simply improve your skills atop the crashing waves in Croyde or Woolacombe. Dive in and explore the artificial reef at Whitsand Bay, created by the sinking of a disused naval ship, and hunt for marine life aboard its many decks. Have your senses shaken at the Extreme Academy in Watergate Bay – try your hand at waveskiing, mountain boarding or kite surfing, and feel your adrenalin levels hit an all-time high.

Lose yourself in a daydream staring out from one of the many beautiful shorelines on the Isles of Scilly. Observe flower fields ablaze with colour and spot puffins diving for unsuspecting fish. Find your bearings along a section of the 630-mile South West Coast Path and enjoy breathtaking views along the way.

Lost worlds

Sense the magic of the mysterious Lost Gardens of Heligan in Pentewan, Cornwall, and unlock the secrets held within its walls. For more inspiration, follow The Forest of Dean Sculpture Trail where you can find thought-provoking work nestling between the trees.

The mighty Stonehenge and Avebury World Heritage Site on Salisbury Plain never ceases to amaze: revel in its 5,000-year history and feel truly humbled by the size of these prehistoric archaeological monuments. Take a stroll around Westonbirt: The National Arboretum in Gloucestershire and allow the colours to mesmerise you whatever the season.

Catch a glimpse of wild red deer or grazing ponies in the stunning Exmoor National Park and gaze at reflections in beautiful lake-like reservoirs on heather-clad Dartmoor. Take your own piece of history home – search for fossils along the Jurassic Coast World Heritage Site in Dorset and East Devon.

Get up and go

Be transported to far-off climates in the transparent biomes of the Eden Project near St Austell. Wander amongst prairie flowers and olive trees and peel back tropical leaves as you pick your way through this remarkable educational centre. Take your chances at the UK's first safari park at Longleat in Warminster, drive amongst prowling tigers and towering giraffes and take a boat trip to Gorilla Island.

Unleash your wild side and try zorbing down a hillside in Dorset. Strap yourself into a large transparent PVC ball (add water for the hydro-zorbing experience), take a deep breath and think of England as you tumble down the hill!

City culture

Head to the vibrant city of Bristol and experience the superb Harbourside complex – admire the water sculpture and pull up a chair at a pavement cafe. Explore At-Bristol, where science, nature and art spring to life in this unique centre of discovery.

Indulge in a Cornish cream tea, tuck into a hearty pub lunch, sample the seafood and don't forget to savour the local pasties. But above all, eat well in this region laden with culinary delights – you're on holiday after all!

Places to **visit**

0 |———————| 50 miles
0 |———————| 75 kms

At-Bristol
Bristol
0845 345 1235
at-bristol.org.uk
*Interactive adventure of
a lifetime*

Bristol Zoo Gardens
Bristol
(0117) 974 7399
bristolzoo.org.uk
*Over 400 exotic and
endangered species*

Cheddar Caves & Gorge
Somerset
(01934) 742343
cheddarcaves.co.uk
A place of wild, rugged beauty

Corfe Castle
Dorset
0870 458 4000
purbeck.gov.uk
Majestic hilltop ruins

Lynton 27

Barnstaple
Clovelly
North Devon
Bude
Okehampton
Tintagel
27
3
DARTMOOR
Tamar Valley
Padstow
Newquay
32
Plymouth
Cornwall
South Devon
St Ives
Truro
St Austell
Penzance
3
Falmouth

Isles of Scilly

Flambards Experience
Helston, Cornwall
(01326) 573404
flambards.co.uk
Fantastic family theme park

The Forest of Dean Sculpture Trail
Gloucestershire
(01594) 833057
forestofdean-sculpture.org.uk
Spot artworks amid the trees

Eden Project
near St Austell, Cornwall
(01726) 811911
edenproject.com
A gateway into the plant world

Longleat
Warminster, Wiltshire
(01985) 844400
longleat.co.uk
*Beautiful stately home, plus
safari park*

Extreme Academy
near Newquay, Cornwall
(01637) 860840
extremeacademy.co.uk
*A Mecca for adventure
enthusiasts*

 National Park
Area of Outstanding Natural Beauty
Heritage Coast
 National Trails
nationaltrail.co.uk
 Sections of the
National Cycle Network
nationalcyclenetwork.org.uk
 Ferry routes

Broadway

Cheltenham

Stow-on-the-Wold

Cotswolds

Wye Valley

OFFA'S DYKE PATH

Gloucester

COTSWOLD WAY

RIDGEWAY

Swindon

Malmesbury

THAMES PATH

4

Bristol

Avebury

Weston-super-Mare

Bath

Mendip Hills

North Wessex Downs

Minehead

Westbury

SOUTH WEST COAST PATH

Quantock Hills

3

Warminster

EXMOOR

33

Salisbury

Taunton

Cranborne Chase & West Wiltshire Downs

3

Blackdown Hills

Yeovil

Exeter

East Devon

Lyme Regis

2

Dorset

Bridport

Bournemouth

Wareham

Poole

Corfe

SOUTH WEST COAST PATH

Weymouth

Swanage

Torbay

Roman Baths
Bath, Somerset
(01225) 477785
romanbaths.co.uk
Fascinating ancient temple and baths

St Michael's Mount
Penzance, Cornwall
(01736) 710507
stmichaelsmount.co.uk
Island crowned by medieval church

Stonehenge and Avebury World Heritage Site
Salisbury, Wiltshire
0870 333 1181
english-heritage.org.uk/stonehenge
World-famous prehistoric monument

Monkey World – Ape Rescue Centre
Wareham, Dorset
(01929) 462537
monkeyworld.org
Internationally acclaimed primate rescue centre

Tate St Ives
Cornwall
(01736) 796226
tate.org.uk/stives
A unique introduction to modern art

Oceanarium
Bournemouth, Dorset
(01202) 311993
oceanarium.co.uk
Embark on an underwater journey

Westonbirt: The National Arboretum
Tetbury, Gloucestershire
(01666) 880220
forestry.gov.uk/westonbirt
A divine collection of trees

The Lost Gardens of Heligan
near St Austell, Cornwall
(01726) 845100
heligan.com
Beautifully restored gardens

Paignton Zoo Environmental Park
Devon
(01803) 697500
paigntonzoo.org.uk
Set in beautiful botanical gardens

Zorb South UK
Dorchester, Dorset
(01929) 426595
zorbsouth.co.uk
Strap in to a PVC ball and let go!

Tourist information centres

When you arrive at your destination, visit a tourist information centre for help with accommodation and information about local attractions and events, or email your request before you go.

Amesbury	Smithfield Street	(01980) 622833	amesburytic@salisbury.gov.uk
Avebury	Green Street	(01672) 539425	all.atic@kennet.gov.uk
Axminster*	Church Street	(01297) 34386	axminstertic@btopenworld.com
Barnstaple	The Square	(01271) 375000	info@staynorthdevon.co.uk
Bath	Abbey Church Yard	0906 711 2000**	tourism@bathnes.gov.uk
Bideford	Victoria Park	(01237) 477676	bidefordtic@torridge.gov.uk
Blandford Forum	1 Greyhound Yard	(01258) 454770	blandfordtic@north-dorset.gov.uk
Bodmin	Mount Folly Square	(01208) 76616	bodmintic@visit.org.uk
Bournemouth	Westover Road	(01202) 451700	info@bournemouth.gov.uk
Bourton-on-the-Water	Victoria Street	(01451) 820211	bourtonvic@cotswold.gov.uk
Bradford-on-Avon	50 St Margaret's Street	(01225) 865797	tic@bradfordonavon2000.fsnet.co.uk
Braunton	Caen Street	(01271) 816400	info@brauntontic.co.uk
Bridgwater	King Square	(01278) 436438	bridgwater.tic@sedgemoor.gov.uk
Bridport	47 South Street	(01308) 424901	bridport.tic@westdorset-dc.gov.uk
Bristol	Harbourside	0906 711 2191**	ticharbourside@destinationbristol.co.uk
Brixham	The Quay	0870 707 0010	brixham.tic@torbay.gov.uk
Bude	The Crescent	(01288) 354240	budetic@visitbude.info
Budleigh Salterton	Fore Street	(01395) 445275	budleigh.tic@btconnect.com
Burnham-on-Sea	South Esplanade	(01278) 787852	burnham.tic@sedgemoor.gov.uk
Camelford*	The Clease	(01840) 212954	manager@camelfordtic.eclipse.co.uk
Cartgate	A303/A3088 Cartgate Picnic Site	(01935) 829333	cartgate.tic@southsomerset.gov.uk
Chard	Fore Street	(01460) 65710	chardtic@chard.gov.uk
Cheddar*	The Gorge	(01934) 744071	cheddar.tic@sedgemoor.gov.uk
Cheltenham	77 Promenade	(01242) 522878	tic@cheltenham.gov.uk
Chippenham	Market Place	(01249) 665970	tourism@chippenham.gov.uk
Christchurch	49 High Street	(01202) 471780	enquiries@christchurchtourism.info
Cirencester	Market Place	(01285) 654180	cirencestervic@cotswold.gov.uk
Coleford	High Street	(01594) 812388	tourism@fdean.gov.uk
Combe Martin*	Cross Street	(01271) 883319	mail@visitcombemartin.co.uk
Corsham	31 High Street	(01249) 714660	corshamheritage@northwilts.gov.uk
Crediton	High Street	(01363) 772006	info@devonshireheartland.co.uk
Dartmouth	Mayor's Avenue	(01803) 834224	holidays@discoverdartmouth.com
Dawlish	The Lawn	(01626) 215665	dawtic@Teignbridge.gov.uk
Devizes	Market Place	(01380) 729408	all.dtic@kennet.gov.uk
Dorchester	11 Antelope Walk	(01305) 267992	dorchester.tic@westdorset-dc.gov.uk
Exeter	Paris Street	(01392) 265700	tic@exeter.gov.uk
Exmouth	Alexandra Terrace	(01395) 222299	info@exmouthtourism.co.uk

Falmouth	28 Killigrew Street	(01326) 312300	info@falmouthtic.co.uk
Fowey	5 South Street	(01726) 833616	info@fowey.co.uk
Frome	Justice Lane	(01373) 467271	frome.tic@ukonline.co.uk
Glastonbury	9 High Street	(01458) 832954	glastonbury.tic@ukonline.co.uk
Gloucester	28 Southgate Street	(01452) 396572	tourism@gloucester.gov.uk
Helston and Lizard Peninsula	79 Meneage Street	(01326) 565431	info@helstontic.demon.co.uk
Honiton	Lace Walk Car Park	(01404) 43716	honitontic@honitontic.freeserve.co.uk
Ilfracombe	The Seafront	(01271) 863001	info@ilfracombe-tourism.co.uk
Isles of Scilly	Hugh Street, Hugh Town	(01720) 422536	tic@scilly.gov.uk
Ivybridge	Leonards Road	(01752) 897035	bookends.ivybridge@virgin.net
Kingsbridge	The Quay	(01548) 853195	advice@kingsbridgeinfo.co.uk
Launceston	Market Street	(01566) 772321	launcestontica@btconnect.com
Looe*	Fore Street	(01503) 262072	looetic@btconnect.com
Lyme Regis	Church Street	(01297) 442138	lymeregis.tic@westdorset-dc.gov.uk
Lynton and Lynmouth	Lee Road	0845 660 3232	info@lyntourism.co.uk
Malmesbury	Market Lane	(01666) 823748	malmesburyip@northwilts.gov.uk
Marlborough	High Street	(01672) 513989	all.tic's@kennet.gov.uk
Melksham	Church Street	(01225) 707424	visitmelksham2@tiscali.co.uk
Mere	Barton Lane	(01747) 861211	MereTIC@Salisbury.gov.uk
Minehead	17 Friday Street	(01643) 702624	info@mineheadtic.co.uk
Modbury*	5 Modbury Court	(01548) 830159	modburytic@lineone.net
Newent	7 Church Street	(01531) 822468	newent@fdean.gov.uk
Newquay	Marcus Hill	(01637) 854020	info@newquay.co.uk
Newton Abbot	6 Bridge House	(01626) 215667	natic@Teignbridge.gov.uk
Okehampton	3 West Street	(01837) 53020	okehamptontic@westdevon.gov.uk
Ottery St Mary	10a Broad Street	(01404) 813964	info@otterytourism.org.uk
Padstow	North Quay	(01841) 533449	padstowtic@btconnect.com
Paignton	The Esplanade	0870 707 0010	paignton.tic@torbay.gov.uk
Penzance	Station Road	(01736) 362207	pztic@penwith.gov.uk
Plymouth (Discovery Centre)	Crabtree	(01752) 266030	mtic@plymouth.gov.uk
Plymouth (Plymouth Mayflower)	3-5 The Barbican	(01752) 306330	barbicantic@plymouth.gov.uk
Poole	Poole Quay	(01202) 253253	info@poole.gov.uk
St Austell	Southbourne Road	0845 094 0428	tic@cornish-riviera.co.uk
St Ives	Street-an-Pol	(01736) 796297	ivtic@penwith.gov.uk
Salcombe	Market Street	(01548) 843927	info@salcombeinformation.co.uk
Salisbury	Fish Row	(01722) 334956	visitorinfo@salisbury.gov.uk
Seaton	The Underfleet	(01297) 21660	info@seatontic.freeserve.co.uk
Sedgemoor Services	M5 Southbound	(01934) 750833	somersetvisitorcentre@somerset.gov.uk
Shaftesbury	8 Bell Street	(01747) 853514	shaftesburytic@north-dorset.gov.uk
Shepton Mallet	48 High Street	(01749) 345258	sheptonmallet.tic@ukonline.co.uk
Sherborne	3 Tilton Court	(01935) 815341	sherborne.tic@westdorset-dc.gov.uk
Sidmouth	Ham Lane	(01395) 516441	sidmouthtic@eclipse.co.uk

South Molton	1 East Street	(01769) 574122	visitsouthmolton@btconnect.com
Stow-on-the-Wold	The Square	(01451) 831082	stowvic@cotswold.gov.uk
Street	Farm Road	(01458) 447384	street.tic@ukonline.co.uk
Stroud	George Street	(01453) 760960	tic@stroud.gov.uk
Swanage	Shore Road	(01929) 422885	mail@swanage.gov.uk
Swindon	37 Regent Street	(01793) 530328	infocentre@swindon.gov.uk
Taunton	Paul Street	(01823) 336344	tauntontic@tauntondeane.gov.uk
Tavistock	Bedford Square	(01822) 612938	tavistocktic@westdevon.gov.uk
Teignmouth	Sea Front	(01626) 215666	teigntic@teignbridge.gov.uk
Tetbury	33 Church Street	(01666) 503552	tourism@tetbury.org
Tewkesbury	64 Barton Street	(01684) 295027	tewkesburytic@tewkesburybc.gov.uk
Tiverton	Phoenix Lane	(01884) 255827	tivertontic@btconnect.com
Torquay	Vaughan Parade	0870 707 0010	torquay.tic@torbay.gov.uk
Torrington	Castle Hill	(01805) 626140	info@great-torrington.com
Totnes	Coronation Road	(01803) 863168	enquire@totnesinformation.co.uk
Trowbridge	St Stephen's Place	(01225) 710530	tic@trowbridge.gov.uk
Truro	Boscawen Street	(01872) 274555	tic@truro.gov.uk
Wadebridge	Eddystone Road	0870 122 3337	wadebridgetic@btconnect.com
Wareham	South Street	(01929) 552740	tic@purbeck-dc.gov.uk
Warminster	off Station Rd	(01985) 218548	visitwarminster@btconnect.com
Wellington	30 Fore Street	(01823) 663379	wellingtontic@tauntondeane.gov.uk
Wells	Market Place	(01749) 672552	touristinfo@wells.gov.uk
Westbury	Edward Street	(01373) 827158	visitwestbury@westwiltshire.gov.uk
Weston-super-Mare	Beach Lawns	(01934) 888800	westontouristinfo@n-somerset.gov.uk
Weymouth	The Esplanade	(01305) 785747	tic@weymouth.gov.uk
Wimborne Minster	29 High Street	(01202) 886116	wimbornetic@eastdorset.gov.uk
Winchcombe*	High Street	(01242) 602925	winchcombetic@tewkesbury.gov.uk
Woolacombe	The Esplanade	(01271) 870553	info@woolacombetourism.co.uk
Yeovil Heritage & Visitor Information Centre	Hendford	(01935) 845946	yeoviltic@southsomerset.gov.uk

*seasonal opening ** calls to this number are charged at premium rate

Alternatively, you can text **TIC LOCATE** to **64118** to find your nearest tourist information centre

Find out **more**

Visit the following websites for further information on South West England (or call **0870 442 0800**):

> **visitsouthwest.co.uk**

> **swcp.org.uk**

Also available from South West Tourism:

> **The Trencherman's Guide to Fine Food in South West England**

Gaze in awe at the mighty Stonehenge on Salisbury Plain

Travel **info**

By road:

The region is easily accessible from London, the South East, the North and the Midlands by the M6/M5 which extends just beyond Exeter, where it links in with the dual carriageways of the A38 to Plymouth, the A380 to Torbay and the A30 into Cornwall. The North Devon Link Road A361 joins junction 27 with the coast of North Devon and the A39, which then becomes the Atlantic Highway into Cornwall.

By rail:

The main towns and cities in the South West are served throughout the year by fast, direct and frequent rail services from all over the country. Trains operate from London (Paddington) to Chippenham, Swindon, Bath, Bristol, Weston-super-Mare, Taunton, Exeter, Plymouth and Penzance. A service runs from London (Waterloo) to Exeter, via Salisbury, Yeovil and Crewkerne.

By air:

Daily flights into Bristol, Bournemouth, Exeter, Gloucester, Isles of Scilly, Newquay and Plymouth operate from airports around the UK and Europe. For schedules, log on to visitsouthwest.co.uk/flights.

Official tourist board publication **Camping & Caravan Parks**

where to stay in
South West England

All place names in the blue bands are shown on the maps at the front of this guide.

A complete listing of all VisitBritain assessed parks in England appears at the back.

Accommodation symbols
Symbols give useful information about services and facilities. Inside the back-cover flap you can find a key to these symbols. Keep it open for easy reference.

ALDERHOLT, Dorset Map ref 3B3

★★★★
TOURING &
CAMPING PARK

🚐 £12.00–£14.00
🚙 £12.00–£14.00
⛺ £10.00–£12.00
34 touring pitches

Hill Cottage Farm Touring Caravan Park

Sandleheath Road, Alderholt, Fordingbridge SP6 3EG **t** (01425) 650513 **f** (01425) 652339

Set in 47 acres of Dorset countryside on the Hampshire/Dorset border. New Forest approximately two miles. Luxury facilities. Coarse fishing. Open March to October.

open All year
payment Cash/cheques

General P 🅿 🛈 🍴 🚐 🐾 📶 🔆   Leisure 🎣 🚤

ASHBURTON, Devon Map ref 2C2

Parkers Farm Holiday Park

Higher Mead Farm, Ashburton, Devon, TQ13 7LJ
Tel: 01364 654869 • Fax: 01364 654004
E-mail: parkersfarm@btconnect.com • Web: www.parkersfarm.co.uk

ROSE
AWARD
CARAVAN
HOLIDAY
PARK
2005

Friendly family run site on edge of Dartmoor National Park. Enjoy a relaxing holiday and visit the animals on a genuine working farm. The touring site has large level terraced pitches, fully tiled shower blocks, laundry room, shop, telephone and family bar and restaurant, all with disabled facilities. Gold award for quality & service 2006. British Farm Tourist award.

Discover Britain's heritage

Discover the history and beauty of over 250 of Britain's best-known historic houses, castles, gardens and smaller manor houses. You can purchase Britain's Historic Houses and Gardens – Guide and Map from good bookshops and online at visitbritaindirect.com.

BATH, Somerset Map ref 3B2

★★★★
TOURING &
CAMPING PARK

🚐 (90) £17.50–£19.50
🚎 (90) £17.50–£19.50
⛺ (105) £14.50–£17.00
195 touring pitches

Newton Mill Camping

Newton Road, Bath BA2 9JF t (01225) 333909 e newtonmill@hotmail.com w campinginbath.co.uk

open All year
payment Credit/debit cards, cash/cheques

Situated in an idyllic hidden valley close to the city centre with easy access by frequent, local buses or nearby level, traffic-free cycle path. Superb heated amenities (5-star Loo of the Year 2006) including showers, bathrooms and private facilities. Old Mill bar/restaurant open all year. David Bellamy Gold Award for Conservation. ADAC Campingplatz Auszeichnung 2006.

⊕ On A4 on outskirts of Bath towards Bristol, take exit signposted Newton St Loe at roundabout by the Globe pub. Site is 1 mile on left.

♥ 5% discount on stays of 7 days (selected periods). New Year package.

General 🔲🚎P🔌🔆☂🗪🅿⊙📧🔋🗙🐕🛖☀ Leisure 📺🍽🍴🎢⋃🎣🏊

BEETHAM, Somerset Map ref 2D2

★★★★
TOURING PARK

🚐 (74) £10.35–£21.40
🚎 (74) £10.35–£21.40
74 touring pitches

See Ad on inside back cover

Five Acres Caravan Club Site

Beetham, Chard TA20 3QA t (01460) 234519 w caravanclub.co.uk

payment Credit/debit cards, cash/cheques

This peaceful, open site is near Chard (six miles) – a busy market town. A wonderful spot from which to explore the lovely South Somerset countryside. Open March to October.

⊕ From east on A303, 5.25 miles past roundabout at end of Ilminster bypass, turn left at crossroads into narrow lane signposted Crickleaze, Whitestaunton. Site 2nd entrance on left in 250yds.

♥ Special member rates mean you can save your membership subscription in less than a week. Visit our website to find out more.

General 🔲P🔌🔆☂🗪🅿⊙📧🐕

BICKINGTON, Devon Map ref 2D2

★★★★★
HOLIDAY, TOURING
& CAMPING PARK

🚐 (50) £8.00–£12.00
🚎 (15) £8.00–£12.00
⛺ (20) £8.00–£12.00
🏠 (12) £160.00–£420.00
80 touring pitches

Lemonford Caravan Park

Bickington, Newton Abbot TQ12 6JR t (01626) 821242 f (01626) 821263 e mark@lemonford.co.uk w lemonford.co.uk

In a beautiful setting and scrupulously clean, superb facilities for touring caravans and tents. Holiday homes to buy or hire. Tourers available mid-March to end October, statics mid-March to mid-January.

payment Cash/cheques

General 🔋🔲🚎P🔌🔆☂🅿⊙📧🔋🐕☀ Leisure 🎢⋃🎣

Don't forget www.

Web addresses throughout this guide are shown without the prefix www. Please include www. in the address line of your browser. If a web address does not follow this style it is shown in full.

BLACKWATER, Cornwall Map ref 2B3

★★★★
TOURING &
CAMPING PARK

🚐(30)   £9.00–£13.50
🚎(30)   £9.00–£13.50
⛺ (30)   £9.00–£13.50
🏠 (20) £130.00–£530.00
30 touring pitches

Trevarth Holiday Park

Blackwater, Truro TR4 8HR **t** (01872) 560266 **f** (01872) 560379 **e** trevarth@lineone.net
w trevarth.co.uk

payment Credit/debit cards, cash/cheques

Luxury caravan holiday homes, touring and camping. A small, quiet park conveniently situated for north- and south-coast resorts. Level touring and tent pitches with electric hook-up. Open April to October.

⊕ Leave A30 at Chiverton roundabout (signed St Agnes). At the next roundabout take the road to Blackwater. Park on right after 200m.

General 🖼️ 🚐 🛁 🚽 🔌 🌳 ☉ 🛢️ ☼ Leisure ⚓ ⛰️

BLANDFORD FORUM, Dorset Map ref 3B3

★★★★
TOURING &
CAMPING PARK

🚐   £11.00–£18.00
🚎   £11.00–£18.00
🏕   £11.00–£18.00
125 touring pitches

The Inside Park

Down House Estate, Blandford St Mary, Blandford Forum DT11 9AD **t** (01258) 453719
f (01258) 459921 **e** inspark@aol.com **w** members.aol.com/inspark/inspark

Secluded park and woodland with facilities built into 18thC stable and coach house. Ideal location for touring the county. One-and-a-half miles south west of Blandford on road to Winterborne Stickland. Open 1 April to 31 October.

payment Credit/debit cards, cash/cheques

General 🖼️ P 🚐 🛁 🚽 🌳 ☉ 🛢️ 🐴 ☼ Leisure ⚓ ⛰️ ∪ ⤵

BOURNEMOUTH, Dorset Map ref 3B3

★★★★★
HOLIDAY, TOURING
& CAMPING PARK

🚐(41)   £7.00–£26.00
🚎(41)   £7.00–£26.00
🏠 (136)   £160.00–£675.00
41 touring pitches

Meadow Bank Holidays

Stour Way, Christchurch BH23 2PQ **t** (01202) 483597 **f** (01202) 483878
e enquiries@meadowbank-holidays.co.uk **w** meadowbank-holiday.co.uk

payment Credit/debit cards, cash/cheques

Bournemouth's closest combined holiday and touring park. Ideally located on the pretty River Stour, between Christchurch, Bournemouth and the New Forest. Open March to October.

⊕ A35 from Christchurch, west 1.5 miles, turn right at Crooked Beam Restaurant into The Grove, site 3rd left.

General P 🚐 🛁 🚽 🔌 🌳 ☉ 🛢️ ☼ Leisure ⚓ ⛰️ ⤵ ⤷

BOURNEMOUTH, Dorset Map ref 3B3

★★
TOURING &
CAMPING PARK

🚐(151)   £9.00–£16.00
🚎(151)   £9.00–£16.00
🏕 (151)   £9.00–£16.00
151 touring pitches

St Leonards Farm Caravan and Camping Park

Ringwood Road, West Moors, Ferndown BH22 0AQ **t** (01202) 872637 **f** (01202) 855683
w stleonardsfarm.biz

Quiet, level site, near Bournemouth, Poole, Channel ferries and New Forest, with modern facilities. Entrance on A31, five miles west of Ringwood opposite Texaco garage. Special facilities for disabled. Electrical hook-ups.

payment Cash/cheques

General 🚐 🛁 🚽 🌳 ☉ 🛢️ Leisure ⛰️ ⤵

BRAUNTON, Devon Map ref 2C1

★★★★
TOURING &
CAMPING PARK

🚐 (100) £7.50–£23.00
🚙 (40)   £7.50–£23.00
⛺ (40)   £6.00–£23.00
180 touring pitches

Lobb Fields Caravan and Camping Park

Saunton Road, Braunton EX33 1EB t (01271) 812090 f (01271) 812090 e info@lobbfields.com
w lobbfields.com

Fourteen-acre grassy park with panoramic views across the Taw Estuary. Situated one mile from Braunton centre on B3231 and 1.5 miles from Saunton beach and Biosphere reserve. Open 23 March to 28 October.

payment Credit/debit cards, cash/cheques

General 🖼 P 🚗 🚿 🔌 📶 ☉ 📧 🔌 🐾 🅿 ☼ Leisure ⩘ ∪ ⤵ 🚲

BREAN, Somerset Map ref 2D1

★★★
TOURING &
CAMPING PARK

🚐 (40)   £7.00–£13.00
🚙 (40)   £7.00–£13.00
⛺ (80)   £7.00–£13.00
🏠 (1) £200.00–£400.00
200 touring pitches

Diamond Farm

Weston Road, Brean, Burnham-on-Sea TA8 2RL t (01278) 751263
e trevor@diamondfarm42.freeserve.co.uk w diamondfarm.co.uk

Quiet family site alongside River Axe and five minutes from beach. Fishing on site. Brean coast road and beach 800yds. Open March to October.

payment Cash/cheques

General 🔌 🖼 🎿 P 🚗 🚿 🔌 📶 ☉ 📧 🅿 ✕ 🐾 🅿 ☼ Leisure ⩘ ∪ ⤵ ▶

BREAN, Somerset Map ref 2D1

★★★★
HOLIDAY, TOURING
& CAMPING PARK

🚐 (350) £5.50–£18.50
🚙 (350) £5.50–£18.50
⛺ (150) £5.50–£16.25
350 touring pitches

Northam Farm Touring Park

Brean Sands, Burnham-on-Sea TA8 2SE t (01278) 751244 f (01278) 751150
e enquiries@northamfarm.co.uk w northamfarm.co.uk

A 30-acre, family-run park adjacent to five miles of sandy beach. Ideal base for exploring Somerset. Central for children's amusements and nightly family entertainment. Free fishing on park. Open March to October.

payment Credit/debit cards, cash/cheques

General P 🚗 🚿 🔌 📶 📶 ☉ 📧 🅿 ✕ 🐾 🅿 ☼ Leisure ⩘ 🌳 ⤵ 🚲

BREAN, Somerset Map ref 2D1

★★★★
HOLIDAY, TOURING
& CAMPING PARK

🚐   £6.00–£13.00
🚙   £6.00–£13.00
⛺   £6.00–£13.00
🏠 (11) £170.00–£440.00
575 touring pitches

Warren Farm Holiday Centre

Warren Road, Brean Sands, Burnham-on-Sea TA8 2RP t (01278) 751227 f (01278) 751033
e enquiries@warren-farm.co.uk w warren-farm.co.uk

payment Credit/debit cards, cash/cheques

Award-winning, family-run holiday centre close to the beach offering a friendly atmosphere, with high standards of cleanliness, modern facilities and excellent value. Spacious, level grass pitches are complemented by indoor and outdoor play facilities, pub, restaurant and nightly entertainment in high season. No pets in caravan holiday homes. Open March to October.

⊕ M5 south. Jct 22 onto B3140 through Burnham-on-Sea, to Berrow and Brean. 1.5 miles past Brean Leisure Park, on the right.

General 🖼 P 🚗 🚿 🔌 📶 📶 ☉ 📧 🅿 ✕ 🅿 ☼ Leisure 📺 🍴 🎵 ♦ ⩘ ∪ ⤵ 🚲

Check it out

Information on parks listed in this guide has been supplied by proprietors. As changes may occur you should remember to check all relevant details at the time of booking.

Official tourist board publication **Camping & Caravan Parks**

BRIDGWATER, Somerset Map ref 2D1

★★
TOURING &
CAMPING PARK

🔌 £9.00–£16.50
🚐 £9.00–£16.50
⛺ £6.00–£55.00

200 touring pitches

Fairways International Touring Caravan and Camping Park

Bath Road, Bawdrip, Bridgwater TA7 8PP **t** (01278) 685569 **f** (01278) 685569
e fairwaysint@btinternet.com **w** fairwaysint.btinternet.co.uk

payment Credit/debit cards, cash/cheques, euros

International touring park in countryside, two miles off motorway in Glastonbury direction. On-site accessory centre for tents, caravans and motor homes. Storage, store and stay, storage on pitch, seasonals and rallies welcomed. Tents charged on size; caravans and motor homes charged on length. Fishing one mile, seaside six miles. Open 1 March to mid-November.

⊕ *From M5 take signs towards Glastonbury/Street. At junction, again head towards Glastonbury/Street. Take left turning to Woolavington, approx 75yds on right. Park is behind garage.*

♥ *7 nights for 6. For Senior Citizens only: 7-day booking during Mar, Jun, Sep, Oct 2007/Mar 2008 – £55 per week (with this advert only).*

General 🖵 P 🔌 🕒 🍴 🏠 ☉ 🏕 🗑 🐾 ☼ Leisure 📺 🔍 ⚠ ♩

BRIDPORT, Dorset Map ref 3A3

★★★★
HOLIDAY, TOURING
& CAMPING PARK

🔌 (350) £9.00–£30.00
🚐 (50) £9.00–£30.00
⛺ (100) £4.00–£30.00
🏠 (60) £150.00–£715.00

500 touring pitches

Freshwater Beach Holiday Park

Burton Bradstock, Bridport DT6 4PT **t** (01308) 897317 **f** (01308) 897336
e office@freshwaterbeach.co.uk **w** freshwaterbeach.co.uk

payment Credit/debit cards, cash/cheques

Family park with a large touring and camping field. Own private beach on Dorset's spectacular World Heritage Coastline. Surrounded by countryside and within easy reach of Dorset's features and attractions. Free nightly family entertainment and children's activities. Horse and pony rides, donkey derby, beach fishing, cliff and seaside walks. Open mid-March to mid-November.

⊕ *From Bridport take B3157, situated 2 miles on the right.*

♥ *Pitch prices include up to 6 people and club membership.*

General 🖵 P 🔌 🕒 🍴 🚐 🏠 ☉ 🏕 🗑 ✕ 🐾 ☼ Leisure ⚡ 📺 🍷 🎵 🔍 ⚠ ∪ ♩ ►

BRIDPORT, Dorset Map ref 3A3

★★★★★
HOLIDAY, TOURING
& CAMPING PARK
ROSE AWARD

🔌 £12.00–£25.00
🚐 £12.00–£25.00
⛺ (159) £12.00–£19.50
🏠 (12) £250.00–£550.00

108 touring pitches

Golden Cap Holiday Park

Seatown, Chideock, Bridport DT6 6JX **t** (01308) 422139 **f** (01308) 425672 **e** holidays@wdlh.co.uk
w wdlh.co.uk

One hundred metres from beach overlooked by Dorset's highest cliff top – Golden Cap – surrounded by countryside on this Heritage Coast. Open March to November.

payment Credit/debit cards, cash/cheques

General P 🔌 🕒 🍴 🏠 ☉ 🏕 🗑 🐾 ☼ Leisure ⚠ ♩ ►

Check the maps

Colour maps at the front pinpoint all the places you will find accommodation entries in the regional sections. Pick your location and then refer to the place index at the back to find the page number.

BRIDPORT, Dorset Map ref 3A3

★★★★★
HOLIDAY, TOURING
& CAMPING PARK
ROSE AWARD

🛏 £12.00–£22.00
🚐 £12.00–£22.00
⛺ (75) £9.00–£16.00
🚊 (18) £200.00–£550.00
120 touring pitches

Highlands End Holiday Park

Eype, Bridport DT6 6AR **t** (01308) 422139 **f** (01308) 425672 **e** holidays@wdlh.co.uk **w** wdlh.co.uk

Quiet, select, family park overlooking sea with exceptional views of Heritage Coast and Lyme Bay. Indoor swimming pool. Open March to November.

payment Credit/debit cards, cash/cheques

General 🔌 P 🔟 🛢 🚾 🌣 Leisure

BRIXHAM, Devon Map ref 2D2

★★★★
TOURING &
CAMPING PARK

🛏 (60) £9.10–£16.40
🚐 (10) £9.10–£16.40
⛺ (60) £9.10–£16.40
🚊 (4) £195.00–£490.00
120 touring pitches

Galmpton Touring Park

Greenway Road, Galmpton, Brixham TQ5 0EP **t** (01803) 842066 **f** (01803) 844458
e galmptontouringpark@hotmail.com **w** galmptontouringpark.co.uk

payment Credit/debit cards, cash/cheques

Overlooking the River Dart with superb views from pitches. A quiet base for families and couples to explore Torbay and South Devon. Open Easter to September.

⊕ Take A380 Torbay ring road then A379 to Brixham. Take 2nd right to Galmpton Park through village to park. Site signposted.

♥ Off-peak reductions.

General 🔌 P 🔟 🛢 🚾 🌣 Leisure

BRIXHAM, Devon Map ref 2D2

★★★★★
TOURING &
CAMPING PARK

🛏 (239) £12.60–£28.00
🚐 (239) £12.60–£28.00
239 touring pitches

See Ad on inside back cover

Hillhead Holiday Park

Hillhead, Brixham TQ5 0HH **t** (01803) 853204 **w** caravanclub.co.uk

open All year
payment Credit/debit cards, cash/cheques

In a great location, with many pitches affording stunning sea views. Swimming pool, evening entertainment, bar, restaurant and much more! Open March to October.

⊕ Right off A380 (Newton Abbot). Three miles onto ring road (Brixham). Seven miles turn right, A3022. In 0.75 miles, right onto A379. Two miles keep left onto B3025. Site entrance on left.

♥ Special member rates mean you can save your membership subscription in less than a week. Visit our website to find out more.

General P 🔟 🛢 🚾 🌣 Leisure

Friendly help and advice

Did you know there are more than 700 tourist information centres throughout Britain? It adds up to a lot of friendly help and advice. You'll find contact details at the beginning of each regional section.

BUDE, Cornwall Map ref 2C2

★★★★★
TOURING PARK

🛋 (145) £8.60–£19.80
🚐 (145) £8.60–£19.80
⛺ (145) £8.60–£19.80
145 touring pitches

Budemeadows Touring Holiday Park

Budemeadows, Bude EX23 0NA **t** (01288) 361646 **f** (01288) 361646
e holiday@budemeadows.com **w** budemeadows.com

open All year
payment Credit/debit cards, cash/cheques

Superb centre for surfing, scenery and sightseeing. All usual facilities including heated pool, licensed bar, shop, launderette, playground. Large pitches – no overcrowding.

⊕ Signposted on A39, 3 miles south of Bude, 200yds past crossroad to Widemouth Bay.

General 🔲 🚲 P 🔌 🚻 🍴 🍽 🕍 ☉ 🏧 📷 🛒 🐾 ☼ Leisure ⚓ 📺 🍷 🔍 ⌂ ♨ 🎣

BUDE, Cornwall Map ref 2C2

★★★
TOURING &
CAMPING PARK

🛋 (30) £7.00–£15.00
🚐 (30) £7.00–£15.00
⛺ (78) £6.00–£13.00
🏠 (2) £120.00–£400.00
98 touring pitches

Penhalt Farm Holiday Park

Widemouth Bay, Poundstock, Bude EX23 0DG **t** (01288) 361210 **f** (01288) 361210
e den&jennie@penhaltfarm.fsnet.co.uk **w** holidaybank.co.uk/penhaltfarmholidaypark

payment Credit/debit cards, cash/cheques

Spectacular, panoramic sea views from most pitches. Friendly, family-run site, ideal for walking, surfing, touring. Site shop, play area, games room. Dogs welcome. Open Easter to October.

⊕ Travelling south, 4.5 miles from Bude on A39. 2nd right into Widemouth Bay, left at bottom. Widemouth Manor Hotel on left. Sign 0.75 miles on the left.

General 🔲 P 🔌 🚻 🍴 📷 ☉ 🏧 📷 🛒 🐾 ☼ Leisure 🔍 ♨ 🎣

BUDE, Cornwall Map ref 2C2

★★★★
HOLIDAY &
TOURING PARK

🛋 (20) £8.30–£16.80
🚐 (20) £8.30–£16.80
⛺ (20) £8.30–£16.80
🏠 (150) £135.00–
£430.00
60 touring pitches

Sandymouth Bay Holiday Park

Sandymouth Bay, Bude EX23 9HW **t** (01288) 352563 **f** (01288) 354822
e reception@sandymouthbay.co.uk **w** dolphinholidays.co.uk

payment Credit/debit cards, cash/cheques

Friendly family park set in 24 acres of meadowland in an area rich with beautiful beaches, busting coastal resorts and picturesque fishing villages. Inland, the rolling countryside is a fascinating contrast to the rugged coast. Licensed club, indoor pool, sauna, solarium, crazy golf, toilets and launderette. Open March to October.

⊕ On M5 from north, exit jct 27. Travel on A361/A39 towards Bude. Just past the village of Kilkhampton, take right-hand turning signposted Sandymouth.

♥ Various promotions for certain times of the year – call us or see website.

General 🔊 🔲 🚲 P 🔌 🚻 🍴 📷 ☉ 🏧 📷 🛒 ✗ ☼ Leisure ⚓ 📺 🍷 🎵 🔍 ♨ 🎣 ⚙

Key to symbols

Open the back flap for a key to symbols.

BUDE, Cornwall Map ref 2C2

★★★★
HOLIDAY, TOURING & CAMPING PARK
(65) £8.50–£15.50
(65) £8.50–£15.50
(65) £8.50–£15.50
(18) £150.00–£475.00
65 touring pitches

Upper Lynstone Caravan and Camping Site

Upton, Bude EX23 0LP **t** (01288) 352017 **f** (01288) 359034 **e** reception@upperlynstone.co.uk
w upperlynstone.co.uk

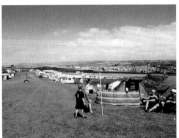

payment Credit/debit cards, cash/cheques

A quiet family-run park just 0.75 miles from the sandy beach and town centre. Enjoy the beauty of the coastal path from our site. Spacious camping and electric hook-up patches. Modern, well-equipped caravans for hire. Families and couples only. Open Easter to October.

⊕ *Half a mile south of Bude on coastal road to Widemouth Bay. Signposted.*

General P Leisure

BUDE, Cornwall Map ref 2C2

★★★★★
HOLIDAY & TOURING PARK
(50) £9.50–£17.00
(50) £9.50–£17.00
(40) £9.50–£17.00
(55) £170.00–£680.00
60 touring pitches

Wooda Farm Park

Poughill, Bude EX23 9HJ **t** (01288) 352069 **f** (01288) 355258 **e** enquiries@wooda.co.uk
w wooda.co.uk

Stunning views over Bude Bay and countryside; 1.5 miles from safe, sandy beaches. Family owned and run with all facilities, fishing, sports barn, tennis court, woodland walks, golf. An ideal base. Open April to October.

payment Credit/debit cards, cash/cheques

General P Leisure

BURNHAM-ON-SEA, Somerset Map ref 2D1

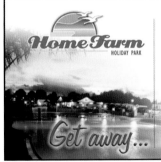

HomeFarm
HOLIDAY PARK
Get away...
Welcome to Somerset's ultimate holiday destination set in forty-four acres of beautiful parkland.
Home Farm has everything you could wish for to make your holiday a truly memorable experience, with fun for all the family including:
• Top-class entertainment in the Home Farm Country Club.
• A new colourful, safe playground for the children.
• Home Farm Country Club restaurant and bar and all day takeaway.
We have some great summer offers so why not give us a call today or check out our new website:
www.homefarmholidaypark.co.uk
The UK's favourite holiday park runner up in 2003 – voted by the readers of Caravan Magazine.
Booking hotline
01278 788888

BURTON BRADSTOCK, Dorset Map ref 3A3

★★★
HOLIDAY, TOURING & CAMPING PARK
£10.00–£17.50
£10.00–£17.50
£8.00–£14.50
40 touring pitches

Coastal Caravan Park

Annings Lane, Burton Bradstock, Bridport DT6 4QP **t** (01308) 422139 **f** (01308) 425672
e holidays@wdlh.co.uk **w** wdlh.co.uk

Small, non-commercial park in beautiful surroundings, situated 2.5 miles from A35 east of Bridport. Mainly privately owned caravan holiday homes. Open March to November.

payment Cash/cheques

General P Leisure

You're welcome at our Sites!
For details of Caravan Club sites in this region, where high standards, excellent facilities and a warm welcome are assured, please see our website
THE CARAVAN CLUB
www.caravanclub.co.uk

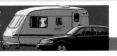

CAMELFORD, Cornwall Map ref 2B2

★★★
HOLIDAY, TOURING
& CAMPING PARK

(35) £10.00–£16.00
(35) £10.00–£16.00
Å (35) £10.00–£14.00
£199.00–£720.00
70 touring pitches

Juliot's Well Holiday Park

Camelford PL32 9RF t (01840) 213302 f (01840) 212700 e juliotswell@holidaysincornwall.net
w holidaysincornwall.net

Quiet park in 31 acres of beautiful woodland and meadows. Facilities include a swimming pool, bar and restaurant, plus more. Close to beach and moor.

open All year
payment Credit/debit cards, cash/cheques

General 🔌P 🔲 🌀 🍴 📺 🛁 ✕ 🐾 Leisure 🏊 ⚟ 🎵 🎯 ⏶ 🎣 ∪ ▶

CHARMOUTH, Dorset Map ref 2D2

★★★
HOLIDAY, TOURING
& CAMPING PARK

(300) £10.00–£19.00
(300) £10.00–£19.00
Å (300) £10.00–£19.00
(6) £200.00–£650.00
300 touring pitches

Manor Farm Holiday Centre

The Street, Charmouth, Bridport DT6 6QL t (01297) 560226 f (01297) 560429
e enq@manorfarmholidaycentre.co.uk w manorfarmholidaycentre.co.uk

Large, open site in Area of Outstanding Natural Beauty close to the sea. From east end of Charmouth bypass, come into Charmouth and the site is 0.75 miles on the right.

open All year
payment Credit/debit cards, cash/cheques

General 🔌🔲P 🔲 🌀 🍴 🌀 🍴 ☺ 📺 🛁 ✕ 🐾 ☼ Leisure 🏊 ⚟ 🎵 🎯 ⏶ ∪ 🎣 ▶

CHARMOUTH, Dorset Map ref 2D2

★★★★
TOURING &
CAMPING PARK

£8.50–£18.00
£8.50–£18.00
Å £8.50–£18.00
60 touring pitches

Monkton Wyld Farm Caravan & Camping Park

Monkton Wyld, Bridport DT6 6DB t (01297) 34525 f (01297) 33594 e simonkewley@mac.com
w monktonwyld.co.uk

payment Credit/debit cards, cash/cheques, euros

Beautifully landscaped, level park. Only three miles from sandy beaches and surrounded by lovely countryside. Excellent access, yet away from noisy main roads. All the amenities you would expect to find in a quality park. Open Easter to 31 October.

⊕ A35 from west towards Charmouth, cross Dorset county boundary, next lane left (brown tourist sign), 2nd campsite on left.

♥ Weekly special-offer rates: £65 low season, £75 mid-season.

General 🔲🚗P 🔲 🌀 🍴 🌀 ☺ 📺 🐾 🐕 ☼ Leisure ⏶ ∪ 🎣 ▶

CHARMOUTH, Dorset Map ref 2D2

★★★★★
HOLIDAY, TOURING
& CAMPING PARK

(40) £12.00–£18.00
(10) £12.00–£18.00
Å (10) £12.00–£18.00
(62) £160.00–£550.00
60 touring pitches

See Ad on page opposite

Seadown Holiday Park

Bridge Road, Charmouth, Bridport DT6 6QS t (01297) 560154 f (01297) 561130
w seadowncaravanpark.co.uk

payment Credit/debit cards, cash/cheques

Quiet, family-run park which runs alongside the River Char. It has its own direct access to Charmouth's famous fossil beach which is situated on the World Heritage Coastline. Open mid-March to end October.

General 🔲P 🚗 🍴 🌀 🌀 📺 🛁 🐾 ☼ Leisure ∪ 🎣

CHARMOUTH, Dorset Map ref 2D2

SEADOWN HOLIDAY PARK
Bridge Road, Charmouth, Dorset DT6 6QS

Quiet family run park situated on Dorset's World Heritage Coast. The park has its own direct access to Charmouth's famous fossil beach.

T: (01297) 560154 F: (01297) 561130 www.seadownholidaypark.co.uk

CHARMOUTH, Dorset Map ref 2D2

★★★★★
HOLIDAY, TOURING
& CAMPING PARK
ROSE AWARD

🚐 (186) £12.50–£26.00
🚐 £12.50–£26.00
▲ (20) £10.50–£22.00
🏠 (3) £210.00–£550.00
206 touring pitches

Wood Farm Caravan and Camping Park
Charmouth, Bridport DT6 6BT t (01297) 560697 f (01297) 561243 e holidays@woodfarm.co.uk w woodfarm.co.uk

payment Credit/debit cards, cash/cheques

Breathtaking views and superb facilities are both on offer at Wood Farm. Our Heritage Coast and spectacular rural scenery are just waiting to amaze you. Open Easter to October.

⊕ From M5 jct 25 follow A358 to Chard then Axminster. Join A35 towards Bridport. After 4 miles, at roundabout take 1st exit to Wood Farm.

♥ Low- and mid-season offers for 1- and 2-week stays.

General 🔌 🎫 P 🔌 🕒 🍴 ⓦ 🏧 ☉ 🗑 🔋 🐕 Leisure 🎣 📺 🔍 🎱 🏊 ►

CHEDDAR, Somerset Map ref 2D1

★★★★
HOLIDAY, TOURING
& CAMPING PARK
ROSE AWARD

🚐 (100) £13.00–£23.00
🚐 (20) £10.00–£21.00
▲ (80) £10.00–£21.00
🏠 (37) £180.00–£600.00
200 touring pitches

Broadway House Holiday Touring Caravan and Camping Park
Axbridge Road, Cheddar BS27 3DB t (01934) 742610 f (01934) 744950 e info@broadwayhouse.uk.com w broadwayhouse.uk.com

payment Credit/debit cards, cash/cheques, euros

Nestling at the foot of the Mendip Hills, this family-run park is only one mile, and the closest of its kind, to England's Grand Canyon: Cheddar Gorge. We have every facility your family could ever want: shop, bar, launderette, swimming pool, BMX track, skateboard park, nature trails, archery, caving and canoeing. Open March to November.

⊕ M5 jct 22. Eight miles. Midway between Cheddar and Axbridge on A371.

General 🎫 P 🔌 🕒 🍴 ⓦ 🏧 ☉ 🗑 🔋 ✕ 🐕 ☀ Leisure 🎣 📺 🍴 🔍 🎢 ∪ ► 🚴

CHEDDAR, Somerset Map ref 2D1

★★★★
TOURING &
CAMPING PARK

🚐 £8.90–£26.75
🚐 £8.90–£26.75
▲ £8.90–£26.75
🏠 (2) £248.00–£480.00
90 touring pitches

Cheddar, Mendip Heights Camping and Caravanning Club Site
Townsend, Priddy, Wells BA5 3BP t (01749) 870241 e cheddar@campingandcaravanningclub.co.uk w campingandcaravanningclub.co.uk

Peaceful park in the Mendip Hills in an Area of Outstanding Natural Beauty. Ideal for Cheddar and Wells. Outdoor pursuits nearby. Open March to November.

payment Credit/debit cards, cash/cheques

General P 🔌 🕒 🍴 ⓦ 🏧 ☉ 🗑 🔋 🐕 ☀ Leisure 🎢 ∪ 🎣

CHELTENHAM, Gloucestershire Map ref 3B1

★★
TOURING &
CAMPING PARK

🚐(68) £9.50–£21.40
🚍(68) £9.50–£21.40
⛺ on application
68 touring pitches

See Ad on inside back cover

THE
CARAVAN
CLUB
2007

Cheltenham Racecourse Caravan Club Site

Prestbury Park, Evesham Road, Cheltenham GL50 4SH t (01242) 523102 w caravanclub.co.uk

payment Credit/debit cards, cash/cheques

In a sophisticated location right on the edge of the elegant spa town of Cheltenham. Walk, or use Park and Ride, into the town centre. Open April to October.

⊕ M25 onto A40, turn left onto A4013, turn right and cross level crossing. After 1 mile turn left into racecourse. Follow Club signs.

♥ Special member rates mean you can save your membership subscription in less than a week. Visit our website to find out more.

General P 🚗 🕁 🖭 📶 🗑

CHRISTCHURCH, Dorset Map ref 3B3

★★★
CAMPING PARK

🚐(60) £12.75–£25.50
🚍(60) £12.75–£22.00
⛺(14) £12.75–£18.50
60 touring pitches

Harrow Wood Farm Caravan Park

Poplar Lane, Bransgore, Christchurch BH23 8JE t (01425) 672487 f (01425) 672487
e harrowwood@caravan-sites.co.uk w caravan-sites.co.uk

Quiet site bordered by woods and meadows. Take A35 from Lyndhurst, after approximately 11 miles turn right at Cat and Fiddle pub, site approximately 1.5 miles into Bransgore, first right after school. Open March to January.

payment Credit/debit cards, cash/cheques

General P 🚗 🕁 🍴 🖭 📶 ⊙ 🏠🗑 ☼ Leisure ∪ ✈ 🚲

COMBE MARTIN, Devon Map ref 2C1

★★★★
TOURING &
CAMPING PARK

🚐(610) £7.00–£20.00
🚍(50) £8.00–£20.00
⛺(50) £7.00–£23.00
710 touring pitches

Stowford Farm Meadows

Combe Martin, Ilfracombe EX34 0PW t (01271) 882476 f (01271) 883053
e enquiries@stowford.co.uk w stowford.co.uk

open All year
payment Credit/debit cards, cash/cheques

Recent winner of numerous awards and situated on the fringe of the Exmoor National Park, this park has a reputation for superb facilities and unrivalled value.

⊕ Situated on the A3123 Woolacombe to Combe Martin road, 4 miles west of Combe Martin.

♥ Low season: one week, only £39.90 (incl electric hook-up). Mid season: one week, only £59.90 (incl electric hook-up).

General 🖭 P 🚗 🕁 🍴 📶 🏠🗑 🥄 ✕ 🐕 ✈.☼ Leisure 🎣 📺 🍸 🎵 🎯 ⚲ ∪ ✈ 🚲

COTSWOLDS

See under Cheltenham, Moreton-in-Marsh
See also Cotswolds in South East England section

visitBritain.com

Big city buzz or peaceful panoramas? Take a fresh look at Britain and you may be surprised at what's right on your doorstep. Explore the diversity online at visitbritain.com.

CRACKINGTON HAVEN, Cornwall Map ref 2C2

★★★
HOLIDAY, TOURING
& CAMPING PARK
(20) £10.00–£16.50
(12) £10.00–£16.50
Å (35) £10.00–£14.00
(8) £160.00–£495.00
43 touring pitches

Hentervene Caravan & Camping Park

Crackington Haven, Bude EX23 0LF t (01840) 230365 f (01840) 230065
e contact@hentervene.co.uk w hentervene.co.uk

Peaceful park in an Area of Outstanding Natural Beauty. Sandy beaches and coastal path nearby. Spacious, level pitches. Modern caravans to hire/buy. Excellent base for exploring North Cornwall and Devon.

open All year
payment Credit/debit cards, cash/cheques

General 🏕 P 🍳 🛁 🍽 🛒 ⊙ 🚿 🛎 ★ ☼ Leisure 📺 ❤ ⅄ ∪ ⤷

CROYDE BAY, Devon Map ref 2C1

★★★★
HOLIDAY, TOURING
& CAMPING PARK
(92) £13.00–£37.00
(92) £11.00–£33.00
Å (220) £8.00–£29.00
(289) £179.00–
£899.00
92 touring pitches

Ruda Holiday Park

Croyde Bay EX33 1NY t 0870 420 2997 f (0191) 268 5986 e enquiries@parkdeanholidays.co.uk
w parkdeanholidays.co.uk

payment Credit/debit cards, cash/cheques

Ruda is a firm favourite with families who return year after year to Croyde Bay's coveted Blue Flag beach, a stunning beach for surfing. You can also enjoy coastal walks with superb views. The excellent facilities include the Cascades Tropical Adventure Pool, mountain boarding and surfing lessons. Open March to November and over Christmas.

⊕ In the centre of Braunton, turn left after 2nd traffic lights onto B3231. Enter Croyde village and follow signs.

♥ Short breaks available.

General 🏕 P 🍳 🛁 🍽 🛒 🗑 ✕ ☼ Leisure 🏊 📺 🍴 ♫ ❤ ⅄ ♦ ∪ ⤷ 🚲

DARTMOOR

See under Ashburton, Bickington, Tavistock

DAWLISH, Devon Map ref 2D2

★★★★
HOLIDAY, TOURING
& CAMPING PARK
(450) £12.50–£21.00
(450) £12.50–£21.00
Å (450) £9.00–£21.00
(66) £170.00–£645.00
450 touring pitches

Cofton Country Holidays

Cofton, Starcross, Exeter EX6 8RP t (01626) 890111 f (01626) 891572 e info@coftonholidays.co.uk
w coftonholidays.co.uk

payment Credit/debit cards, cash/cheques

A glorious corner of Devon. Family-run holiday park in 30 acres of delightful parkland. Some of the finest pitches in South Devon. Heated outdoor swimming pools. Fun-packed visitor attractions to suit all. David Bellamy Gold Conservation Award. Two minutes from Blue Flag beach. Open April to October.

⊕ A379 Exeter to Dawlish road, 3 miles Exeter side of Dawlish.

♥ £2 off standard pitch per night, low and mid season. Senior Citizens save an extra £1 each per night (advance bookings, minimum 3 nights' stay).

General 🏕 P 🍳 🛁 🍽 🛒 ⊙ 🗑 ✕ ☼ Leisure 🏊 🍴 ❤ ⅄ ⤷

Place index

If you know where you want to stay the index at the back of the guide will give you the page number which lists parks in or near your chosen town, city or village. Check out the other useful indexes too.

DAWLISH, Devon Map ref 2D2

DORCHESTER, Dorset Map ref 3B3

★★
TOURING &
CAMPING PARK

🚐 (50) £7.00–£12.00
🚏 (50) £7.00–£12.00
Ⓐ (50) £7.00–£12.00
50 touring pitches

Giants Head Caravan & Camping Park

Old Sherborne Road, Dorchester DT2 7TR t (01300) 341242 e holidays@giantshead.co.uk
w giantshead.co.uk

Two miles north-east of Cerne Abbas, three miles   **payment** Cash/cheques
south of Middlemarsh, eight miles from
Dorchester.

General 🔌🖥️🎣P🔌💧🍴🕪☺️🅾️🐕🏕️. Leisure ⚓🏊

EXFORD, Somerset Map ref 2D1

★★
CAMPING PARK

🚏 (60) Min £10.00
Ⓐ (60) Min £10.00
60 touring pitches

Westermill Farm

Exford, Minehead TA24 7NJ t (01643) 831238 f (01643) 831216 e BC@westermill.com
w westermill.com

Natural and uncommercialised. David Bellamy   **open** All year
Gold Award for Conservation site beside river.   **payment** Cash/cheques
Beautiful valley, centre of Exmoor National Park.
Four way-marked walks over 500-acre farm.

General 🔌P💧🍴🕪☺️🖥️🚿🐕🏕️. Leisure ⚓

EXMOOR

See under Combe Martin, Exford, Lynton, Porlock, Winsford

Using map references

The map references refer to the colour maps at the front of this guide. The first
figure is the map number; the letter and figure that follow indicate the grid
reference on the map.

EXMOUTH, Devon Map ref 2D2

★★★★★
TOURING PARK
£12.00–£18.00
(2) £160.00–£480.00
115 touring pitches

See Ad below

Webbers Caravan & Camping Park

Castle Lane, Woodbury, Exeter EX5 1EA **t** (01395) 232276 **f** (01395) 233389
e reception@webberspark.co.uk **w** webberspark.co.uk

payment Credit/debit cards, cash/cheques

Set in a tranquil corner of East Devon, this quiet, family-run park has breathtaking views of Dartmoor and the Exe Estuary. Just a short distance from Woodbury Common, with some 3,000 acres of unspoilt open heathland to roam. Relax, and enjoy this outstanding piece of countryside. Open mid-March to end October.

General 🔌📺 P 🔌 🚿 🚽 📶 📮 🏧 🛒 🐕 Leisure ⛲ ⚓ 🎣

FOWEY, Cornwall Map ref 2B3

★★★★
TOURING &
CAMPING PARK
(65) £7.00–£17.00
(65) £7.00–£17.00
Å (65) £7.00–£17.00
65 touring pitches

Penmarlam Caravan & Camping Park

Bodinnick by Fowey, Fowey PL23 1LZ **t** (01726) 870088 **f** (01726) 870082
e info@penmarlampark.co.uk **w** penmarlampark.co.uk

payment Credit/debit cards, cash/cheques, euros

A quiet, grassy site on the Fowey Estuary, an Area of Outstanding Natural Beauty. Choose from our lawned, sheltered field or enjoy breathtaking views from the upper field. Shop and off-licence, immaculately clean heated amenity block, electric hook-ups and serviced pitches, WI-FI Internet access, boat launching and storage adjacent. Open April to October.

⊕ *A38 in Dobwalls, take A390 (signposted St Austell). In East Taphouse, left onto B3359 (signposted Looe, Polperro). After 5 miles, right (signposted Bodinnick, Fowey via ferry). Site 5 miles.*

General 🏕 P 🔌 🚿 🚽 📶 📮 ⊙ 📮 🛒 🐕 ⛺ ☀ Leisure ⛲ ⚓ 🎣

Friendly help and advice

Tourist information centres offer friendly help with accommodation and holiday ideas as well as suggestions of places to visit and things to do. You'll find contact details at the beginning of each regional section.

GLASTONBURY, Somerset Map ref 3A2

★★★★★
HOLIDAY PARK

🚐(40) £10.50–£20.00
🚏(20) £10.50–£20.00
▲ (20) £10.50–£16.00
80 touring pitches

The Old Oaks Touring Park

Wick, Glastonbury BA6 8JS **t** (01458) 831437 **e** info@theoldoaks.co.uk **w** theoldoaks.co.uk

An award-winning park, exclusively for adults, set in tranquil, unspoilt countryside with panoramic views, offering spacious, landscaped pitches and excellent amenities. Open 17 March to 31 October.

payment Credit/debit cards, cash/cheques

General 🛢 P 🖪 🗑 🍴 🖳 🍵 ☉ 🕮 🗑 🔋 🐕 🥾 ☼ Leisure 🚣 🚲

HAYLE, Cornwall Map ref 2B3

★★★★
HOLIDAY, TOURING
& CAMPING PARK

🚐 £8.00–£24.50
🚏 £8.00–£24.50
▲ £8.00–£24.50
🚅 £85.00–£725.00
84 touring pitches

Beachside Holiday Park

Lethlean Lane, Phillack, Hayle TR27 5AW **t** (01736) 753080 **f** (01736) 757252
e reception@beachside.demon.co.uk **w** beachside.co.uk

Beachside is a family holiday park amidst sand dunes beside the sea in the famous St Ives Bay. Our location is ideal for the beach and for touring the whole of West Cornwall. Open Easter to October.

payment Credit/debit cards, cash/cheques

General 🛢 P 🖪 🍴 🖳 ☉ 🕮 🗑 🔋 ☼ Leisure ⌇ 💈 🎵 🥂 🎢 🚣

HELSTON, Cornwall Map ref 2B3

★★★★
HOLIDAY PARK
ROSE AWARD

🚅 (132) £159.00–£779.00

Sea Acres Holiday Park

Kennack Sands, Nr Helston TR12 7LT **t** 0870 420 2997 **f** (0191) 268 5986
e enquiries@parkdeanholidays.co.uk **w** parkdeanholidays.co.uk

payment Credit/debit cards, cash/cheques

From the park's cliff-top position you can savour the stunning sea views over Kennack Sands. Explore the dramatic coastline of The Lizard; there's even a PADI diving centre on site! Other facilities include an indoor pool and kids' clubs. Enjoy light evening entertainment in the Family Club House. Open March to October.

⊕ *Take the A3083 from Helston, then the B3293 to Coverack, turn right at crossroads signed Kennack Sands, site on right overlooking beach.*

♥ *Short breaks available.*

General P 🕮 🗑 🔋 ✕ 🐕 Leisure ⌇ 📺 💈 🎵 🥂 🎢 🏇 🚴

ILFRACOMBE, Devon Map ref 2C1

★★★★★
HOLIDAY PARK

🚅 (27) £165.00–£650.00

Beachside Holiday Park

33 Beach Road, Hele, Ilfracombe EX34 9QZ **t** (01271) 863006 **f** (01271) 867296
e enquiries@beachsidepark.co.uk **w** beachsidepark.co.uk

payment Credit/debit cards, cash/cheques

At Beachside, the sea views and the beach are right outside your door; you don't have to get in the car and drive. Peaceful, relaxing, tranquil, unspoilt, quiet, great for all ages and families alike – these are words often used to describe a holiday at Beachside. Open mid-March to end of October.

⊕ *Just off the A399 between Ilfracombe and Combe Martin.*

♥ *Short breaks out of high season. For specials see our website.*

General 🛢 P 🕮 🗑 🐕 ☼ Leisure ∪ 🎵 🏇

ILFRACOMBE, Devon Map ref 2C1

★★★★
HOLIDAY PARK
ROSE AWARD

🏠 (30) £215.00–£570.00

Mullacott Park

Mullacott Cross, Ilfracombe EX34 8NB **t** (01271) 862212 **f** (01271) 862979
e info@mullacottpark.co.uk **w** mullacottpark.co.uk

Mullacott Park is a new and exclusive lodge and caravan holiday home development offering only the highest-quality accommodation, with panoramic ocean and meadow views. The perfect base for North Devon

open All year
payment Credit/debit cards, cash/cheques

General 🔌P🟦🔋✕🐕🐾☼ Leisure ►

KENNFORD, Devon Map ref 2D2

★★★
TOURING &
CAMPING PARK

🚐(100) £9.35–£19.60
🚙(100) £9.35–£19.60
▲ on application
100 touring pitches

See Ad on inside back cover

CARAVAN
CLUB
2007

Exeter Racecourse Caravan Club Site

Kennford, Exeter EX6 7XS **t** (01392) 832107 **w** caravanclub.co.uk

payment Credit/debit cards, cash/cheques

Elevated position with open views of Exeter Forest. Good walks on the site, and marked footpaths through the forest. Non-members and tent campers welcome. Open March to October.

⊕ *At end of M5 continue onto A38, turn left at top of hill and then immediately right.*

♥ *Special member rates mean you can save your membership subscription in less than a week. Visit our website to find out more.*

General P🔌⏱🏧📖🐕 Leisure ⚓

KENTISBEARE, Devon Map ref 2D2

★★★★
HOLIDAY &
TOURING PARK
ROSE AWARD

🚐 £12.00–£16.50
🚙 £12.00–£16.50
▲ £9.50–£13.50
🏠 (26) £185.00–£450.00
80 touring pitches

Forest Glade Holiday Park

Kentisbeare, Cullompton EX15 2DT **t** (01404) 841381 **f** (01404) 841593
e nwellard@forest-glade.co.uk **w** forest-glade.co.uk

payment Credit/debit cards, cash/cheques

Free indoor heated pool on small, family-managed park surrounded by forest with deer. Large, flat, sheltered pitches. Luxury, all-serviced holiday homes for hire. Open mid-March to end of October.

⊕ *From Honiton, take Dunkerswell road, follow Forest Glade signs. From M5, A373, 2.5 miles at Keepers Cottage inn then 2.5 miles on Sheldon road.*

♥ *Club members £1 per night discount on pitch fees. Short breaks available in holiday homes during most of season. Pet-free and non-smoking holiday homes available.*

General 🔌📺🚐P🔌⏱🍴☕🏧☉📖🔋🐕☼ Leisure 🎣♠⛰🎱U⚓

Key to symbols

Symbols at the end of each entry help you pick out the services and facilities which are most important for your stay. A key to the symbols can be found inside the back-cover flap. Keep this open for easy reference.

KINGSBRIDGE, Devon Map ref 2C3

Challaborough Bay Holiday Park

★★★★
HOLIDAY PARK
ROSE AWARD

🏠 (64) £179.00–£779.00

Challaborough Beach, Nr Bigbury-on-Sea TQ7 4HU **t** 0870 420 2997 **f** (0191) 268 5986
e enquiries@parkdeanholidays.co.uk **w** parkdeanholidays.co.uk

payment Credit/debit cards, cash/cheques

An intimate park, nestling in a quiet, sheltered bay on South Devon's Heritage Coast. Located in an Area of Outstanding Natural Beauty, take time to explore the scenery and coastal walks. Excellent leisure facilities, including an indoor pool, gym, sauna and solarium, ensure your stay will be totally relaxing. Open March to October.

General 🎣 P 🏢 🖥 ⛟ ✕ ⼽   Leisure ⚑ ♟ ♫ ● ∪ ♪ ⼽

LACOCK, Wiltshire Map ref 3B2

Piccadilly Caravan Park

★★★★★
TOURING &
CAMPING PARK

🚐 (39)   £11.50–£13.50
🚍 (39)   £11.50–£13.50
🛆 (4)   £11.50–£13.50
43 touring pitches

Folly Lane (West), Lacock, Chippenham SN15 2LP **t** (01249) 730260 **e** piccadillylacock@aol.com

This well-maintained and peaceful site stands in open countryside 0.5 miles from the historic National Trust village of Lacock. Open April to October.

payment Cash/cheques

General P 🏢 ⼽ 🏢 🏢 ⊙ 🏢 🖥 ⼽ ☼   Leisure 冂 ⼽

LANDRAKE, Cornwall Map ref 2C2

Dolbeare Caravan and Camping Park

★★★★
TOURING &
CAMPING PARK

🚐 (60)   £10.80–£18.60
🚍 (60)   £10.80–£18.60
🛆 (11)   £3.50–£18.60
60 touring pitches

St Ive Road, Landrake, Saltash PL12 5AF **t** (01752) 851332 **f** (01752) 851332
e dolbearepark@btconnect.com **w** dolbeare.co.uk

Friendly, well-maintained park which offers you that personal touch. Set amidst rolling countryside from which to explore varied coastal resorts. Enjoy both Cornwall and Devon from Dolbeare. Internet and WI-FI available.

open All year
payment Credit/debit cards, cash/cheques

General 🖳 P 🏢 ⼽ 🏢 🚐 🏢 ⊙ 🏢 🖥 ⛟ ⼽ ⼯ ☼   Leisure 冂 ⼽ ⼽

LAND'S END, Cornwall Map ref 2A3

Cardinney Caravan and Camping Park

★★★
TOURING &
CAMPING PARK

🚐   £7.50–£14.00
🚍   £7.50–£14.00
🛆   £7.50–£14.00
105 touring pitches

Penberth Valley, St Buryan, Penzance TR19 6HJ **t** (01736) 810880 **f** (01736) 810998
e cardinney@btinternet.com **w** cardinney-camping-park.co.uk

Quiet, family-run site set in rural area. Peaceful, central for the Land's End peninsula.

payment Credit/debit cards, cash/cheques

General P 🏢 ⼽ 🏢 🏢 ⊙ 🖥 ⛟ ✕ ⼽ ☼   Leisure 📺 ♟ ● ∪

Great-value offers

Many parks offer a variety of special rates (highlighted in colour). Why not check the main attractions and places to visit listed for each area and then plan that great, super-value break?

LANGPORT, Somerset Map ref 2D1

★★★
HOLIDAY, TOURING
& CAMPING PARK

🚐	£10.00–£18.00
🚎	£10.00–£18.00
⛺	£5.00–£16.00
🏠 (13)	£150.00–£450.00

30 touring pitches

Bowdens Crest Caravan and Camping Park

Bowdens, Langport TA10 0DD **t** (01458) 250553 **f** (01458) 253360 **e** bowcrest@btconnect.com
w Bowdenscrest.co.uk

Tranquil park with panoramic views across Somerset Levels. No charge for under 18s when with parents. Dogs welcome.

open All year
payment Credit/debit cards, cash/cheques

General 🖥 ♿ P 🚐 🚻 🚿 🏪 ⊙ 📷 🧺 ✕ 🐕 🛒 ☀ Leisure 📺 ⚲ 🔍 ⛰ 🎣 🚲

LANGTON MATRAVERS, Dorset Map ref 3B3

★★★
CAMPING PARK

🚎	£9.00–£11.00
⛺ (100)	£9.00–£11.00

100 touring pitches

Tom's Field Campsite & Shop

Tom's Field Road, Langton Matravers, Swanage BH19 3HN **t** (01929) 427110 **f** (01929) 427110
e tomsfield@hotmail.com **w** tomsfieldcamping.co.uk

payment Credit/debit cards, cash/cheques

Peaceful site. World Heritage coastal path 20 minutes' walk. Ideal base for family holidays, walkers, climbers. Shop has general camping supplies. Open mid-March to end of October.

General P 🚐 🚻 🚿 🏪 ⊙ 📷 🧺 🐕

LOOE, Cornwall Map ref 2C2

★★★★
HOLIDAY &
TOURING PARK

🚐	£9.00–£14.75
🚎	£9.00–£14.75
⛺	£9.00–£14.75
🏠 (5)	£160.00–£395.00

31 touring pitches

Polborder House Caravan and Camping Park

Bucklawren Road, St Martin PL13 1NZ **t** (01503) 240265 **e** reception@peaceful-polborder.co.uk
w peaceful-polborder.co.uk

Small, select, peaceful park in a beautiful countryside location. Only 2.5 miles from the picturesque fishing port of Looe and 1.5 miles from the sea. No noisy club or bar. Open April to October.

payment Credit/debit cards, cash/cheques

General P 🚐 🚻 🚿 🏪 ⊙ 📷 🧺 🐕 ☀ Leisure ⛰ 🎣

LOOE, Cornwall Map ref 2C2

★★★★
HOLIDAY &
TOURING PARK

🚐 (100)	£8.90–£13.50
🚎 (40)	£8.90–£13.50
⛺ (100)	£8.90–£13.50
🏠 (100)	£120.00–£445.00

240 touring pitches

Tencreek Holiday Park

Polperro Road, Looe PL13 2JR **t** (01503) 262447 **f** (01503) 262760 **e** reception@tencreek.co.uk
w dolphinholidays.co.uk

open All year
payment Credit/debit cards, cash/cheques

Lying close to the South Cornwall coast, in a rural but not isolated position, Tencreek Holiday Park is ideal for exploring Cornwall and South Devon. Tencreek is the closest park to Looe and lies in Daphne du Maurier Country; beyond are Bodmin Moor, Dartmoor, traditional Cornish towns and picturesque beaches and ports.

⊕ A38 from Tamar bridge. Left at roundabout. follow Looe signs. Right onto A387, becomes B3253. Through Looe towards Polperro. Tencreek 1.25 miles from Looe bridge.

♥ Various promotions for certain times of the year – call us or see website.

General 🖥 ♿ P 🚐 🚻 🚿 🏪 ⊙ 📷 🧺 ✕ 🐕 🛒 ☀ Leisure 🎿 🏹 ⚲ 🎵 🔍 ⛰ ∪ 🎣 ⛳ 🚲

LUXULYAN, Cornwall Map ref 2B2

★★★★
HOLIDAY, TOURING
& CAMPING PARK

🚐(52) £9.60–£13.80
🚛(52) £9.60–£13.80
🅰 (52) £6.60–£13.80
🏠(16) £145.00–£438.00
52 touring pitches

Croft Farm Holiday Park

Luxulyan PL30 5EQ t (01726) 850228 f (01726) 850498 e lynpick@ukonline.co.uk
w croftfarm.co.uk

A small, beautifully secluded touring park, ideally situated one mile from the Eden Project, offering a peaceful and friendly base from which to explore the county.

payment Credit/debit cards, cash/cheques

General 🔌🗄🛗P🔷🛒🚻🚿⛲☺🛝🖼🧺🐕🐾 Leisure 🎣🎡🌊

LYME REGIS, Dorset Map ref 2D2

10 acre level site • On the Devon & Dorset border • Pitches for tents, motor vans & caravans • Electric hook ups • Spacious modern shower block • Large children's play area • Crazy golf • Dog walking area • Rallies welcome • Off peak special offers • Colour brochure
ROUSDON • LYME REGIS • DORSET DT7 3XW
TEL: (01297) 442227 FAX (01297) 446086
www.ukparks.co.uk/shrubbery

LYNTON, Devon Map ref 2C1

★★★★
HOLIDAY &
TOURING PARK
ROSE AWARD

🚐   £9.00–£14.00
🚛   £8.50–£13.00
🅰   £8.50–£13.00
🏠(5) £230.00–£430.00
69 touring pitches

Channel View Caravan and Camping Park

Manor Farm, Lynton EX35 6LD t (01598) 753349 f (01598) 752777 e relax@channel-view.co.uk
w channel-view.co.uk

Rural site situated on main A39 with panoramic views over Lynton/Lynmouth and Bristol Channel. Within Exmoor National Park. Open 15 March to 15 November.

payment Credit/debit cards, cash/cheques

General P🔷🛒🚻🚿🖼🧺🐕🐾☀ Leisure ∪🌊

MODBURY, Devon Map ref 2C3

★★★★
TOURING PARK

🚐(112) £11.00–£24.00
🚛(112) £11.00–£24.00
112 touring pitches

See Ad on inside back cover

Broad Park Caravan Club Site

Higher East Leigh, Modbury, Ivybridge PL21 0SH t (01548) 830714 w caravanclub.co.uk

payment Credit/debit cards, cash/cheques

Situated between moor and sea, this makes a splendid base from which to explore South Devon. Head for Dartmoor, or seek out the small villages of the South Hams. Open March to October.

⊕ From B3207, site on left.

♥ Special member rates mean you can save your membership subscription in less than a week. Visit our website to find out more.

General P🔷🛒🚿🖼🐕🐾

MOORSHOP, Devon Map ref 2C2

★★★★
TOURING &
CAMPING PARK

🚐(80) £6.00–£12.00
🚛(10) £6.00–£12.00
🅰(40) £5.00–£12.00
🏠(4) £150.00–£480.00
100 touring pitches

Higher Longford Caravan & Camping Park

Moorshop, Tavistock PL19 9LQ t (01822) 613360 f (01822) 618722 e stay@higherlongford.co.uk
w higherlongford.co.uk

Friendly park set in the foothills of Dartmoor. Spacious pitches, electric hook-ups, grass, hardstanding and serviced pitches. Deluxe toilet/shower block, bath, shop, off-licence, takeaway, camper lounge and launderette. Dogs welcome.

open All year
payment Credit/debit cards, cash/cheques

General 🔌🛗P🔷🛒🚻🚿⛲☺🖼🧺🐕🐾☀ Leisure 📺🎣🌊∪🌙🏐

MORETON-IN-MARSH, Gloucestershire Map ref 3B1

★★★★★
TOURING &
CAMPING PARK

🚐 (183) £12.50–£25.10
🚏 (183) £12.50–£25.10
183 touring pitches

See Ad on inside back cover

Moreton-in-Marsh Caravan Club Site

Bourton Road, Moreton-in-Marsh GL56 0BT t (01608) 650519 w caravanclub.co.uk

open All year
payment Credit/debit cards, cash/cheques

An attractive, well-wooded site within easy walking distance of the market town of Moreton-in-Marsh. On-site facilities include crazy golf, volleyball and boules. Large dog-walking area.

⊕ *From Moreton-in-Marsh on A44 the site entrance is on the right 250yds past the end of the speed limit sign.*

♥ *Special member rates mean you can save your membership subscription in less than a week. Visit our website to find out more.*

General 🔲 P 🚗 🕐 🍴 🚐 📻 ☺ 📶 🐕 🔧 ☼ Leisure 🏔 ⚓

MORTEHOE, Devon Map ref 2C1

★★★★
HOLIDAY, TOURING
& CAMPING PARK

🚐 (25)   £10.00–£17.00
🚏   £10.00–£17.00
⛺ (150) £10.00–£14.00
🏠 (24) £225.00–£515.00

North Morte Farm Caravan and Camping Park

North Morte Road, Mortehoe, Woolacombe EX34 7EG t (01271) 870381 f (01271) 870115
e info@northmortefarm.co.uk w northmortefarm.co.uk

Open April to September.   **payment** Credit/debit cards, cash/cheques

General P 🚗 🕐 🍴 📻 ☺ 📶 🐄 🐕 🔧 ☼ Leisure 🏔 ☾ ⚓

NEWQUAY, Cornwall Map ref 2B2

NEWQUAY, Cornwall Map ref 2B2

★★★★
HOLIDAY PARK
ROSE AWARD

🏠 (142)   £159.00–
          £799.00

Crantock Beach Holiday Park

Crantock, Newquay TR8 5RH t 0870 420 2997 f (0191) 268 5986
e enquiries@parkdeanholidays.co.uk w parkdeanholidays.co.uk

payment Credit/debit cards, cash/cheques

Resting just outside the charming village of Crantock, this tranquil park is the perfect location to get away from it all. The park overlooks secluded Crantock beach, with its rock pools and hidden caves, and is a great base for exploring. Enjoy light evening entertainment in the Wavecrest Pub. Open March to October.

⊕ *A30 to Newquay, then the A392. A3075 to Redruth, then take right turn to Crantock beach.*

♥ *Short breaks available.*

General P 📻 📶 🐄 🐕 Leisure 📺 🍴 🎵 🔍

Check it out

Please check prices, quality ratings and other details when you book.

NEWQUAY, Cornwall Map ref 2B2

★★★★
HOLIDAY PARK
ROSE AWARD

🚐 (244) £10.00–£28.00
🚚 (244) £10.00–£28.00
⛺ (244) £7.00–£25.00
🏠 (162) £149.00–
 £689.00
244 touring pitches

Holywell Bay Holiday Park

Holywell Bay, Newquay TR8 5PR **t** 0870 420 2997 **f** (0191) 268 5986
e enquiries@parkdeanholidays.co.uk **w** parkdeanholidays.co.uk

payment Credit/debit cards, cash/cheques

Nestling in the Ellenglaze Valley, this park is small, friendly and simply perfect for beach lovers, being a short stroll from the stunning beach of Holywell Bay. The excellent facilities include heated outdoor pools with waterslide, kids' clubs and evening entertainment. Newquay is just a few miles away. Open March to October.

⊕ Turn right off the A3075, signposted Holywell Bay, 3 miles west of Newquay.

♥ Short breaks available.

General 🔌🖭P🔌🖑☂🏠📶🖵🍴 Leisure ⚡🖵🍴♪🔍⚙▶

NEWQUAY, Cornwall Map ref 2B2

★★★★
HOLIDAY PARK
ROSE AWARD

🚐   £9.00–£14.90
🚚   £9.00–£14.90
⛺   £9.00–£14.90
🏠 (5) £235.00–£620.00
395 touring pitches

Newperran Holiday Park

Rejerrah, Newquay TR8 5QJ **t** (01872) 572407 **f** (01872) 571254 **e** holidays@newperran.co.uk
w newperran.co.uk

Peaceful family holiday park renowned for its spacious perimeter pitching, with breathtaking open countryside and sea views. Caravans, motor homes, tents and holiday caravans for hire. Open Easter to 31 October.

payment Credit/debit cards, cash/cheques

General 🔌🖭P🔌🖑☂🚙🏠☉📶🖵🍴✕🐴🎠☼ Leisure ⚡🖵🍴♪🔍⚙☾♪▶

NEWQUAY, Cornwall Map ref 2B2

★★★★
HOLIDAY PARK
ROSE AWARD

🚐 (60) £12.00–£30.00
🚚 (60) £10.00–£28.00
⛺ (60) £7.00–£25.00
🏠 (104) £159.00–
 £749.00
60 touring pitches

Newquay Holiday Park

Newquay TR8 4HS **t** 0870 420 2997 **f** (0191) 268 5986 **e** enquiries@parkdeanholidays.co.uk
w parkdeanholidays.co.uk

payment Credit/debit cards, cash/cheques

A spacious park surrounded by luscious rolling countryside, Newquay Holiday Park is ideal for all the family! There's so much to do! Three heated outdoor pools, a giant waterslide, amusements and children's playground keep the kids happy, whilst the bar and entertainment complex are great for some evening family fun. Open March to October.

⊕ Follow A30 Bodmin to Redruth road, after iron bridge turn right signed RAF St Mawgan. 2nd exit off roundabout signposted Newquay A3059. Right at bottom of hill.

♥ Short breaks available.

General P🔌🖑☂🏠📶🖵🍴✕🐴 Leisure ⚡🖵🍴♪🔍⚙▶

NEWQUAY, Cornwall Map ref 2B2

★★★★
HOLIDAY PARK

🚐   £10.00–£15.00
🚚   £10.00–£15.00
⛺   £10.00–£15.00
🏠 (19) £185.00–£651.00
98 touring pitches

Riverside Holiday Park

Gwills Lane, Newquay TR8 4PE **t** (01637) 873617 **f** (01637) 877051
e info@riversideholidaypark.co.uk **w** riversideholidaypark.co.uk

Peaceful riverside family park. Two miles to Newquay. Sheltered, level touring pitches, luxury lodges and caravans. Covered, heated pool and bar. Open March to October.

payment Credit/debit cards, cash/cheques

General 🔌P🔌🖑☂🏠📶🖵🍴✕🐴 Leisure ⚡🖵🍴🔍♪

NEWQUAY, Cornwall Map ref 2B2

★★★★
TOURING &
CAMPING PARK

🚐(140) £10.00–£14.00
🚍(140) £10.00–£14.00
▲(140) £10.00–£14.00
140 touring pitches

Treloy Touring Park

Newquay TR8 4JN t (01637) 872063 & (01637) 876279 f (01637) 876279
e treloy.tp@btconnect.com w treloy.co.uk

A quiet families' and couples' park in a pleasant
setting, with a good range of facilities. Adjacent
own golf course, driving range. Nearby fishing.
Brochure available. Off A3059, Newquay three
miles. Open April to September.

payment Credit/debit cards, cash/cheques

General 🛇P🔌🎧🚽🚿🌂☉🚮🗑🛒✕🐾🚿🌞 Leisure ⟲📺🍷🎵🔍⛰⛵⛳►

NEWTON ABBOT, Devon Map ref 2D2

★★★★★
TOURING &
CAMPING PARK

🚐(135) £12.50–£19.80
🚍 £12.50–£19.80
▲ £13.50–£20.80

Dornafield

Two Mile Oak, Newton Abbot TQ12 6DD t (01803) 812732 f (01803) 812032
e enquiries@dornafield.com w dornafield.com

payment Credit/debit cards, cash/cheques

Beautiful 14thC farmhouse located in 30 acres of
glorious South Devon countryside. So quiet and
peaceful, yet so convenient for Torbay and
Dartmoor. Superb facilities to suit the discerning
caravanner, including many hardstanding, all-service
pitches. Shop, games room, adventure play area,
tennis and golf. Our brochure is only a phone call
away.

⊕ Take A381 Newton Abbot to Totnes road. In 2.5 miles at
Two Mile Oak Inn turn right. In 0.5 miles 1st turn to left.
Site 200yds on right.

♥ Early- and late-season bookings. Book for 7 days and only
pay for 5. Details on request.

General 🛇P🔌🎧🚽🚿🚐🌂☉🚮🗑🛒🐾🚿🌞 Leisure 📺🔍⛰🔍►

NORTH PETHERTON, Somerset Map ref 2D1

★★★
TOURING PARK

🚐 £10.00–£12.00
🚍 £10.00–£12.00
50 touring pitches

Somerset View Caravan Park

Taunton Road, North Petherton, Bridgwater TA6 6NW t (01278) 661294 & 07767 032687
e qcs@somersetview.co.uk w somersetview.co.uk

Modern site for caravans and campers. Only five
minutes from M5 junction 24. Close to coast,
Glastonbury and Exmoor. Stay or stop over en
route to/from the South West.

open All year
payment Cash/cheques

General 🛇P🔌🚽🚿🚿☉🚮🗑🐾 Leisure ⛰⛵►♿

ORGANFORD, Dorset Map ref 3B3

★★★
HOLIDAY, TOURING
& CAMPING PARK

🚐(30) £10.50–£12.00
🚍(10) £9.50–£11.00
▲(30) £10.50–£12.00
🚎(4) £180.00–£250.00
70 touring pitches

Organford Manor Caravans & Holidays

The Lodge, Organford, Poole BH16 6ES t (01202) 622202 f (01202) 623278 e organford@lds.co.uk
w organfordmanor.co.uk

payment Cash/cheques, euros

A quiet country site in the wooded grounds of the
manor-house, level and grassy. Good facilities;
surrounded by farmland but centrally placed.

⊕ From Poole, A35 towards Dorchester. 1st turning left off
A35 after roundabout, junction with A351 to Wareham. 1st
drive entrance on right.

♥ 10% discount off a 4-night stay in May, Jun and Sep, low
season times only (excl Bank Holiday weeks).

General 🚐🛇P🔌🎧🚽🚿🚿☉🚮🗑🛒🐾🌞 Leisure ⛵⛵►🛶

OWERMOIGNE, Dorset Map ref 3B3

Sandyholme Holiday Park

★★★★
HOLIDAY, TOURING
& CAMPING PARK

🚐(50) £13.00–£19.00
🚃(52) £13.00–£19.00
🛆 (70) £13.00–£19.00
🏠 (26) £175.00–£520.00
50 touring pitches

Moreton Road, Owermoigne, Dorchester DT2 8HZ **t** (01305) 852677 **f** (01305) 854677
e smeatons@sandyholme.co.uk **w** sandyholme.co.uk

Quiet, family-run park with all amenities. Situated in Hardy Country, central for Weymouth, Dorchester and Lulworth Cove.

payment Credit/debit cards, cash/cheques

General 🚐P🚗🅿️🔆🎣⊙📶🎱✕🐕☼ Leisure 🏆🎣⚲▶

PADSTOW, Cornwall Map ref 2B2

Carnevas Farm Holiday Park

★★★★
HOLIDAY, TOURING
& CAMPING PARK
ROSE AWARD

🚐   £8.00–£15.00
🚃   £8.00–£15.00
🛆   £8.00–£15.00
🏠 (9) £175.00–£550.00
198 touring pitches

St Merryn, Padstow PL28 8PN **t** (01841) 520230 **f** (01841) 520230 **e** carnevascampsite@aol.com
w carnevasholidaypark.com

payment Cash/cheques

Family-run park for families. Situated on the North Cornish coast. Padstow four miles. Nearest beach 0.5 miles. Great surfing. Excellent facilities. Cleanliness assured. Open April to October.

⊕ *Bodmin bypass, A30, carry on under iron bridge. Right towards Newquay Airport. A39, then left onto B3271, Padstow. At St Merryn, left onto B3276. Two miles, opposite Tredrea Inn.*

General 🚐P🚗🅿️🔆🎣⊙📶✕🐕☼ Leisure 🏆🎣⚲◡⚲

PADSTOW, Cornwall Map ref 2B2

Padstow Touring Park

★★★★
TOURING &
CAMPING PARK

🚐   £9.50–£16.00
🚃   £9.50–£16.00
🛆   £9.50–£16.00
120 touring pitches

Padstow PL28 8LE **t** (01841) 532061 **e** mail@padstowtouringpark.co.uk **w** padstowtouringpark.co.uk

Located one mile from Padstow with footpath access; panoramic views; quiet family park; open all year; sandy beaches two miles; some en suite pitches; easy access from main road.

open All year
payment Credit/debit cards, cash/cheques

General 🚐🔌P🚗🅿️🚐🎣⊙📶🎱🐕🐾☼ Leisure ⚲⚲🚲

PAIGNTON, Devon Map ref 2D2

Mention our name
Please mention this guide when making your booking.

PAIGNTON, Devon Map ref 2D2

★★★★
HOLIDAY, TOURING & CAMPING PARK

🚐 (80) £8.00–£13.00
🚎 (80) £8.00–£13.00
⛺ (80) £8.00–£13.00
🏠 (18) £140.00–£450.00
80 touring pitches

Higher Well Farm Holiday Park

Waddeton Road, Stoke Gabriel, Totnes TQ9 6RN **t** (01803) 782289 **e** higherwell@talk21.com **w** higherwellfarmholidaypark.co.uk

Secluded farm park with static caravans and separate area welcoming touring caravans, tents and motor homes. Within one mile of Stoke Gabriel and the River Dart. Four miles to Paignton.

payment Credit/debit cards, cash/cheques

General 🅿 ❓ 🛜 ⊙ 🎱 🐕 ☼ Leisure ▶

PAIGNTON, Devon Map ref 2D2

CC

Beautiful South Devon

- Modern touring facilities and holiday homes
- 10 acres of woodland • Outdoor heated pool
- Hayloft Bar & family room • Childrens' play areas
- Woodland walks • Shop, café & takeaway
- David Bellamy Gold Award

Stoke Road, Paignton, South Devon TQ4 7PF
info@whitehill-park.co.uk

Tel: 01803 782 338 www.whitehill-park.co.uk

PENZANCE, Cornwall Map ref 2A3

★★★
HOLIDAY & TOURING PARK

🚐 £7.75–£10.50
🚎 £7.75–£10.50
⛺ £6.75–£9.50
🏠 (5) £142.00–£307.00
102 touring pitches

Tower Park Caravans and Camping

St Buryan, Penzance TR19 6BZ **t** (01736) 810286 **f** (01736) 810286 **e** enquiries@towerparkcamping.co.uk **w** towerparkcamping.co.uk

Peaceful site in rural setting, adjoining St Buryan village. Sheltered, level pitches. All facilities, ideally situated for beaches and Minack Theatre. Caravans, motor homes, tents and holiday caravans for hire. Open March to January.

payment Credit/debit cards, cash/cheques

General 🅿 ❓ 🛜 ⊙ 🐕 ☼ Leisure 📺 ⚡ 🎣 ♨ 🚣 ⛳

PLYMOUTH, Devon Map ref 2C2

★★★★
HOLIDAY & TOURING PARK

🚐 (60) £7.90–£17.10
🚎 (60) £7.90–£17.10
60 touring pitches

See Ad on inside back cover

THE CARAVAN CLUB

Plymouth Sound Caravan Club Site

Bovisand Lane, Down Thomas, Plymouth PL9 0AE **t** (01752) 862325 **w** caravanclub.co.uk

payment Credit/debit cards, cash/cheques

Within easy reach of the historic port. Superb views over the Sound. Close to the South West Coast Path and lovely beaches. Open April to October.

✛ Turn right at village signposted Down Thomas into Bovisand Lane. Site on right.

♥ Special member rates mean you can save your membership subscription in less than a week. Visit our website to find out more.

General 🅿 ❓ 🐕 ☼ Leisure ▶

Using map references

Map references refer to the colour maps at the front of this guide.

POLGOOTH, Cornwall Map ref 2B3

★★★★★
HOLIDAY PARK
(27) £125.00–£645.00

Saint Margaret's Holiday Bungalows

Tregongeeves Lane, St Austell PL26 7AX t (01726) 74283 f (01726) 71680
e reception@stmargaretsholidays.co.uk w stmargaretsholidays.co.uk

Timber bungalows set in lovely tranquil park.
Convenient central location in pleasant village,
three miles from beaches, 500m to shop and inn.
Seven miles to Eden Project. Open March to
January.

payment Credit/debit cards, cash/cheques

General 🔌P🛢👟🖪 Leisure 🏔 ∪ ✈▸ 🚲

POLRUAN-BY-FOWEY, Cornwall Map ref 2B3

★★★★
HOLIDAY, TOURING
& CAMPING PARK

🚐(7)	£10.00–£15.00
🚍(7)	£10.00–£15.00
⛺(40)	£7.50–£15.00
🏠(10)	£165.00–£470.00

47 touring pitches

Polruan Holidays (Camping & Caravanning)

Townsend, Polruan PL23 1QH t (01726) 870263 f (01726) 870263 e polholiday@aol.com

Small, peaceful, coastal holiday park surrounded
by sea, river and National Trust farmland.
Walking, sailing, fishing, boating and beaches
nearby.

payment Cash/cheques

General 🏕P🔌👟🖪 Leisure 🏔 ∪ ✈

POOLE, Dorset Map ref 3B3

★★★
TOURING &
CAMPING PARK

🚐(120)	£11.50–£25.50
🚍(50)	£11.50–£30.50
⛺(50)	£10.00–£25.50

170 touring pitches

Beacon Hill Touring Park

Blandford Road North, Nr Lytchett Minster, Poole BH16 6AB t (01202) 631631 f (01202) 625749
e bookings@beaconhilltouringpark.co.uk w beaconhilltouringpark.co.uk

Thirty acres of wooded heathland with open
grassy spaces and two small lakes. Set at the foot
of Beacon Hill, a local beauty spot and view point
for Poole, Poole Harbour and the Purbecks.

payment Cash/cheques

General 📺🏕P🔌👟🖪✕👟 Leisure ➰📺🍴🎵🎯🏔🔍∪✈▸🚲

PORLOCK, Somerset Map ref 2D1

★★★★
HOLIDAY, TOURING
& CAMPING PARK

🚐(54)	£10.00–£15.00
🚍(54)	£10.00–£15.00
⛺(66)	£8.00–£13.00
🏠(19)	£140.00–£375.00

120 touring pitches

Burrowhayes Farm Caravan and Camping Site and Riding Stables

West Luccombe, Porlock, Minehead TA24 8HT t (01643) 862463 e info@burrowhayes.co.uk
w burrowhayes.co.uk

payment Credit/debit cards, cash/cheques

Real family site situated in glorious National Trust
scenery in Exmoor National Park. Ideal for walking
and riding, with stables on site. New heated toilet
and shower block with disabled and baby-changing
facilities. Open mid-March to end October.

⊕ From Minehead, A39 towards Porlock; 1st left after
Allerford to Horner and West Luccombe; Burrowhayes is
0.25 miles along on right before hump-backed bridge.

General 📺P🔌👟🖪👟 Leisure ∪✈

It's all quality-assessed accommodation

Our commitment to quality involves wide-ranging accommodation assessment.
Ratings and awards were correct at the time of going to press but may change
following a new assessment. Please check at the time of booking.

PORLOCK, Somerset Map ref 2D1

★★★★
HOLIDAY, TOURING
& CAMPING PARK
ROSE AWARD

Min £11.00
Min £12.00
Min £11.00
(9) £255.00–£420.00
40 touring pitches

Porlock Caravan Park

High Bank, Porlock, Minehead TA24 8ND t (01643) 862269 f (01643) 862269
e info@porlockcaravanpark.co.uk w porlockcaravanpark.co.uk

Quiet, select site, ideal for walking, touring and beaches. Five acres, grassy, level and sheltered. Open 15 March to 15 January. A39 from Minehead, in Porlock village take B3225 to Porlock Weir, site signposted.

payment Cash/cheques

General P ⚡ ☕ 🚿 🅟 ☺ 📻 🐕 ⛱ ☼ Leisure ∪ ♪ ►

PORTHTOWAN, Cornwall Map ref 2B3

★★★★
TOURING &
CAMPING PARK

(22) £8.50–£14.00
(6) £8.50–£14.00
(22) £8.50–£14.00
50 touring pitches

Porthtowan Tourist Park

Mile Hill, Porthtowan, Truro TR4 8TY t (01209) 890256 e admin@porthtowantouristpark.co.uk
w porthtowantouristpark.co.uk

payment Cash/cheques

This quiet, family-run park offers plenty of space and level pitches. Superb new toilet/laundry facilities with family rooms. Close to a sandy surfing beach, coastal path and Portreath to Devoran cycle trail, it is an excellent base from which to discover the delights of Cornwall. David Bellamy Silver Award. Open April to October.

⊕ From A30, take 3rd exit off the roundabout signed Redruth/Porthtowan. Follow this road for 2 miles. Turn right at T-junction. Site on left after 0.5 miles.

♥ Off-peak special offers – see our website for details.

General P ⚡ ☕ 🚿 🅟 ☺ 📻 🐕 ⛱ ☼ Leisure ♠ 𝄞 ∪ ♪ ⚲

PORTREATH, Cornwall Map ref 2B3

★★★
TOURING &
CAMPING PARK

£7.50–£13.00
£7.50–£13.00
£7.50–£13.00
60 touring pitches

Cambrose Touring Park

Portreath Road, Cambrose, Redruth TR16 4HT t (01209) 890747 f (01209) 891665
e cambrosetouringpark@supanet.com w cambrosetouringpark.co.uk

Six acres of well-sheltered land in a valley. Excellent suntrap. Most roads are tarmac finished. Facilities for the disabled. Open April to October inclusive.

payment Cash/cheques

General P ⚡ ☕ 🚿 🅟 ☺ 📻 🐕 ☼ Leisure ⌇ ♠ 𝄞 ∪ ♪ ⚲ 🏊

PORTREATH, Cornwall Map ref 2B3

★★★★
HOLIDAY PARK

(18) £8.00–£12.00
(3) £8.00–£12.00
(18) £8.00–£12.00
(20) £115.00–£455.00

Tehidy Holiday Park

Harris Mill, Illogan, Redruth TR16 4JQ t (01209) 216489 e holiday@tehidy.co.uk w tehidy.co.uk

payment Credit/debit cards, cash/cheques

Come and visit our beautifully landscaped, family-run park set in a peaceful wooded valley. Ideally situated to explore north and south coastlines. Accommodation includes static caravans and bungalows – two wheelchair friendly. Tents and tourers welcome. Facilites include new ablution block, play area, launderette, games room and licensed shop. Open April to October.

⊕ Off A30 at Redruth, turn right to Porthtowan. After 300 yds turn left onto B3300 (Portreath). Straight over at crossroads. Uphill, past Cornish Arms. Site is 500 yds on left.

General ⚡ P ⚡ ☕ 🚿 🅟 ☺ 📻 ⛝ Leisure 📺 ♠ 𝄞

REDRUTH, Cornwall Map ref 2B3

★★★★
HOLIDAY, TOURING
& CAMPING PARK
ROSE AWARD

⊕ (25)　£14.00–£17.00
⊞ (25)　£14.00–£17.00
▲ (50)　£14.00–£17.00
⊡ (16)　£160.00–£530.00
25 touring pitches

Lanyon Caravan & Camping Park

Loscombe Lane, Four Lanes, Redruth TR16 6LP　t (01209) 313474　e jamierielly@btconnect.com
w lanyoncaravanandcampingpark.co.uk

Lovely, well-kept, friendly park set in the heart of
the beautiful Cornish countryside with distant sea
views. Ideal touring base. Three modern toilet/
shower blocks. Free hot water. Pets welcome.

open All year
payment Credit/debit cards, cash/cheques

General ▨ P ⊕ 🐾 🖟 🖥 🏊 ✕ 🐕 🐾 ☼　Leisure ⌕ ⛾ 🎵 🍺 🎡 ∪ 🎣 🏊 ⚲

RELUBBUS, Cornwall Map ref 2B3

★★★★★
HOLIDAY PARK
ROSE AWARD

⊕ (70)　£8.50–£13.50
⊞ (10)　£8.50–£12.50
▲ (19)　£7.00–£12.00
⊡ (45)　£115.00–£505.00

River Valley Country Park

Relubbus, Penzance TR20 9ER　t (01736) 763398　f (01736) 763398
e rivervalley@surfbay.dircon.co.uk　w surfbayholidays.co.uk

payment Credit/debit cards, cash/cheques

Eighteen-acre, partly wooded park situated along the
banks of a clear, shallow stream. Spacious, well-kept,
individual pitches for touring caravans, motor homes
and tents. Luxury lodges, some with hot tubs, and
caravan holiday homes also available to hire or to buy
as a second home. Shop and launderette. David
Bellamy Silver Award. Open March to December.

⊕ From A394, A30 St Michael's Mount roundabout, left A394
Helston road, left next roundabout B3280. Straight through
to Relubbus.

♥ 10% discount on pitches booked for 14 nights or more
between 1 Apr and 21 Jul.

General 🔌 ▨ P ⊕ 🖐 🐾 🖟 ☉ 🗐 🏊 ☼　Leisure 🎣 🏊

ROSUDGEON, Cornwall Map ref 2B3

★★★★
HOLIDAY, TOURING
& CAMPING PARK
ROSE AWARD

⊕　£10.00–£16.00
⊞　£10.00–£16.00
▲　£10.00–£16.00
⊡ (9)　£155.00–£455.00
50 touring pitches

Kenneggy Cove Holiday Park

Higher Kenneggy, Rosudgeon, Penzance TR20 9AU　t (01736) 763453
e enquiries@kenneggycove.co.uk　w kenneggycove.co.uk

payment Cash/cheques

Flat, lawned pitches in a beautiful garden setting with
panoramic sea views. Twelve minutes' walk to South
West Coast Path and secluded, sandy beach. Home-
made meals available May to September. Please
note: this is a quiet site, operating a policy of no
noise between 2200 and 0800. German and French
spoken. Open March to November.

⊕ Take the lane to Higher Kenneggy, south off the A394 at
the Helston end of Rosudgeon. The park is 0.5 miles down
the lane on the left.

♥ 10% discount for Senior Citizens Mar-May and Sep-Oct
(static hire only). No single-sex groups or large parties.

General ▨ P ⊕ 🖐 🐾 🖾 🖟 ☉ 🗐 🏊 🐕 ☼　Leisure 🎡 ∪ 🎣 🏊 ⚲

Our quality rating schemes

For a detailed explanation of the quality and
facilities represented by the stars please refer to
the back of this guide.

RUAN MINOR, Cornwall Map ref 2B3

★★★★
HOLIDAY, TOURING
& CAMPING PARK

🚐(15) £11.00–£16.97
🚍(15) £11.00–£16.97
Å (20) £9.50–£13.97
🚉(14) £97.00–£417.00
35 touring pitches

Silver Sands Holiday Park

Gwendreath, Kennack Sands, Ruan Minor, Helston TR12 7LZ **t** (01326) 290631 **f** (01326) 290631
e enquiries@silversandsholidaypark.co.uk **w** silversandsholidaypark.co.uk

payment Credit/debit cards, cash/cheques

A quiet family park set in nine acres of landscaped grounds, offering peace and tranquillity. The large, well-spaced touring emplacements are individually marked and bounded by trees and shrubs. A short, enchanting woodland walk through the Lizard nature reserve brings you to award-winning sandy beaches. Open Easter to September.

⊕ *A3083 from Helston past RNAS Culdrose, left onto B3293 (St Keverne). Right turn after passing Goonhilly satellite station. Left after 1.5 miles to Gwendreath.*

General 🏕️P🔌🛁🚿🅿️☉🏧🐕🥾☀️ Leisure 🏔️∪🎣

ST AGNES, Cornwall Map ref 2B3

★★★★
TOURING PARK

🚐(70) £14.00–£19.00
🚍(70) £14.00–£19.00
Å (70) £14.00–£19.00
70 touring pitches

Beacon Cottage Farm Touring Park

Beacon Drive, St Agnes TR5 0NU **t** (01872) 552347 **e** beaconcottagefarm@lineone.net
w beaconcottagefarmholidays.co.uk

Peaceful, secluded park on a working farm in an Area of Outstanding Natural Beauty. Pitches in six small, landscaped paddocks. Beautiful sea views, lovely walks, ten minutes' walk to sandy beach. Open April to October.

payment Credit/debit cards, cash/cheques

General 🔌📺🏕️P🔌🛁🚿🅿️☉🏧🐕🥾☀️ Leisure 🏔️∪🎣🚲🏇

ST AUSTELL, Cornwall Map ref 2B3

★★★★★
HOLIDAY, TOURING
& CAMPING PARK
ROSE AWARD

🚐 £10.00–£25.00
🚍 £10.00–£25.00
Å £10.00–£20.00
🚉(40) £200.00–£600.00
45 touring pitches

River Valley Holiday Park

Pentewan Road, London Apprentice, St Austell PL26 7AP **t** (01726) 73533 **f** (01726) 73533
w cornwall-holidays.co.uk

payment Credit/debit cards, cash/cheques

Stay at River Valley and you will enjoy our high standards. Quality caravans to hire, or bring your own and stay in our level, sheltered meadow. Surrounded by woodlands and bordered by a river with lots of walks. Indoor swimming pool, cycle trail to the beach, immaculate toilet block. Open April to October.

⊕ *Take B3273 from St Austell to Mevagissey. When entering London Apprentice, park is on left-hand side.*

♥ *Short-break offers in static vans. 7 nights for the price of 5 in the touring meadow.*

General 📺P🔌🚿🏕️🅿️☉🏧🐕☀️ Leisure 🎣🎾🏔️🚲

★★★
HOLIDAY, TOURING
& CAMPING PARK

🚐 (35) £8.95–£15.50
🚐 £8.95–£15.50
▲ £7.00–£13.50
🏠 (40) £115.00–£510.00
184 touring pitches

Trencreek Farm Country Holiday Park

Hewas Water, St Austell PL26 7JG t (01726) 882540 f (01726) 883254
e reception@trencreek.co.uk w surfbayholidays.co.uk

payment Credit/debit cards, cash/cheques

Fifty-six acres of idyllic open meadows, woodland and lakes in a fun farm setting. Six miles from the Eden Project. On-park facilities include tennis court, outdoor swimming pool, fishing lakes, farm animals, entertainment, bar, restaurant and takeaway. Bungalows or Luxury Lodges with hot tubs also available. Open March to October.

⊕ Four miles south west of St Austell on the A390; fork left onto B3287. Continue for 1 mile and Trencreek is on the left.

♥ 8 Apr-21 Jul, 7 nights or more: £52pw (electric pitch) or £45pw (non-electric pitch) – for up to 6 people and a pet!

General 🔧P🚐♿🍴🛁☎⊙🏧🛒✖🐕🚫☼ Leisure ⚡📺🍽🎵🎣🐟⚲♨

HOLIDAY, TOURING
& CAMPING PARK

🚐 (105) £5.50–£20.00
🚐 (105) £5.50–£20.00
▲ (105) £5.50–£20.00
🏠 (40) £149.00–£600.00
105 touring pitches

Trewhiddle Village

Pentewan Road, St Austell PL26 7AD t (01726) 879420 f (01726) 879421
e holidays@trewhiddle.co.uk w trewhiddle.co.uk

open All year
payment Credit/debit cards, cash/cheques

Under new management! A great family park superbly situated for beaches, the Eden project, Lost Gardens of Heligan and for touring Cornwall. A fantastic escape for a peaceful and relaxing holiday.

⊕ From the A390 turn south on B3273 to Mevagissey, site 0.75 miles from the roundabout on the right-hand side.

General 🔧📶🏠P🚐♿🍴☎📶⊙🏧🛒✖🐕🚫☼ Leisure ⚡🍽🎣🐟♨∪🎵🐾⛳

★★★★
TOURING &
CAMPING PARK

🚐 (168) £10.50–£18.00
🚐 (168) £10.50–£18.00
▲ (235) £10.50–£18.00
235 touring pitches

Little Trevarrack Touring Park

Laity Lane, Carbis Bay, St Ives TR26 3HW t (01736) 797580 e littletrevarrack@hotmail.com
w littletrevarrack.co.uk

payment Credit/debit cards, cash/cheques

A well-maintained and spacious landscaped park, ideal for family holidays with a range of superb modern facilities. Some pitches with sea views. Approximately one mile from the stunning Carbis Bay beach and the coastal footpath into St Ives. High season bus service from the site into St Ives.

⊕ From A30 take A3074 to St Ives. Signposted left opposite turning for Carbis Bay beach. Straight across at next crossroads. Approx 200m on right.

♥ Please telephone reception for details.

General 📶P🚐♿🍴☎⊙🏧🛒🐕🚫☼ Leisure ⚡🐟♨∪🎣🐾

What's in a quality rating?

Information about ratings can be found at the back of this guide.

ST IVES, Cornwall Map ref 2B3

★★★★★
TOURING &
CAMPING PARK

🚐 £11.00–£27.00
🚙 £11.00–£27.00
⛺ £11.00–£25.00
260 touring pitches

Polmanter Touring Park

St Ives TR26 3LX   t (01736) 795640   f (01736) 793607   e reception@polmanter.com
w polmanter.com

Family park in lovely countryside with sea views, within walking distance of St Ives and beaches. Heated toilets/showers. Hard-standings. Open April to October.

payment Credit/debit cards, cash/cheques

General 🖼 P 🚐 🗓 🚻 🖨 🏧 ☉ 🛒 🖳 ✕ 🐕 🎿 ☼   Leisure ⚓ 🍴 🍷 🔦 🛝 🎣 ∪ ♪ ▸

ST JUST IN ROSELAND, Cornwall Map ref 2B3

★★★★★
TOURING &
CAMPING PARK

🚐 (84) £11.00–£16.00
🚙 (84) £11.00–£16.00
⛺ (84) £11.00–£16.00
84 touring pitches

Trethem Mill Touring Park

Trethem, St Just in Roseland TR2 5JF   t (01872) 580504   f (01872) 580968   e reception@trethem.com
w trethem.com

payment Credit/debit cards, cash/cheques

We offer peace and tranquillity with an exceptional standard of facilities. Cornwall Tourism Awards: 'Consistent winners offering consistent quality.' Open April to mid-October. Say hello to a new experience.

⊕ *A3078 towards Tregony/St Mawes, over Tregony bridge. After 5 miles follow brown caravan and camping signs from Trewithian. Site 2 miles beyond on right-hand side.*

General P 🚐 🗓 🚻 🖨 🏧 ☉ 🛒 🖳 🐕 🎿 ☼   Leisure 🛝 ∪ 🚴

ST MERRYN, Cornwall Map ref 2B2

★★★★
TOURING &
CAMPING PARK

🚐 £8.00–£12.00
🚙 £8.00–£12.00
⛺ £8.00–£12.00
🏠 (3) £175.00–£425.00
70 touring pitches

Trevean Farm

St Merryn, Padstow PL28 8PR   t (01841) 520772   f (01841) 520722   e trevean.info@virgin.net

Small, pleasant farm site one mile from the sea. Ideally situated for beaches, walking and many visitor attractions. Open Easter to end of October.

payment Cash/cheques, euros

General 🖼 🚐 P 🚐 🗓 🚻 🏧 ☉ 🛒 🖳 🐕 ☼   Leisure 🛝 ∪

ST MINVER, Cornwall Map ref 2B2

★★★★
HOLIDAY, TOURING
& CAMPING PARK
ROSE AWARD

🏠 (87) £159.00–£999.00

St Minver Holiday Park

St Minver, Wadebridge PL27 6RR   t 0870 420 2997   f (01208) 268 5986
e enquiries@parkdeanholidays.co.uk   w parkdeanholidays.co.uk

payment Credit/debit cards, cash/cheques

A delightful woodland park nestled in the grounds of an old manor-house, St Minver provides a base for exploring the pretty fishing harbours of Padstow and Port Isaac, or the famous beaches of Rock and Polzeath. Facilities include an indoor heated pool, kids' clubs and evening family entertainment. Open March to October.

⊕ *Head for Port Isaac on the B3314. After 3.5 miles turn left towards Rock. The park is 250yds along on the right-hand side.*

♥ *Short breaks available.*

General 🖼 P 🖨 🖳 ✕ 🐕   Leisure ⚓ 📺 🍷 ♫ 🔦 🛝

SIDBURY, Devon Map ref 2D2

★★★★★
TOURING PARK

(113) £11.00–£24.00
(113) £11.00–£24.00
113 touring pitches

See Ad on inside back cover

CARAVAN CLUB

Putts Corner Caravan Club Site

Sidbury, Sidmouth EX10 0QQ **t** (01404) 42875 **w** caravanclub.co.uk

payment Credit/debit cards, cash/cheques

A quiet site in pretty surroundings, with a private path to the local pub. Bluebells create a sea of blue in spring, followed by foxgloves. Open March to October.

⊕ *From M5 jct 25, A375 signposted Sidmouth. Turn right at Hare and Hounds onto B3174. In about 0.25 miles turn right into site entrance.*

♥ *Special member rates mean you can save your membership subscription in less than a week. Visit our website to find out more.*

General 🖭 P 🔌 🗘 🎦 🚾 🌣 ⊙ 📧 🐕 ✦ ☼ Leisure ⚏ ↑

SIDMOUTH, Devon Map ref 2D2

★★★★★
HOLIDAY, TOURING & CAMPING PARK
ROSE AWARD

(40) £9.50–£14.50
(40) £9.50–£14.50
▲ (60) £9.50–£14.50
(10) £190.00–£515.00
100 touring pitches

Salcombe Regis Camping and Caravan Park

Salcombe Regis, Sidmouth EX10 0JH **t** (01395) 514303 **f** (01395) 514314
e info@salcombe-regis.co.uk **w** salcombe-regis.co.uk

Situated 1.5 miles east of Sidmouth in Area of Outstanding Natural Beauty. A good base for visiting East Devon. Short walk to coastal path. Great walking country.

payment Credit/debit cards, cash/cheques

General 🖭 P 🔌 🗘 🎦 🚾 🌣 ⊙ 📧 🐕 ✦ ☼ Leisure ⚏ ↑

SIXPENNY HANDLEY, Dorset Map ref 3B3

★★★
TOURING & CAMPING PARK

(35) £10.00–£13.25
(35) £10.00–£13.25
▲ (35) £10.00–£13.25
(2) £180.00–£270.00
35 touring pitches

Church Farm Caravan & Camping Park

High Street, Sixpenny Handley, Salisbury SP5 5ND **t** (01725) 552563 **f** (01725) 552563
e churchfarmcandcpark@yahoo.co.uk **w** churchfarmcandcpark.co.uk

Partially sheltered site on farm near village. Within walking distance of shops, pubs etc. One mile from A354 Handley roundabout on B3081.

open All year
payment Cash/cheques

General 🚲 P 🔌 🗘 🎦 🚾 🌣 ⊙ 🗎 🐕 ☼ Leisure ⚏ ⚲ ∪ ♪ ↑ 🏊

SOUTH MOLTON, Devon Map ref 2C1

HOLIDAY, TOURING & CAMPING PARK

(45) £13.50–£18.00
(5) £13.50–£18.00
▲ (10) £11.00–£13.50
(5) £210.00–£480.00
65 touring pitches

Yeo Valley Holiday Park

c/o Blackcock Inn, Molland, South Molton EX36 3NW **t** (01769) 550297
e info@yeovalleyholidays.com **w** yeovalleyholidays.com

In a beautiful, secluded valley on the edge of Exmoor, this small, family-run park is the ideal place to relax or enjoy many activities. Open February to November inclusive.

payment Credit/debit cards, cash/cheques

General 🔌 P 🔌 🗘 🎦 🚾 🌣 ⊙ 📧 ✕ 🐕 ☼ Leisure ⚲ ❣ ♪ ● ⚏ ∪ ♪ ⚘

To your credit

If you book by phone you may be asked for your credit card number. If so, it is advisable to check the proprietor's policy in case you have to cancel your reservation at a later date.

SWANAGE, Dorset Map ref 3B3

TAUNTON, Somerset Map ref 2D1

★★★
HOLIDAY, TOURING
& CAMPING PARK

(20)	£9.00–£11.00
(10)	£9.00–£11.00
▲ (10)	£9.00–£11.00
(2)	£115.00–£170.00

30 touring pitches

Ashe Farm Caravan and Campsite

Thornfalcon, Taunton TA3 5NW **t** (01823) 442567 **f** (01823) 443372
e camping@ashe-farm.fsnet.co.uk

Quiet farm site, lovely views, easy access. Central for touring. Easy reach coast and hills. Family run and informal. Open April to October.

payment Cash/cheques

General ♿ P 🅿 ♿ ♿ 🎔 ☉ 🔲 🐾 🛝. Leisure ♨ ♿ ▶

TAVISTOCK, Devon Map ref 2C2

★★★★
HOLIDAY, TOURING
& CAMPING PARK

(40)	£9.50–£18.00
(40)	£9.50–£18.00
▲ (40)	£9.50–£13.50
(12)	£195.00–£440.00

120 touring pitches

Harford Bridge Holiday Park

Peter Tavy, Tavistock PL19 9LS **t** (01822) 810349 **f** (01822) 810028 **e** enquiry@harfordbridge.co.uk
w harfordbridge.co.uk

open All year
payment Credit/debit cards, cash/cheques

Beautiful, level, sheltered park set in Dartmoor with delightful views of Cox Tor. The River Tavy forms a boundary, offering riverside and other spacious, level camping pitches. Luxury, self-catering caravan holiday homes. Ideal for exploring Devon and Cornwall, walking the moor or just relaxing on this beautiful park.

⊕ M5 onto A30 to Sourton Cross; take left turn onto A386 Tavistock Road; 2 miles north of Tavistock, take the Peter Tavy turning; entrance 200yds on left.

♥ Camping: 10% discount for week paid in full on arrival. Holiday let: £15 off 2-week booking. £10 Senior Citizen discount.

General ♿ ♿ P 🅿 ♿ ♿ ♿ ♿ ☉ ♿ 🔲 🐾 🛝. Leisure 📺 ♿ ⑁ ♿ ☉ ♪ ▶ 🚲 ⛵

TAVISTOCK, Devon Map ref 2C2

★★★★
HOLIDAY, TOURING
& CAMPING PARK
ROSE AWARD

Langstone Manor Caravan and Camping Park

Moortown, Tavistock PL19 9JZ t (01822) 613371 f (01822) 613371 e jane@langstone-manor.co.uk
w langstone-manor.co.uk

🚐 (40) £9.00–£11.00
🚎 (40) £9.00–£11.00
⛺ (40) £9.00–£11.00
🏠 (7) £160.00–£400.00
40 touring pitches

payment Credit/debit cards, cash/cheques

Fantastic location with direct access onto moor. Peace and quiet, with secluded pitches. Bar and restaurant. Excellent base for South Devon and Cornwall. Discover Dartmoor's secret!

⊕ *Take the B3357 Princetown road from Tavistock. After approx 1.5 miles, signs to Langstone Manor. Turn right, go over cattle grid, up hill, left following signs.*

♥ *£15 discount for 2-week booking in holiday homes. £30 discount for 2 people sharing, on weekly bookings, booked on certain weeks.*

General 🛋 🖛 P 🔌 🛱 🐾 ⦿ 🎒 ✕ 🐾 ☼ Leisure 📺 🍽 🔍 ⋔ ∪ 🎵 ▸ ♿

TEDBURN ST MARY, Devon Map ref 2D2

★★★
HOLIDAY, TOURING
& CAMPING PARK

Springfield Holiday Park

Tedburn St Mary, Exeter EX6 6EW t (01647) 24242 e enquiries@springfieldholidaypark.co.uk
w springfieldholidaypark.co.uk

🚐 (38) £12.00–£15.00
🚎 (2) £12.00–£20.00
⛺ (10) £10.00–£15.00
🏠 (6) £200.00–£450.00
50 touring pitches

Peaceful, beautiful location in central Devon. Ideal family park, close to Dartmoor National Park, coastal resorts and Exeter.

open All year except Christmas and New Year
payment Credit/debit cards, cash/cheques, euros

General 🖛 P 🔌 🛱 🐾 ⦿ 🔟 ☼ Leisure ⋔ 🔍 ∧ 🎵 ▸

TEIGNGRACE, Devon Map ref 2D2

★★★★
TOURING &
CAMPING PARK

Twelve Oaks Farm Caravan Park

Teigngrace, Newton Abbot TQ12 6QT t (01626) 352769 f (01626) 352769
e info@twelveoaksfarm.co.uk w twelveoaksfarm.co.uk

🚐 (25) £7.50–£13.00
🚎 (25) £7.50–£13.00
⛺ £7.50–£13.00
25 touring pitches

open All year
payment Credit/debit cards, cash/cheques

General 🖥 P 🔌 🛱 🐾 ⦿ 🎒 🐾 ☼ Leisure ⋔ ∪ 🎵

TORQUAY, Devon Map ref 2D2

Rating Applied For
TOURING &
CAMPING PARK

Torquay Holiday Park

Kingskerswell Road, Torquay TQ2 8JU t 0870 420 2997 f (0191) 268 5986
e enquiries@parkdeanholidays.co.uk w parkdeanholidays.co.uk

🏠 (221) £169.00–£759.00

payment Credit/debit cards, cash/cheques

A great park which enjoys a countryside hillside setting just minutes from Torquay. As well as being a great base for exploring South Devon and the English Riviera, the park offers fantastic facilities, a range of accommodation, an indoor pool, kids' clubs, family entertainment and much more! Open March to November.

⊕ *Take A380 towards Torquay, continue to A3022. Turn left at Currys. At roundabout, turn left onto Barton Road. Continue up hill and turn left.*

♥ *Short breaks available.*

General 🛋 🐾 🎒 🐾 Leisure 🏊 🍽 🎵 🔍 ∧

TOTNES, Devon Map ref 2D2

★★★★
TOURING &
CAMPING PARK

🚐 £8.00–£14.00
🚚 £8.00–£12.50
⛺ £8.00–£15.00
35 touring pitches

Broadleigh Farm Park

Coombe House Lane, Aish, Stoke Gabriel, Totnes TQ9 6PU **t** (01803) 782309 **f** (01803) 782422
e enquiries@broadleighfarm.co.uk **w** gotorbay.com/accommodation

Situated in beautiful South Hams village of Stoke Gabriel close to the River Dart and Torbay's wonderful, safe beaches. Many local walks. Bus stop at end of lane. Dartmoor within easy reach by car.

open All year
payment Cash/cheques

General P 🚗 🚻 ⛽ 🚰 ☉ 🗓 🐕 ✕ ☼

TRURO, Cornwall Map ref 2B3

★★★★
TOURING PARK

🚐 (40) £10.00–£13.00
🚚 (5) £10.00–£13.00
⛺ (15) £10.00–£13.00
60 touring pitches

Summer Valley Touring Park

Shortlanesend, Truro TR4 9DW **t** (01872) 277878 **e** res@summervalley.co.uk **w** summervalley.co.uk

Situated in a sheltered valley surrounded by woods and farmland, we have been awarded for our peaceful, rural environment. We have the ideal site for visiting the gardens in spring. Open April to October.

payment Credit/debit cards, cash/cheques

General 🏕 P 🚗 ☕ 🚻 ⛽ 🚰 ☉ 🛒🗓 🛠 🐕 ☼ Leisure 🏔 🕊

WAREHAM, Dorset Map ref 3B3

"At the gateway to the beautiful Purbeck Hills"

★ Many electric hook-ups ★ Superb amenity blocks ★ Shop & Off-licence ★ Games Room
★ No dogs ★ 150 Touring pitches ★ 95 Hardstandings ★ Modern Launderette
★ Open all year ★ All year storage ★ Large Children's adventure playground

THE
Lookout
HOLIDAY PARK

RAC APPOINTED

Ideally situated: 3 miles from Corfe Castle –
1¼ miles from Wareham and within easy reach of
Studland Bay Swanage and Bournemouth.
STATIC HOLIDAY CARAVANS ALSO AVAILABLE.
THE LOOKOUT HOLIDAY PARK STOBOROUGH,
WAREHAM, DORSET BH20 5AZ
Or call WAREHAM (01929) 552546 (24 Hours)
E-mail: enquiries@caravan-sites.co.uk

★★★★
HOLIDAY PARK

WARMWELL, Dorset Map ref 3B3

★★★★
HOLIDAY, TOURING
& CAMPING PARK

🚐 (37) £11.95–£15.95
🚚 (9) £11.95–£15.95
⛺ (5)
40 touring pitches

Warmwell Caravan Park

Warmwell, Dorchester DT2 8JD **t** (01305) 852313 **f** (01305) 851824
e stay@warmwellcaravanpark.co.uk **w** warmwellcaravanpark.co.uk

The park is set in an Area of Outstanding Natural Beauty in the heart of Thomas Hardy country in Dorset. Open 1 March to 2 January.

payment Credit/debit cards, cash/cheques

General 🖥 🏕 P 🚗 ☕ 🚻 🚰 🛒🗓 🛠 🐕 ☼ Leisure 🍴 🕊

Key to symbols

Symbols at the end of each entry help you pick out the services and facilities which are most important for your stay. A key to the symbols can be found inside the back-cover flap. Keep this open for easy reference.

WARMWELL, Dorset Map ref 3B3

★★★★
HOLIDAY PARK

🏠 (185)   £199.00–
£1,089.00

Warmwell Holiday Park

Warmwell, Nr Weymouth DT2 8JE t 0870 420 2997 f (0191) 268 5986
e enquiries@parkdeanholidays.co.uk w parkdeanholidays.co.uk

payment Credit/debit cards, cash/cheques

Combine relaxation and fun at Warmwell! With lodges set in peaceful, landscaped woodland and unrivalled leisure facilities, you really can enjoy the best of both worlds. Try skiing and snowboarding on our 110m SnowFlex ski slope. Other facilities include an indoor pool, roller rink, fishing lakes and much more. Open February to December.

General 🛄 P 📠 🖾 🛒 ✕ 🐕   Leisure 🎣 📺 🍽 🎵 🔍 ⛰ 🌙

WATERROW, Somerset Map ref 2D1

★★★★★
TOURING &
CAMPING PARK
ROSE AWARD

🚐 (37)   £11.00–£19.00
🚍 (27)   £11.00–£19.00
▲ (8)   £11.00–£16.00
🏠 (1)   £255.00–£350.00
45 touring pitches

Waterrow Touring Park

Waterrow, Taunton TA4 2AZ t (01984) 623464 f (01984) 624280 w waterrowpark.co.uk

A gently sloping, grassy site with landscaped hardstandings in the peaceful Tone Valley. An ideal base from which to explore this beautiful unspoilt area. One holiday caravan for hire. Adults only.

open All year
payment Credit/debit cards, cash/cheques

General P 📠 🖾 🍽 🎏 ⊙ 📠 🖾 🐕 🐾 ☀   Leisure 🌙 ⛵

WEST BAY, Dorset Map ref 3A3

★★★★
HOLIDAY, TOURING
& CAMPING PARK

🚐 (131) £12.00–£30.00
🚍 (131) £12.00–£30.00
▲ (131)   £9.00–£27.00
🏠 (39) £159.00–£769.00
131 touring pitches

West Bay Holiday Park

West Bay, Bridport DT6 4HB t 0870 420 2997 f (0191) 268 5986
e enquiries@parkdeanholidays.co.uk w parkdeanholidays.co.uk

payment Credit/debit cards, cash/cheques

Set in the heart of a pretty harbour village, just two minutes' walk to the beach at West Bay and the stunning coastline. There's so much to do! Facilities include an indoor pool, crazy golf and the Riverside Entertainment Club, where the whole family can enjoy some evening fun. Open March to November.

⊕ M5 jct 25, leave main Dorchester road (A35), heading for Bridport. 1st exit at 1st roundabout, 2nd exit at 2nd roundabout into West Bay. Park on right.

♥ Short breaks available.

General 🖾 P 📠 🖾 🍽 🎏 📠 🖾 🛒 ✕ 🐕   Leisure 🎣 📺 🍽 🎵 🔍 ⛰ ▶

WESTON-SUPER-MARE, Somerset Map ref 2D1

★★★★
HOLIDAY, TOURING
& CAMPING PARK

🚐 (120) £11.00–£21.00
🚍 (120) £11.00–£21.00
▲ (120) £10.00–£20.00
120 touring pitches

Country View Holiday Park

29 Sand Road, Sand Bay, Weston-super-Mare BS22 9UJ t (01934) 627595 w cvhp.co.uk

Country View is a beautifully kept site surrounded by the countryside and just 200yds from the Sand Bay beach. Heated pool, bar, shop and children's play area.

open All year
payment Cash/cheques

General 🏕 P 📠 🍽 🖾 🎏 ⊙ 📠 🖾 🐕 ☀   Leisure 🎣 🍽 🔍 ⛰ ▶

WESTON-SUPER-MARE, Somerset Map ref 2D1

★★★
**TOURING &
CAMPING PARK**

🚐(57) £10.00–£15.00
🚏(5) £10.00–£15.00
Å (25) £8.00–£14.00
87 touring pitches

Dulhorn Farm Camping Site

Weston Road, Lympsham, Weston-super-Mare BS24 0JQ **t** (01934) 750298 **f** (01934) 750913

A family site on a working farm set in the countryside, approximately four miles from the beach, midway between Weston and Burnham. Ideal for touring. Easily accessible from M5. Open March to October.

payment Cash/cheques

General ⚏🖳P🔌🖰🍴🚾☎☉🗑🐕🐾☀ Leisure ⛰∪🎣

WHITE CROSS, Cornwall Map ref 2B2

★★★★★
HOLIDAY PARK
ROSE AWARD

🚐(40) £15.00–£35.00
🚏(40) £13.00–£33.00
Å (40) £10.00–£29.00
🚍(254) £189.00–
£849.00
40 touring pitches

White Acres Country Park

White Cross, Newquay TR8 4LW **t** 0870 420 2997 **f** (0191) 268 5986
e enquiries@parkdeanholidays.co.uk **w** parkdeanholidays.co.uk

payment Credit/debit cards, cash/cheques

This park is the perfect place to escape to. Surrounded by tranquil countryside, White Acres is also a premier UK fishing destination. The unrivalled park facilities include indoor heated pool, kids' clubs and family entertainment. The lively resort of Newquay is just a few minutes' drive away. Open March to November and over Christmas.

⊕ *Take the Indian Queens exit from A30. Follow A392 towards Newquay. White Acres Holiday Park is approx 1 mile on right-hand side.*

♥ *Short breaks available.*

General ⚏P🔌🖰🍴🚾☉🗑🗑🛒✕🐾 Leisure 🎣📺🍴🎵🎯⛰∪🎣►

WINCANTON, Somerset Map ref 3B3

★★★
**TOURING &
CAMPING PARK**

🚐(57) £9.35–£19.60
🚏(57) £9.35–£19.60
Å on application
57 touring pitches

See Ad on inside back cover

Wincanton Racecourse Caravan Club Site

Wincanton BA9 8BJ **t** (01963) 34276 **w** caravanclub.co.uk

payment Credit/debit cards, cash/cheques

Attractive site set in open countryside, with beautiful views to Bruten Forest and the Downs. Golf course within racecourse. Open April to October.

⊕ *From A303, onto B3081 (signposted Racecourse). Follow B3081 for 4.5 miles. Site on right.*

♥ *Special member rates mean you can save your membership subscription in less than a week. Visit our website to find out more.*

General P🔌🖰🍴🗑🗑🐕🐾 Leisure ►

WINSFORD, Somerset Map ref 2D1

★★★★
TOURING & CAMPING PARK

(22)	£9.50–£11.50
(22)	£9.50–£11.50
(22)	£9.50–£11.50

44 touring pitches

Halse Farm Caravan & Tent Park

Winsford, Minehead TA24 7JL **t** (01643) 851259 **f** (01643) 851592 **e** brit@halsefarm.co.uk
w halsefarm.co.uk

payment Credit/debit cards, cash/cheques

Exmoor National Park, small, peaceful, working farm with spectacular views. Paradise for walkers and country lovers. David Bellamy Gold Conservation Award. Open 23 March to 31 October.

⊕ *Signposted from A396. In Winsford turn left and bear left past Royal Oak Inn. One mile up hill. Entrance immediately after cattle grid on left.*

♥ *10% discount for 1 week or more, paid 10 days in advance.*

General Leisure

WOOL, Dorset Map ref 3B3

★★★★
TOURING & CAMPING PARK

(95)	£8.00–£13.00
(95)	£8.00–£13.00
(95)	£8.00–£13.00

95 touring pitches

Whitemead Caravan Park

East Burton Road, Wool, Wareham BH20 6HG **t** (01929) 462241 **f** (01929) 462241
e whitemeadcp@aol.com **w** whitemeadcaravanpark.co.uk

Within easy reach of beaches and beautiful countryside, this friendly site is maintained to a high standard of cleanliness. Turn west off the A352 near Wool level crossing. Open 18 March to 31 November 2006.

payment Cash/cheques

General Leisure

Quality
visitor attractions
Enjoy England operates a Visitor Attraction Quality Assurance Service.
Participating attractions are visited annually by trained, impartial assessors who look at all aspects of the visit, from initial telephone enquiries to departure, customer service to catering, as well as all facilities and activities.
Only those attractions which have been assessed by Enjoy England and meet the standard receive the quality marque, your sign of a Quality Assured Visitor Attraction.
enjoyEngland.com
QUALITY ASSURED VISITOR ATTRACTION
Look out for the quality marque and visit with confidence.

Country ways

The Countryside Rights of Way Act gives people new rights to walk on areas of open countryside and registered common land.

To find out where you can go and what you can do, as well as information about taking your dog to the countryside, go online at countrysideaccess.gov.uk.

And when you're out and about...

Always follow the Country Code
- Be safe – plan ahead and follow any signs
- Leave gates and property as you find them
- Protect plants and animals, and take your litter home
- Keep dogs under close control
- Consider other people

Scotland

A challenge on the rocks at St Monance, Fife

VisitScotland
Ocean Point One
94 Ocean Drive, Leith,
Edinburgh EH6 6JH
(0131) 472 2222
visitscotland.com

soaring
peaks,
sparkling
lochs,
creative
cities

Main Stunning views of the
Old Man of Hoy, Orkney
Left Drama at the famous
Edinburgh Festival; casting off –
fly fishing on the River Tay; the
sweet sound of Scotland,
outside the Kelvingrove
Museum and Art Gallery,
Glasgow; perching on the edge
of the world at Loch Lomond &
The Trossachs National Park

Dramatic landscapes and mist on the lochs. Or world-class shopping and an unrivalled arts festival. Can you stay the course at St Andrews, or indeed on the Malt Whisky Trail? **Rediscover yourself in some of Europe's finest landscapes and enjoy a leisurely break or an action-packed holiday**.

Explore
Scotland

Take the high road

Scotland is easy to get to, with excellent motorway links from most parts of the UK, and wherever your journey takes you, you're in for a treat. Linger in the Borders and explore the dignified ruins of once-powerful abbeys or follow in the footsteps of Rob Roy and Walter Scott through the Trossachs. Potter around picturesque fishing villages in the Kingdom of Fife and tee off on the legendary Old Course in St Andrews. Or venture into Speyside to tickle your tastebuds on the Malt Whisky Trail.

If it's drama you're after, head for the Highlands, a vast swathe of untamed wilderness where land and sea collide to create stunning perspectives. Discover the most perfect vista at Eilean Donan where the dramatic castle ruins and surrounding mountains are reflected in the waters of the loch. Both landscapes and wildlife are at their most spectacular in Scotland's two National Parks – Loch Lomond & The Trossachs, and Cairngorms.

Ancient heritage

Whichever part of Scotland takes your fancy, history is never far away – from the Neolithic ruins of Skara Brae on Orkney to Scotland's dramatic capital city. Here you can stroll through the cobbled streets of the medieval Old Town, visit the castle and uncover 1,000 years of Scotland's tumultuous past or stop for refreshment in Deacon Brodie's Tavern and learn about the devious Edinburgh citizen who inspired Robert Louis Stevenson's tale of Dr Jekyll and Mr Hyde.

Highland fling

If it's festivals you want – they're here in abundance. Apart from Edinburgh's celebrated arts and fringe festivals, there's traditional music and celebration at the Shetland Folk Festival, caber tossing and games aplenty at the Cowal Highland Gathering and Scotland's national poet Robert Burns is celebrated at venues throughout the Scottish Borders in May each year.

The Scots are fiercely proud of their heritage, which they celebrate in a thousand different ways, from the pomp and splendour of the Edinburgh Military Tattoo to the more intimate appeal of an impromptu ceilidh in a cosy pub. If this leads you to assume that they only look back to the past, a trip to Glasgow will set you straight. Scotland's largest city has reinvented itself to become one of Europe's great cultural capitals. It also has shopping to rival London's best and an abundance of stylish restaurants and cafe-bars that will seduce the most adventurous gourmet.

Escape to the outer islands for a unique experience. Dreamy beaches are found in the Outer Hebrides, folk music draws the finest performers to Orkney, and puffins by the million await bird-watchers in Shetland.

Places to **visit**

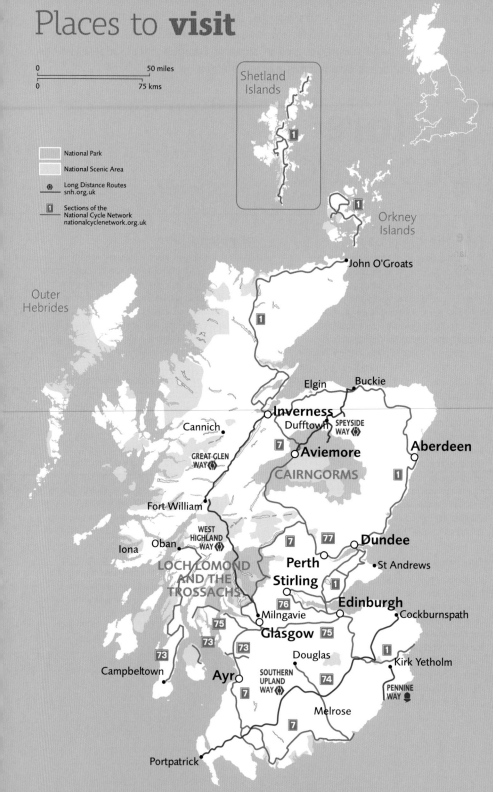

0 |————————————————| 50 miles
0 |————————————————| 75 kms

Shetland Islands

National Park

National Scenic Area

Long Distance Routes
snh.org.uk

1 Sections of the
National Cycle Network
nationalcyclenetwork.org.uk

Outer Hebrides

Orkney Islands

John O'Groats

Elgin   Buckie

Cannich   **Inverness**
Dufftown   SPEYSIDE WAY

7   **Aviemore**   **Aberdeen**

GREAT GLEN WAY

CAIRNGORMS   1

Fort William

WEST HIGHLAND WAY   7   77   **Dundee**

Iona   Oban   7

Perth   St Andrews

LOCH LOMOND AND THE TROSSACHS   **Stirling**   1

76   **Edinburgh**
Milngavie   Cockburnspath

75   **Glasgow**   75

73   73   Douglas   1
Campbeltown   Kirk Yetholm

Ayr   SOUTHERN UPLAND WAY   74   PENNINE WAY

7   Melrose

7

Portpatrick

CairnGorm Mountain Railway
Near Aviemore, Inverness-shire
(01479) 861261
cairngormmountain.com
*Scale outstanding peaks
in a funicular*

Culzean Castle and Country Park
Maybole, South Ayrshire
0870 1181 945
culzeanexperience.org
*Stunning castle with exquisite
furnishings and outstanding
surrounding gardens*

Deep Sea World
North Queensferry, Fife
(01383) 411880
deepseaworld.com
*Take a dip with the sharks or
stroll through the remarkable
underwater tunnel*

Edinburgh Castle
(0131) 225 9846
historic-scotland.gov.uk
*Achieve panoramic views
of the city*

Edinburgh Zoo
(0131) 334 9171
edinburghzoo.org.uk
*Beautiful parkland setting
on the edge of the city*

Eilean Donan Castle and Visitor Centre
By Kyle of Lochalsh
(01599) 555202
eileandonancastle.com
*Outstanding and
explorable castle*

Falkirk Wheel
0870 0500 208
thefalkirkwheel.co.uk
The world's only rotating boat lift

Gallery of Modern Art
Glasgow
(0141) 229 1996
glasgowmuseums.com
*Thought-provoking
contemporary gallery*

Glasgow Science Centre
(0141) 420 5000
glasgowsciencecentre.org
*Challenging and entertaining
hands-on exhibits*

The Lighthouse
Glasgow
(0141) 221 6362
thelighthouse.co.uk
*National centre for architecture
and design*

Malt Whisky Trail
Speyside
maltwhiskytrail.com
*Discover the secrets of whisky
in many locations*

Museum of Flight
Near Haddington, Edinburgh
(0131) 247 4422
nms.ac.uk/flight
*Protected First and Second
World War airfield*

National Wallace Monument
Causewayhead, Stirling
(01786) 472140
nationalwallacemonument.com
*A stunningly located
national landmark*

Old Course, St Andrews
St Andrews, Fife
(01344) 479050
oldcourse-experience.com
Tee off in a breathtaking setting

Royal Botanic Garden, Edinburgh
(0131) 248 2901
rbge.org.uk
Explore the world of plants

Scotch Whisky Heritage Centre
Edinburgh
(0131) 220 0441
whisky-heritage.co.uk
Scotch whisky in the making

Skara Brae
Orkney
(01856) 841815
orkneyjar.com
*Intriguing remains of
Neolithic village*

Stirling Castle
(01786) 450000
historic-scotland.gov.uk
*Dramatic fortress atop a
great rock*

Tourist information centres

When you arrive at your destination, visit a tourist information centre for help with accommodation and information about local attractions and events. Alternatively call **0845 22 55 121** to receive information and book accommodation before you depart.

Aberdeen	23 Union Street		Crail*	Marketgate
Aberfeldy	The Square		Crathie*	The Car Park
Aberfoyle*	Main Street		Crieff	High Street
Abington	Welcome Break Motorway Service Area		Daviot Wood*	Picnic Area, A9
			Dornoch	The Square
Alford*	Railway Museum		Drumnadrochit	The Car Park
Alva	Mill Trail Visitor Centre		Drymen*	The Square
Anstruther*	Harbourhead		Dufftown*	The Square
Arbroath	Market Place		Dumbarton	Milton
Ardgartan*	By Arrochar		Dumfries	64 Whitesands
Auchterarder	90 High Street		Dunbar*	143A High Street
Aviemore	Grampian Road		Dunblane*	Stirling Road
Ayr	22 Sandgate		Dundee	21 Castle Street
Ballater	Station Square		Dunfermline	1 High Street
Balloch*	The Old Station Building		Dunkeld	The Cross
Banchory*	Bridge Street		Dunoon	7 Alexandra Parade
Banff*	Collie Lodge		Dunvegan*	2 Lochside
Biggar*	155 High Street		Durness*	Durine
Blairgowrie	26 Wellmeadow		Edinburgh	3 Princes Street
Bo'ness*	Union Street		Edinburgh Airport	Main Concourse
Bowmore	The Square		Elgin	17 High Street
Braemar	Mar Road		Eyemouth*	Market Square
Brechin*	Pictavia Centre		Falkirk	2-4 Glebe Street
Brodick	The Pier		Forfar*	45 East High Street
Callander*	Ancaster Square		Forres*	116 High Street
Campbeltown	The Pier		Fort Augustus*	Car Park
Carnoustie*	1B High Street		Fort William	Cameron Square
Castlebay*	Main Street		Forth Bridges	Queensferry Lodge Hotel
Castle Douglas*	Market Hill Car Park		Fraserburgh*	3 Saltoun Square
Craignure	The Pier		Gatehouse of Fleet*	Car Park

Glasgow	11 George Square		Moffat*	Churchgate
Glasgow Airport	International Arrivals Hall		Montrose*	Bridge Street
Grantown on Spey*	54 High Street		Newtongrange*	Scottish Mining Museum
Gretna	Gretna Gateway Outlet Village		Newton Stewart*	Dashwood Square
			North Berwick	Quality Street
Hamilton	Road Chef Services		North Kessock*	Picnic Site
Hawick*	Drumlanrig's Tower		Oban	Argyll Square
Helensburgh*	The Clock Tower		Old Craighall*	Old Craighall Service Area
Huntly*	9a The Square		Paisley	9A Gilmour Street
Inveraray	Front Street		Peebles	High Street
Inverness	Castle Wynd		Perth	West Mill Street
Inverurie	18 High Street		Pitlochry	22 Atholl Road
Jedburgh	Murrays Green		Portree	Bayfield House
John o'Groats*	County Road		Rothesay	Winter Gardens
Kelso	The Square		St Andrews	70 Market Street
Kilchoan*	Pier Road		Selkirk	Halliwells House
Killin*	Main Street		Stirling	41 Dumbarton Road
Kinross	Junction 6, M90		Stirling (Pirnhall)	Motorway Service Area
Kirkcaldy	339 High Street		Stonehaven*	66 Allardice Street
Kirkcudbright	Harbour Square		Stornoway	26 Cromwell Street
Kirkwall	6 Broad Street		Stranraer	28 Harbour Street
Kirriemuir*	Cumberland Close		Stromness	Ferry Terminal Building
Lanark	Ladyacre Road		Strontian*	Acharacle
Largs*	Main Street		Sumburgh	Sumburgh Airport
Lerwick	The Market Cross		Tarbert (Harris)	Pier Road
Linlithgow*	The Cross		Tarbert (Loch Fyne)	Harbour Street
Loch Lomond Gateway Centre	Loch Lomond Shores		Tarbet (Loch Lomond)*	Main Street
Lochboisdale*	Pier Road		Thurso*	Riverside
Lochgilphead*	Lochnell Street		Tobermory*	The Pier
Lochinver*	Kirk Lane		Tomintoul*	The Square
Lochmaddy*	Pier Road		Tyndrum*	Main Street
Melrose	Abbey Street		Ullapool	Argyle Street

* seasonal opening

Alternatively, you can text **TIC LOCATE** to **64118** to find your nearest tourist information centre

Find out **more**

The following publications are available by post or from the online bookshop. Browse VisitScotland.com or phone (0131) 472 2222 for these titles and more:

Where to Stay Hotels & Guest Houses £8.99
Over 800 places to stay in Scotland – from luxury town houses and country hotels to budget-priced guesthouses. Details of prices and facilities, with location maps.

Where to Stay Bed & Breakfast £6.99
Over 1,000 Bed and Breakfast establishments throughout Scotland offering inexpensive accommodation – the perfect way to enjoy a budget trip and meet Scottish folk in their own homes. Details of prices and facilities, with location maps.

Where to Stay Caravan & Camping £4.99
Over 100 parks detailed with prices, available facilities and lots of other useful information. Parks inspected by the British Holiday Parks Grading Scheme. Also includes caravan homes for hire, with location maps.

Where to Stay Self Catering £5.99
Over 700 cottages, apartments and chalets to let – many in scenic areas. Details of prices and facilities, with location maps.

Touring Guide to Scotland £7.99
A fully revised edition of this popular guide which now lists over 1,500 things to do and places to visit in Scotland. Easy to use index and locator maps. Details of opening hours, admission charges, general description and information on disabled access.

Touring Map of Scotland £4.99
An up-to-date touring map of Scotland. Full colour with comprehensive motorway and road information, the map details over 20 categories of tourist information and names over 1,500 things to do and places to visit in Scotland.

Travel **info**

By road:
The A1 and M6 bring you quickly over the border and immerse you in beautiful scenery. Scotland's network of excellent roads span out from Edinburgh – Glasgow takes approximately one hour and 15 minutes by car; Aberdeen two hours 30 minutes and Inverness three hours.

By rail:
The cross-border service from England and Wales to Scotland is fast and efficient, and Scotrail trains offer overnight Caledonian sleepers to make the journey even easier. Telephone 0845 755 0033 for further details.

By air:
Fly into Aberdeen, Dundee, Edinburgh, Glasgow or Inverness.

Spectacular views of Edinburgh from Calton Hill

where to stay in
Scotland

All place names in the blue bands are shown on the maps at the front of this guide.

Accommodation symbols

Symbols give useful information about services and facilities. Inside the back-cover flap you can find a key to these symbols. Keep it open for easy reference.

AYR, South Ayrshire Map ref 7B2

★★★★
HOLIDAY PARK

🚐 (20) £11.50–£16.50
🚐 (8)   £10.00–£15.00
🛆 (8)   £10.00–£16.50
🏠 (10) £160.00–£550.00
36 touring pitches

Heads of Ayr Caravan Park

Dunure Road, Ayr KA7 4LD **t** (01292) 442269 **f** (01292) 500298

Situated five miles south of Ayr on the A719. Facilities include bar, shop, laundry, play area and beach. Seasonal entertainment. Caravans to hire. Tourers and tents welcome. Open weekends-only in winter.

open All year
payment Cash/cheques

General 🔌 P 🔄 🖰 🚽 🆒 🛝 ☉ 🗑 🖩 🗜 🐕 ☼ Leisure 📺 🍽 🎵 🍸 🎣 ⚠ ☂ 🎵 ►

BALMACARA, Highland Map ref 8B3

★★★★
TOURING PARK

🚐 (40) Min £10.30
🚐 (40) Min £10.30
🛆 (5)   Min £10.30
45 touring pitches

Reraig Caravan Site

Balmacara, Kyle of Lochalsh IV40 8DH **t** (01599) 566215 **e** warden@reraig.com **w** reraig.com

Small family-run site, four miles from bridge to Isle of Skye. Booking not necessary. No awnings during July and August. Tents: only small tents permitted. No youth groups. Open May to September.

payment Credit/debit cards, cash/cheques

General 🔌 P 🔄 🚽 🆒 🛝 ☉ 🐕

BRAEMAR, Aberdeenshire Map ref 8C3

★★★★
TOURING PARK

🚐 (97) £11.00–£24.00
🚐 (97) £11.00–£24.00
🛆   on application
97 touring pitches

See Ad on inside back cover

The Invercauld Caravan Club Site

Glenshee Road, Ballater AB35 5YQ **t** (01339) 741373 **w** caravanclub.co.uk

payment Credit/debit cards, cash/cheques

Set on the edge of Braemar village, gateway to the Cairngorms. Ideal centre for mountain lovers. See red deer, capercaillie and golden eagles. Open December 2006 to October 2007.

⊕ *On A93 on southern outskirts of village.*

♥ *Special member rates mean you can save your membership subscription in less than a week. Visit our website to find out more.*

General 📺 P 🔄 🖰 🚽 🆒 🛝 ☉ 🗑 🖩 🐕 ☼ Leisure ⚠ 🎵 ►

BRORA, Highland Map ref 8C2

★★★★★
TOURING PARK
🚐 (52) £12.10–£24.00
🚉 (52) £12.10–£24.00
▲ on application
52 touring pitches

See Ad on inside back cover

Dalchalm Caravan Club Site
Dalchalm, Brora KW9 6LP **t** (01408) 621479 **w** caravanclub.co.uk

payment Credit/debit cards, cash/cheques

A sheltered site where you can play golf or relax on the nearby sandy beach. Marvellous walking, bird-watching, sea and loch fishing. Open April to October.

⊕ 1.25 miles north of Brora on A9, turn right at Dalchalm.

♥ Special member rates mean you can save your membership subscription in less than a week. Visit our website to find out more.

General ▨ P 🔌 🅖 🍴 🚐 🎢 ☉ 📠 🅱 🐾 ☼ Leisure ✈ ↑

CALLANDER, Stirling Map ref 7B1

★★★★★
HOLIDAY PARK
🚐 (128) Min £17.00
🚉 (128) Min £17.00
128 touring pitches

Gart Caravan Park
Stirling Road, Callander FK17 8LE **t** (01877) 330002 **f** (01877) 330002
e enquiries@gart-caravan-park.co.uk **w** gart-caravan-park.co.uk

payment Credit/debit cards, cash/cheques

A peaceful and spacious park maintained to a very high standard with modern, heated shower block facilities. The ideal centre for cycling, walking and fishing.

⊕ Leave jct 10 of the M9, west to Callander.

♥ Reduced rates for the over 50s. Winner – Calor Gas Best Park in Britain 2003.

General ▨ P 🔌 🅖 🍴 🚐 🎢 ☉ 📠 🐾 ☼ Leisure ⛰ ∪ ✈ ↑ 🚲

CULLODEN, Highland Map ref 8C3

★★★★★
TOURING PARK
🚐 (97) £11.00–£24.00
🚉 (97) £11.00–£24.00
▲ on application
97 touring pitches

See Ad on inside back cover

Culloden Moor Caravan Club Site
Newlands, Inverness IV2 5EF **t** (01463) 790625 **w** caravanclub.co.uk

payment Credit/debit cards

A gently sloping site with glorious views over the Nairn Valley. Inverness, with impressive castle, great shops and fascinating museums, is six miles away. Open March to January 2007.

⊕ From A9 south of Inverness, take B9006 signposted Croy, site on left 1 mile past Culloden field memorial.

♥ Special member rates mean you can save your membership subscription in less than a week. Visit our website to find out more.

General ▨ P 🔌 🅖 🍴 🚐 🎢 ☉ 📠 🅱 🐾 ☼ Leisure ⛰ ✈

Check it out
Information on parks listed in this guide has been supplied by proprietors. As changes may occur you should remember to check all relevant details at the time of booking.

DUMFRIES, Dumfries & Galloway Map ref 7C3

★★★
HOLIDAY PARK

🚐 (10) £10.00–£14.00
🚚 (10) £10.00–£14.00
▲ (10) £10.00–£14.00
🏠 £140.00–£230.00
30 touring pitches

Barnsoul Farm

Irongray, Shawhead, Dumfries DG2 9SQ t (01387) 730249 f (01387) 730453
e barnsouldg@aol.com w barnsoulfarm.co.uk

payment Cash/cheques

Barnsoul is one of Galloway's most scenic farms with 200 acres of meadows, ponds, woodlands and heath. Includes two Iron Age forts and medieval farm settlement. A nature lover's paradise. Six wigwam, single-room bunk houses available. Open October to April.

⊕ Off A75 at sign for Shawhead. At Shawhead take right, then within 50m bear left. After 1.5 miles Barnsoul is on left.

General 🔌 🖵 P 🐕 🚻 🚟 🅿 ⊙ 🛢 🐕 ☼ Leisure 📺 ⚠ ⤓ 🎣

DUNBAR, East Lothian Map ref 7D2

★★★★
HOLIDAY PARK
THISTLE AWARD

🚐 (53) £12.00–£20.00
🚚 (53) £12.00–£20.00
▲ (53) £12.00–£21.50
🏠 (5) £245.00–£560.00
53 touring pitches

Belhaven Bay Caravan Park

Belhaven Bay, Dunbar EH42 1TU t (01368) 865956 f (01368) 865022
e belhaven@meadowhead.co.uk w meadowhead.co.uk

Bordered by one of Britain's cleanest beaches and a tranquil pond. Set on the edge of the John Muir Country Park but only 30 minutes to Edinburgh's city centre!

open All year except Christmas and New Year
payment Credit/debit cards, cash/cheques, euros

General 🖵 P 🐕 🚻 🚟 🅿 ⊙ 🛢 🐕 ☼ Leisure ⚠ ⤓

EDINBURGH, Edinburgh Map ref 7C2

★★★★★
TOURING PARK

🚐 (80) £12.00–£15.00
🚚 (40) £12.00–£15.00
▲ (28) £12.00–£15.00
🏠 (12) £300.00–£600.00
108 touring pitches

See Ad on below

Drummohr Caravan Park

Levenhall, Musselburgh, Edinburgh EH21 8JS t (0131) 665 6867 f (0131) 653 6859

payment Credit/debit cards, cash/cheques

Premier park close to Princes Street, Edinburgh and the coast of East Lothian. Excellent bus service to city with many retail outlets in the area.

⊕ From south (A1), take A199 Musselburgh, then B1361. Follow park signs. From west (A1), come off at Wallyford slip road and follow Park and Mining Museum signs.

General 🔌 P 🐕 🚻 🚟 🅿 ⊙ 🛢 🐾 🐕 🎯 ☼ Leisure ⚠

Key to symbols

Open the back flap for a key to symbols.

★★★★★
TOURING PARK

🚐 (197) £12.50–£25.10
🚐 (197) £12.50–£25.10
⛺ on application
197 touring pitches

See Ad on inside back cover

Edinburgh Caravan Club Site

35-37 Marine Drive, Edinburgh EH4 5EN **t** (0131) 312 6874

open All year
payment Credit/debit cards, cash/cheques

Situated to the north of the city on the Firth of Forth, the site provides easy access to Edinburgh. It's a historic setting – yet Edinburgh is a friendly, modern, cosmopolitan city with something for everyone.

⊕ *From A901 turn left at traffic lights; at roundabout turn right into Marine Drive. Site on left.*

♥ *Special member rates mean you can save your membership subscription in less than a week. Visit our website to find out more.*

General **P** 🚑 🕐 🍴 🌳 📶 🐕 🚻 Leisure ►

★★★★
HOLIDAY PARK
THISTLE AWARD

🚐 (100) £11.25–£24.00
🚐 (100) £11.25–£24.00
⛺ (150) £11.25–£24.00
🏠 (19) £245.00–£640.00
250 touring pitches

Mortonhall Caravan Park

38 Mortonhall Gate, Frogston Road East, Edinburgh EH16 6TJ **t** (0131) 664 1533 **f** (0131) 664 5387
e mortonhall@meadowhead.co.uk **w** meadowhead.co.uk

payment Credit/debit cards, cash/cheques, euros

Our park is in unrivalled, historic, landscaped grounds only four miles from the heart of Edinburgh. Great new WCs and showers. Wonderful walks with vistas over Edinburgh and views of highland cattle. Fine fayre at the Stable Bar or nearby coffee shop. Efficient bus routes connect us to the city centre.

⊕ *From city bypass at A701 or A702 junction, follow signs for Mortonhall. From city centre go south on A701 or A702. Follow signs before bypass.*

♥ *Please see website for special promotions and details on our new wigwams too!*

General 📺 **P** 🚑 🕐 🍴 🚐 🌳 ☉ 📶 🏪 ✕ 🐕 🚻 ☼ Leisure 📺 ⛄ 🎱 ⛰ ∪ ► 🎣

★★★
HOLIDAY PARK

🚐 (10) £10.00–£11.50
🚐 (10) £10.00–£11.50
⛺ (10) £8.00–£10.00
🏠 (2) £250.00
10 touring pitches

Brownmuir Caravan Park

Fordoun, Laurencekirk AB30 1SJ **t** (01561) 320786 **f** (01561) 320786
e brownmuircaravanpark@talk21.com **w** brownmuircaravanpark.co.uk

A quiet park set in the Howe-of-the-Mearns not far from Royal Dee Side, ideal for cycling and fishing. Top golf courses are nearby. Children's play area on site. Open April to October.

payment Cash/cheques

General 📺 🏠 **P** 🚑 🕐 🍴 🌳 ☉ 📶 🐕 🚻 ☼ Leisure ⛰ ⚲ ∪ 🎣 ►

Country Code Always follow the Country Code

- Be safe – plan ahead and follow any signs
- Leave gates and property as you find them
- Protect plants and animals, and take your litter home
- Keep dogs under close control
- Consider other people

FORT WILLIAM, Highland Map ref 7B1

Linnhe Lochside Holidays

★★★★★
HOLIDAY PARK

🚐 (65) £15.00–£21.00
🚍 (65) £15.00–£21.00
⛺ (15) £11.50–£13.50
🏠 (60) £210.00–£510.00
80 touring pitches

Corpach, Fort William PH33 7NL **t** (01397) 772376 **f** (01397) 772007
e relax@linnhe-lochside-holidays.co.uk **w** linnhe-lochside-holidays.co.uk

payment Credit/debit cards, cash/cheques

Almost a botanical garden. Winner of 'Best Park in Scotland 1999' award. Free fishing. Colour brochure sent with pleasure. Also self-catering. Open 15 December to 31 October.

⊕ On A830 1.5 miles (3km) west of Corpach village, 5 miles from Fort William.

♥ Discounts for Senior Citizen groups and for 2nd week. Rallies – no charge for awnings.

General 🎣 🚲 P 🔌 🛁 🚽 🚐 🐾 ☉ 🏪 🖥 🛒 🐕 🎪 ☼   Leisure 🏔 🛶 🚲

GAIRLOCH, Highland Map ref 8B2

Gairloch Caravan and Camping Park

★★★★
TOURING PARK

🚐 (20) £10.00–£13.50
🚍 (20) £10.00–£13.50
⛺ (20) £10.00–£13.50
🏠 (2) £210.00–£395.00
20 touring pitches

Strath, Gairloch IV21 2BX **t** (01445) 712373 **e** info@gairlochcaravan park.com
w gairlochcaravanpark.com

Small, friendly site with view of mountains and sea. Walks, fishing, golf, pony-trekking, beach, restaurants, Heritage Museum and Inverewe Gardens all nearby. Open April to October.

payment Credit/debit cards, cash/cheques

General P 🔌 🚽 🐾 ☉ 🏪 🖥 🐕 ☼   Leisure ∪ 🛶 ⚑ 🚲

GAIRLOCH, Highland Map ref 8B2

Sands Holiday Centre

★★★★
HOLIDAY PARK
THISTLE AWARD

🚐 (120) £8.50–£16.50
🚍 (40) £8.50–£15.50
⛺ (120) £8.50–£15.50
🏠 (5) £325.00–£480.00
280 touring pitches

Gairloch IV21 2DL **t** (01445) 712152 **f** (01445) 712518 **e** Litsands@aol.com
w highlandcaravancamping.co.uk

Adjoining sandy beach with boat-launching access to Loch Gairloch. Facilities: children's play area, games room, well-stocked, licensed shop, laundry with washing, drying and ironing facilities. Dish-washing and picnic tables. Open 1 April to 15 October.

payment Credit/debit cards, cash/cheques

General P 🔌 🚽 🐾 ☉ 🏪 🖥 🛒 🐕   Leisure ⚓ 🏔 ∪ 🛶 ⚑

GATEHOUSE OF FLEET, Dumfries & Galloway Map ref 7B3

Auchenlarie Holiday Park

★★★★
HOLIDAY PARK

🚐 (120) £20.00–£25.00
🚍 (120) £20.00–£25.00
⛺ (120) £18.00–£25.00
🏠 (80) £120.00–£460.00
120 touring pitches

Gatehouse of Fleet, Castle Douglas DG7 2EX **t** (01557) 840251 **f** (01557) 840252

Family caravan park with extensive amenities located on the beautiful Galloway coast.

payment Credit/debit cards, cash/cheques, euros

General 🎣 P 🔌 🚽 🚐 🐾 ☉ 🏪 🖥 🛒 ✕ 🐕 🎪 ☼   Leisure 🎣 📺 🍴 🎵 ⚓ 🏔 ∪ 🛶 ⚑

Check the maps

Colour maps at the front pinpoint all the places you will find accommodation entries in the regional sections. Pick your location and then refer to the place index at the back to find the page number.

★★★
HOLIDAY PARK
🚐(15)   Min £14.00
🚏(15)   Min £14.00
🅰 (30)   Min £12.50
🛖(16) £150.00–£350.00
30 touring pitches

Craigendmuir Park

Craigendmuir Park Business Centre, Stepps, Glasgow G33 6AF t (0141) 7794159 f (0141) 779 4057
e info@craigendmuir.co.uk w craigendmuir.co.uk

From M8 take junction 11 to A80, turn right for one mile through Stepps. Turn right onto Cardowan Road. At top of hill turn right onto Claymouse Road and follow to next roundabout. Park on right.

open All year
payment Credit/debit cards, cash/cheques

General 🔌 P 🔌 🚰 🍴 🚿 🛝 ☺ 📻 🖥 🏊 🐾   Leisure ∪ 🎣 ►

★★★★★
HOLIDAY PARK
THISTLE AWARD
🚐   Min £15.00
🚏   Min £15.00
🅰   Min £15.00
🛖 £270.00–£450.00
60 touring pitches

Invercoe Caravan & Camping Park

Invercoe, Glencoe PH49 4HP t (01855) 811210 f (01855) 811210 e invercoe@sol.co.uk
w invercoe.co.uk

open All year
payment Credit/debit cards, cash/cheques

Situated on the shores of Loch Leven and surrounded by spectacular scenery, Invercoe is a small, award-winning, family-run park and is an excellent base for exploring the West Highlands. Booking advisable during high season (minimum three nights).

⊕ *Site is 0.25 miles from Glencoe crossroads (A82) on the Kinlochleven road (B863).*

General 🔌 🔌 🚿 🍴 🚐 🛝 ☺ 📻 🖥 🏊 🐾 ☼   Leisure 🎣 ►

★★★
TOURING PARK
🚐(90)   Min £10.00
🚏(90)   Min £10.00
🅰 (90)   Min £10.00
90 touring pitches

John O' Groats Caravan Park

John O' Groats, Wick KW1 4YR t (01955) 611329 & (01955) 611744
e info@johnogroatscampsite.co.uk w johnogroatscampsite.co.uk

On seashore overlooking Orkney Islands (day trips available). Hotel restaurant 400m, harbour 150m, sea birds 3km. Cliff scenery. Open April to September.

payment Cash/cheques

General P 🔌 🚿 🍴 🚐 🛝 ☺ 📻 🖥 🐾   Leisure ∪ 🎣

★★★★
TOURING PARK
🚐(56) £9.35–£19.60
🚏(56) £9.35–£19.60
56 touring pitches

See Ad on inside back cover

Kinlochewe Caravan Club Site

Achnasheen IV22 2PA t (01445) 760239 w caravanclub.co.uk

payment Credit/debit cards, cash/cheques

Peaceful site near Loch Maree. A rare and very special place with lochs, woodland and mountains – a paradise for climbers and walkers. Non-members welcome. Open March to October.

⊕ *Just north of Kinlochewe at junction of A832 and A896. Signposted.*

♥ *Special member rates mean you can save your membership subscription in less than a week. Visit our website to find out more.*

THE
CARAVAN
CLUB

General 🖥 P 🔌 🚿 🍴 🚐 🛝 ☺ 📻 🖥 🐾 ☼

KIPPFORD, Dumfries & Galloway Map ref 7C3

★★★★★
HOLIDAY PARK
THISTLE AWARD

(30) £12.00–£15.00
(30) £12.00–£15.00
(15) £9.00–£15.00
(24) £245.00–£470.00
45 touring pitches

Kippford Holiday Park

Kippford, Dalbeattie DG5 4LF **t** (01556) 620636 **f** (01556) 620607 **w** kippfordholidaypark.co.uk

open All year
payment Credit/debit cards, cash/cheques, euros

Coastal south-west Scotland by beautiful seaside village. All electric pitches on Bellamy Gold Park, with woodland and coastal walks. Play areas, cycles, fishing, 9-hole golf. Pitches separated for privacy by specimen planting. Touring pitches are grassed hard-standing with water and waste connection. Huge showers in fully heated toilet blocks.

From A711 Dalbeattie take A710 Solway coast road. After 3.5 miles continue straight ahead at junction with Kippford Road. Entrance to park is 200yds on right.

Discounts for large families and Senior Citizens, also seventh night free. Marquee (free) for small rallies.

General P Leisure

LAURENCEKIRK, Aberdeenshire Map ref 7D1

★★★★
HOLIDAY PARK

(25) £10.00–£11.00
(25) £10.00–£11.00
(25) £7.50–£8.50
(1) £200.00–£230.00
25 touring pitches

Dovecot Caravan Park

Northwaterbridge, Laurencekirk AB30 1QL **t** (01674) 840630 **f** (01674) 840630
e info@dovecotcaravanpark.com **w** dovecotcaravanpark.com

Dovecot is a peaceful, rural site located halfway between Dundee and Aberdeen. Ideal location for touring. Sandy beaches eight miles and Angus glens on our doorstep.

payment Cash/cheques

General P Leisure

LINLITHGOW, West Lothian Map ref 7C2

★★★★
TOURING PARK

(36) £12.00–£16.00
(36) £12.00–£16.00
(20) £10.00–£18.00
56 touring pitches

Beecraigs Caravan and Camping Site

Beecraigs Country Park, The Park Centre, Linlithgow EH49 6PL **t** (01506) 844516 **f** (01506) 846256
e mail@beecraigs.com **w** beecraigs.com

open All year
payment Credit/debit cards, cash/cheques

Open all year. Situated near historic Linlithgow town. On-site facilities include electric hook-ups, barbecues, play area, modern toilet facilities with privacy cubicles, baby-change and laundry. Pets welcome. Leaflets available. Great for exploring central Scotland and the Lothians.

From Linlithgow, follow Beecraigs Country Park and International Caravan Park signposts. Park is 2 miles south of Linlithgow. From M8, follow B792. From M9, follow A803.

Sep 2006-Mar 2007: 10% discount for Senior Citizens (proof required) and 10% discount for 7-night stay if paid in advance (excl Senior Citizens).

General P Leisure

LOCKERBIE, Dumfries & Galloway Map ref 7C3

★★★★★
HOLIDAY PARK

(100) £7.50–£14.00
(100) £7.50–£14.00
(30) £6.50–£14.00
130 touring pitches

Hoddom Castle Caravan Park

Hoddom, Lockerbie DG11 1AS **t** (01576) 300251 **e** hoddomcastle@aol.com **w** hoddomcastle.co.uk

Part of 10,000-acre estate. Beautiful, peaceful, award-winning park. Own 9-hole golf course. Salmon, seatrout and coarse fishing. Nature trails and walks in surrounding countryside. Open April to October.

payment Credit/debit cards, cash/cheques

General P Leisure

MARKINCH, Fife Map ref 7C2

★★★★
TOURING PARK

🚐 (77) £9.50–£21.40
🚎 (77) £9.50–£21.40
Å   on application
77 touring pitches

See Ad on inside back cover

CARAVAN
CLUB
2001

Balbirnie Park Caravan Club Site

Balbirnie Road, Markinch, Glenrothes KY7 6NR **t** (01592) 759130 **w** caravanclub.co.uk

payment Credit/debit cards, cash/cheques

Attractive site set in 400 acres of parkland. Thirty golf courses, including one on site. Swimming pool, ice rink, ten-pin bowling, children's farm close by. Open March to October.

⊕ From A92, follow signs to Markinch, then signs to Balbirnie Park Craft Centre. Site entrance is just inside park on right, 0.5 miles west of Markinch.

♥ Special member rates mean you can save your membership subscription in less than a week. Visit our website to find out more.

General 🖭 🔌 🕓 🚻 🚾 📶 ☺ 📶🗑 🐾 ☼   Leisure ⚠

NORTH BERWICK, East Lothian Map ref 7D2

★★★★★
HOLIDAY PARK
THISTLE AWARD

🚐 (147) £16.00–£22.00
🚎 (147) £16.00–£22.00
Å (40)   £12.00–£24.00
🏠 (10) £250.00–£600.00
147 touring pitches

Tantallon Caravan Park

Dunbar Road, North Berwick EH39 5NJ **t** (01620) 893348 **f** (01620) 895623
e tantallon@meadowhead.co.uk **w** meadowhead.co.uk

payment Credit/debit cards, cash/cheques

Relaxing park that's ideal for exploring the classy golfing capital of North Berwick and East Lothian beyond. Overlooks Glen Golf Course with views of the Forth, Bass Rock, Isle of May and Fife. Local bus and trains connect us to Edinburgh, and the park is convenient for local shops.

⊕ From North Berwick, A198 towards Dunbar. From the south, turn off at A1 north of Dunbar and follow signs for North Berwick and Tantallon Park.

♥ Please see our website for special promotions.

General 🖭 P 🔌 🕓 🚻 🚾 📶 ☺ 📶🗑 🐾 ☼   Leisure 📺 ⚡ ⚠ ▶

PORT LOGAN, Dumfries & Galloway Map ref 7B3

★★★★
TOURING PARK

🚐 (158) £9.50–£21.40
🚎 (158) £9.50–£21.40
158 touring pitches

See Ad on inside back cover

CARAVAN
CLUB
2001

New England Bay Caravan Club Site

Port Logan, Stranraer DG9 9NX **t** (01776) 860275 **w** caravanclub.co.uk

payment Credit/debit cards, cash/cheques

On the edge of Luce Bay, an ideal site for children with direct access to a safe, clean, sandy beach. Sailing, sea-angling, golf, green bowling, pony-trekking. Open March to October.

⊕ From Newton Stewart take A75, then A715, then A716. Site on left 2.7 miles past Ardwell Filling Station.

♥ Special member rates mean you can save your membership subscription in less than a week. Visit our website to find out more.

General 🖭 P 🔌 🚻 🚾 📶 ☺ 📶🗑 🐾 ☼   Leisure ⚡ ⚠ ∪

Scotland

STIRLING, Stirling Map ref 7C2

★★★★★
TOURING PARK
🚐(60)　£12.00–£16.00
🚙(60)　£12.00–£16.00
⛺ (60)　£10.00–£16.00
60 touring pitches

Witches Craig Caravan Park

Blairlogie, Stirling FK9 5PX　**t** (01786) 474947　**f** (01786) 447286　**e** info@witchescraig.co.uk
w witchescraig.co.uk

Winner of numerous awards, Witches Craig is attractive and exceptionally well maintained. Peacefully situated below the picturesque Ochil Hills, an ideal place to unwind. Great base for travelling. Superb modern facilities. Open April to October.

payment Credit/debit cards, cash/cheques

General 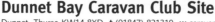 Leisure 🏔 ⛵

THURSO, Highland Map ref 8C1

★★★★★
TOURING PARK
🚐(57)　£11.00–£24.00
🚙(57)　£11.00–£24.00
⛺　on application
57 touring pitches

See Ad on inside back cover

THE
CARAVAN
CLUB
2007

Dunnet Bay Caravan Club Site

Dunnet, Thurso KW14 8XD　**t** (01847) 821319　**w** caravanclub.co.uk

payment Credit/debit cards, cash/cheques

A good place for those who like to be solitary. Views to Dunnet Head, northernmost point of mainland Britain. Good for bird-watching and fishing. Open March to October.

⊕ From east (John O'Groats) on A836. Site on right past Dunnet village.

♥ Special member rates mean you can save your membership subscription in less than a week. Visit our website to find out more.

General P 🚐 🛢 🚙 🔫 🗑 🎣　Leisure ⛵

Ratings

you can trust

When you're looking for a place to stay, you need a rating system you can trust. The British Graded Holiday Parks Scheme, operated jointly by VisitBritain, VisitScotland and Visit Wales, gives you a clear guide as to what to expect.

Based on the internationally recognised rating of one to five stars, the system puts great emphasis on quality and reflects customer expectations.

Parks are visited annually by professional assessors who award a rating based on cleanliness, environment and the quality of services and facilities provided.

Ratings made easy

★	Simple, practical, no frills
★★	Well presented and well run
★★★	Good level of quality and comfort
★★★★	Excellent standard throughout
★★★★★	Exceptional with a degree of luxury

For full details of VisitBritains's Quality Rose assessment schemes, go online at **enjoyengland.com/quality**

Wales

A playful picnic overlooking Three Cliffs Bay on the Gower Peninsula

Visit Wales
Welsh Assembly Government,
Brunel House, 2 Fitzalan Road
Cardiff CF24 0UY

0870 830 0306
0870 121 1255 (minicom)
visitwales.com

lush valleys,
spectacular
coastline,
myths and
legends

Main Biking across the heather-clad Black Mountains, Powys
Left Experience Welsh folklore at the Eisteddfod International Festival, Llangollen; a stunning spectacle – the Cardiff Millennium Centre by night; facing the challenge on the River Tryweryn at the National White Water Centre, Snowdonia; pony-trekking through stunning vistas at Carreg Cennen Castle, Llandelio

For a small country Wales is big on things to see and do. To start with it has three National Parks, each one featuring very different landscapes, and a turbulent history which comes alive in its many castles. **Search out Wales' fascinating industrial heritage and discover its myths and legends.**

Explore
Wales

Nature at its best

In big, bold Snowdonia National Park walk to the summit of Mount Snowdon, or take the little mountain railway. Pembrokeshire has Britain's only coastal-based National Park where the sea air fills your lungs and the wildlife captures your attention. The Brecon Beacons National Park is filled with the greenest, grassiest hills you'll ever see. Walk, cycle, or take a trip on a canal-boat, whichever you prefer.

Cappuccinos and citadels

Europe's youngest capital, Cardiff is just a stone's throw from the Beacons' wide, open spaces. It's cosmopolitan, lively and busy. Join in the cafe culture and don't miss the stunning new waterfront along Cardiff Bay. Make sure you visit the fabulous city-centre castle. Castles, of course, are what Wales does very well. There are hundreds of them, ranging from Harlech, Beaumaris, Caernarfon and Conwy, part of Edward I's mighty iron ring of castles in the north, to romantic hilltop fortresses such as Carreg Cennen near Llandeilo. Here it's easy to conjure up tales of princes, wizards and dragons as you climb its ramparts or explore the eerie underground passage.

Experience the country's fascinating industrial heritage first-hand in places like the Big Pit at Blaenavon and the Llechwedd Slate Caverns where you go underground and find out exactly what it was like to work there.

Get up and go

For all its history, Wales doesn't live in the past. It's an exciting, forward-looking country, full of zest, activity and adventure. You can go mountain biking or try parascending and white-water rafting. For quieter exploration, walk, cycle or ride on waymarked trails through hill and vale. At the Centre for Alternative Technology in Mid Wales you'll find the village of the future with lots of child-friendly exhibits and events throughout the year. Hold your breath as you shoot down Europe's largest wooden rollercoaster at Oakwood Theme Park or ride gently on Wales' charming Great Little Trains – scenic narrow-gauge railways that puff their way to the loveliest corners of the country.

And there's plenty going on all over Wales. Give your tastebuds a treat in September at the Abergavenny Food Festival or at Caerphilly's Big Cheese extravaganza in July. Or for something completely different watch the extraordinary World Bog Snorkelling Championships near Llanwrtyd Wells on August Bank Holiday Monday. As you would expect, there is music everywhere. Tap your foot to the beat at the renowned Brecon International Festival of Jazz or immerse yourself in all things Welsh at the National Eisteddfod near Swansea, both in August.

Places to **visit**

0   50 miles

0   75 kms

Anglesey

Holyhead   **5**

Bangor   Conwy

Prestatyn

5

8

Caernarfon

Clwydian Range

8

SNOWDONIA

OFFA'S DYKE PATH

Lleyn Peninsula

Portmeirion

8

Machynlleth

Welshpool

GLYNDWR'S WAY

81   **81**

Aberystwyth

Knighton

Rhayader

82

St Dogmaels   Cardigan

Llanwrtyd Wells

8

PEMBROKESHIRE COAST

Whitesands Bay

47

4

Fishguard

PEMBROKESHIRE COAST PATH

BRECON BEACONS

42

OFFA'S DYKE PATH

4

47

Blaenafon

42

Wye Valley

Milford Haven

Amroth

8

47

Pembroke   Tenby

Swansea

4

46

Sedbury

Gower

47

Newport

4

4

Cardiff

Legend

- National Park
- Area of Outstanding Natural Beauty
- Heritage Coast
- National Trails
  nationaltrail.co.uk
- **5** Sections of the National Cycle Network
  nationalcyclenetwork.org.uk

Aberystwyth Arts Centre
(01970) 623232
aberystwythartscentre.co.uk
The busiest arts centre in Wales with cinema and exhibitions

Beaumaris Castle

Anglesey
(01248) 810361
beaumaris.com
Symmetrical medieval fortress surrounded by water

Big Pit: National Coal Museum
Blaenafon, Torfaen
(01495) 790311
museumwales.ac.uk/en/bigpit
Take a guided tour underground

Bodnant Garden
Near Colwyn Bay, Conwy
(01492) 650460
bodnantgarden.co.uk
Fabulous gardens with rare, foreign plants

Caernarfon Castle
Gwynedd
(01286) 677617
castlewales.com/caernarf
Vast and beautiful castle located on the shoreline

Cardiff Castle
(02920) 878100
cardiffcastle.com
Splendid city-centre castle alongside the magnificent Bute Park

Carreg Cennen Castle
Llandelio, Carmarthenshire
(0120) 500200
castlewales.com/carreg
Ruined castle in spectacular hilltop setting

Centre for Alternative Technology
Machynlleth, Powys
(01654) 705950
cat.org.uk
Practical solutions to environmental problems

Great Orme Tramway
Llandudno
(01492) 879306
greatormetramway.co.uk
Cable-hauled tramway

Harlech Castle
Gwynedd
(01766) 780552
harlech.com
Truly stunning hilltop fortress

Heatherton Country Sports Park
Tenby, Pembrokeshire
(01646) 652000
heatherton.co.uk
Adventure park with endless entertainment

Llechwedd Slate Caverns
Blaenau Ffestiniog, Gwynedd
(01766) 830306
llechwedd-slate-caverns.co.uk
Fantastic slate mine with railway

Llyn Brenig Reservoir and Visitor Centre
Corwen, Conwy
(01490) 420463
waterscape.com/llyn_brenig
Surrounded by stunning moorland and forest

Oakwood Theme Park
Narbeth, Pembrokeshire
(01834) 861889
oakwood-leisure.com
Ride the thrilling rollercoaster

Penrhyn Castle

Bangor, Gwynedd
(01248) 371337
nationaltrust.org.uk
Stunning castle with views over Snowdonia

Portmeirion

Gwynedd
(01766) 770000
portmeirion-village.com
Beautiful redeveloped cliffside village

Techniquest
Cardiff
(02920) 475475
techniquest.org
Science fun and a planetarium

Wales Millennium Centre: artsExplorer Gallery
Cardiff
0870 040 2000
wmc.org.uk
Enjoy arts and entertainment

Welsh Mountain Zoo and Botanical Gardens
Colwyn Bay, Conwy
(01492) 532938
welshmountainzoo.org
Watch sealions dive and swim

Tourist information centres

When you arrive at your destination, visit a tourist information centre for help with accommodation and information about local attractions and events, or email your request before you go.

Aberaeron	The Quay	(01545) 570602	aberaerontic@ceredigion.gov.uk
Aberdyfi*	The Wharf Gardens	(01654) 767321	tic.aberdyfi@eryri-npa.gov.uk
Abergavenny	Monmouth Road	(01873) 857588	abergavenny.tic@monmouthshire.gov.uk
Aberystwyth	Terrace Road	(01970) 612125	aberystwythtic@ceredigion.gov.uk
Bala*	Pensarn Road	(01678) 521021	bala.tic@gwynedd.gov.uk
Bangor*	Deiniol Road	(01248) 352786	bangor.tic@gwynedd.gov.uk
Barmouth*	Station Road	(01341) 280787	barmouth.tic@gwynedd.gov.uk
Barry Island*	The Promenade	(01446) 747171	tourism@valeofglamorgan.gov.uk
Beddgelert*	Canolfan Hebog	(01766) 890615	tic.beddgelert@eryri-npa.gov.uk
Betws y Coed	Royal Oak Stables	(01690) 710426	tic.byc@eryri-npa.gov.uk
Blaenau Ffestiniog*	High Street	(01766) 830360	tic.blaenau@eryri-npa.gov.uk
Blaenavon*	North Street	(01495) 792615	blaenavon.ironworks@btopenworld.com
Borth*	Cambrian Terrace	(01970) 871174	borthtic@ceredigion.gov.uk
Brecon	Cattle Market Car Park	(01874) 622485	brectic@powys.gov.uk
Bridgend	McArthur Glen Design Outlet (Wales)	(01656) 654906	bridgendtic@bridgend.gov.uk
Builth Wells	The Groe Car Park	(01982) 553307	builtic@powys.gov.uk
Caerleon	5 High Street	(01633) 422656	caerleon.tic@newport.gov.uk
Caernarfon	Castle Street	(01286) 672232	caernarfon.tic@gwynedd.gov.uk
Caerphilly	Lower Twyn Square	(029) 2088 0011	tic@caerphilly.gov.uk
Cardiff	The Old Library	0870 121 1258	visitor@cardiff.gov.uk
Cardigan	Bath House Road	(01239) 613230	cardigantic@ceredigion.gov.uk
Carmarthen	113 Lammas Street	(01267) 231557	carmarthentic@carmarthenshire.gov.uk
Chepstow	Bridge Street	(01291) 623772	chepstow.tic@monmouthshire.gov.uk
Colwyn Bay	Princess Drive	(01492) 530478	colwynbaytic@conwy.gov.uk
Conwy	Castle Buildings	(01492) 592248	conwytic@conwy.gov.uk
Dolgellau	Eldon Square	(01341) 422888	tic.dolgellau@eryri-npa.gov.uk
Fishguard Harbour	The Parrog	(01348) 872037	fishguardharbour.tic@pembrokeshire.gov.uk
Fishguard Town	The Library, High Street	(01348) 873484	fishguard.tic@pembrokeshire.gov.uk
Harlech*	High Street	(01766) 780658	tic.harlech@eryri-npa.gov.uk
Haverfordwest	Old Bridge	(01437) 763110	haverfordwest.tic@pembrokeshire.gov.uk
Holyhead	Terminal 1	(01407) 762622	holyhead@nwtic.com
Kilgetty*	Kingsmoor Common	(01834) 814161	info@kilgettytic.fsnet.co.uk
Knighton	West Street	(01547) 529424	oda@offasdyke.demon.co.uk
Lake Vyrnwy*	Vyrnwy Craft Workshops	(01691) 870346	laktic@powys.gov.uk

Llanberis	41b High Street	(01286) 870765	llanberis.tic@gwynedd.gov.uk
Llandovery	Kings Road	(01550) 720693	llandovery.ic@breconbeacons.org
Llandrindod Wells	Memorial Gardens	(01597) 822600	llandtic@powys.gov.uk
Llandudno	1-2 Chapel Street	(01492) 876413	llandudnotic@conwy.gov.uk
Llanfairpwllgwyngyll	Station Site	(01248) 713177	llanfairpwll@nwtic.com
Llangollen	Castle Street	(01978) 860828	llangollen@nwtic.com
Llanidloes*	54 Longbridge Street	(01686) 412605	llantic@powys.gov.uk
Machynlleth	Canolfan Owain Glyndwr	(01654) 702401	mactic@powys.gov.uk
Merthyr Tydfil	14a Glebeland Street	(01685) 379884	tic@merthyr.gov.uk
Milford Haven*	94 Charles Street	(01646) 690866	milford.tic@pembrokeshire.gov.uk
Mold	Earl Road	(01352) 759331	mold@nwtic.com
Monmouth	Agincourt Square	(01600) 713899	monmouth.tic@monmouthshire.gov.uk
Mumbles	Mumbles Road	(01792) 361302	info@mumblestic.co.uk
New Quay*	Church Street	(01545) 560865	newquaytic@ceredigion.gov.uk
Newport	John Frost Square	(01633) 842962	newport.tic@newport.gov.uk
Newport (pembs)*	2 Bank Cottages	(01239) 820912	info@newporttic.fsnet.co.uk
Newtown	Back Lane	(01686) 625580	newtic@powys.gov.uk
Oswestry Mile End	Mile End Services	(01691) 662488	tic@oswestry-bc.gov.uk
Oswestry Town	2 Church Terrace	(01691) 662753	ot@oswestry-welshborders.org.uk
Pembroke Ferry*	Ferry Terminal	(01646) 622753	pembrokedock.tic@pembrokeshire.gov.uk
Pembroke*	Commons Road	(01646) 622388	pembroke.tic@pembrokeshire.gov.uk
Penarth*	The Esplanade	(029) 2070 8849	tourism@valeofglamorgan.gov.uk
Pont Nedd Fechan*	Pontneathvaughan Road	(01639) 721795	pnf-tic@btconnect.com
Pontypridd	Bridge Street	(01443) 490748	tourism@pontypriddmuseum.org.uk
Porthcawl	John Street	(01656) 786639	porthcawltic@bridgend.gov.uk
Porthmadog	High Street	(01766) 512981	porthmadog.tic@gwynedd.gov.uk
Presteigne*	Broad Street	(01544) 260650	presteignetic@powys.gov.uk
Pwllheli	Station Square	(01758) 613000	pwllheli.tic@gwynedd.gov.uk
Rhayader	North Street	(01597) 810591	rhayader.tic@powys.gov.uk
Rhyl	West Parade	(01745) 355068	rhyl.tic@denbighshire.gov.uk
Ruthin	Park Road	(01824) 703992	ruthin@nwtic.com
Saundersfoot*	Harbour Car Park	(01834) 813672	saundersfoot.tic@pembrokeshire.gov.uk
St Davids	The Grove	(01437) 720392	enquiries@stdavids.pembrokeshirecoast.org.uk
Swansea	Plymouth Street	(01792) 468321	tourism@swansea.gov.uk
Tenby	The Gateway Complex	(01834) 842402	tenby.tic@pembrokeshire.gov.uk
Tywyn*	High Street	(01654) 710070	tywyn.tic@gwynedd.gov.uk
Welshpool	Church Street	(01938) 552043	weltic@powys.gov.uk
Wrexham	Lambpit Street	(01978) 292015	tic@wrexham.gov.uk

* seasonal opening

Alternatively, you can text TIC LOCATE to 64118 to find your nearest tourist information centre

Feeling the breeze across Breacon Beacons

Find out **more**

For any further information contact:

Visit Wales
Welsh Assembly Government, Brunel House,
2 Fitzalan Road, Cardiff CF24 0UY
t 0870 830 0306
   0870 121 1255 (minicom)
w visitwales.com

Travel **info**

By road:

Travelling to South and West Wales is easy on
the M4 and the dual carriageway network. The
new Second Severn Crossing gives two ways
to enter Wales, but those wishing to visit
Chepstow and the Wye Valley should use the
original Severn Bridge and the M48 (originally
part of the M4). In North Wales the A55
'Expressway' has made travelling speedier,
whilst Mid Wales is accessible via the M54
which links with the M6, M5 and M1.

By rail:

Fast and frequent Great Western Intercity trains
travel between London Paddington and Cardiff,
departing hourly and half-hourly at peak times,
and taking only two hours. Newport, Bridgend,
Port Talbot, Neath and Swansea are also
accessible through this service, which
encompasses most of West Wales.

London Euston links to the North Wales coast
via Virgin Trains, who also run a service
between the North East of England and South
Wales. In addition, Wales and West Passenger
Trains run Alphaline services from London
Waterloo, Manchester and the North East,
Brighton and the South, and Nottingham and
the Heart of England. For further rail enquiries,
please telephone 0845 748 4950.

By air:

Fly into Cardiff International Airport.

where to stay in
Wales

All place names in the blue bands are shown on the maps at the front of this guide.

Accommodation symbols
Symbols give useful information about services and facilities. Inside the back-cover flap you can find a key to these symbols. Keep it open for easy reference.

ABERAERON, Ceredigion Map ref 1A2

★★★★
HOLIDAY, TOURING
& CAMPING PARK

🚐	£12.00–£17.00
🚏	£12.00–£17.00
Å	£12.00–£17.00
100 touring pitches	

Aeron Coast Caravan Park

North Road, Aberaeron SA46 0JF **t** (01545) 570349 **e** enquiries@aeroncoast.com **w** aeroncoast.com

Flat coastal park only 500yds from the picturesque harbour and shops of Aberaeron. Quiet out of season but good facilities for families and free evening entertainment in school holidays.

payment Credit/debit cards, cash/cheques

General P 🚗 ⏻ 🍴 🚿 📻 ☉ 🛢🗑 🛁 ⌁ ☼   Leisure 🏊 📺 🍸 🎵 🎯 🎡 🎣 ⛱ 🎶 ⛳

BANGOR, Gwynedd Map ref 1A1

★★
HOLIDAY &
TOURING PARK

🚐	£12.00–£19.00
🚏	£12.00–£19.00
Å (75)	Min £7.00
🚃 (3)	Max £270.00
29 touring pitches	

Treborth Hall Farm Caravan Site

The Old Barn, Treborth Hall Farm, Bangor LL57 2RX **t** (01248) 364104 **f** (01248) 364333
e enquiries@treborthleisure.co.uk **w** treborthleisure.co.uk

Well-located site within walled area of beautiful countryside, located between Britannia and Menai Bridge on mainland, close to Snowdon, Anglesey and A55 expressway. Golf and fishing on site. Open Easter to end of September.

payment Cash/cheques

General P 🚗 🍴 📻 🛁 ⌁ ☼   Leisure 🎡 🎶 ⛳

BARMOUTH, Gwynedd Map ref 1A2

★★★★
HOLIDAY PARK

🚃 (70) £264.00–£490.00

Parc Caerelwan

Talybont, Barmouth LL43 2AX **t** (01341) 247236 **f** (01341) 247711 **e** parc@porthmadog.co.uk
w porthmadog.co.uk/parc/

Top-quality caravan-bungalows and caravans available at quiet, family-run park. Near safe, sandy beach with mountain views. Low season short breaks available. Pets welcome.

open All year
payment Credit/debit cards, cash/cheques

General 🛗 P ⏻ 📻 🛢🗑 🛁 ⌁ ☼   Leisure 🏊 🎯 🎡 ⛱ 🎶

Check it out

Information on parks listed in this guide has been supplied by proprietors. As changes may occur you should remember to check all relevant details at the time of booking.

BEAUMARIS, Isle of Anglesey Map ref 1A1

★★★
HOLIDAY, TOURING & CAMPING PARK

(55) £11.50–£13.50
(2) £11.50–£13.50
(20) £11.50–£13.50
(2) £150.00–£295.00
99 touring pitches

Kingsbridge Caravan and Camping Park

Camp Road, Llanfaes, Beaumaris LL58 8LR **t** (01248) 490636 **f** (01248) 490736
w kingsbridgecaravanpark.co.uk

A quiet, family-run park located in an Area of Outstanding Natural Beauty. We aim to provide first-class facilities for those wishing to escape the hectic pace of modern living.

payment Cash/cheques

General P Leisure

BENLLECH, Isle of Anglesey Map ref 1A1

★★★★★
TOURING PARK

(93) £11.00–£24.00
(93) £11.00–£24.00
93 touring pitches

See Ad on inside back cover

Penrhos Caravan Club Site

Brynteg, Benllech LL78 7JH **t** (01248) 852617 **w** caravanclub.co.uk

payment Credit/debit cards, cash/cheques

An ideal site for a family holiday, five minutes' drive from a safe, sandy beach. Open March to October.

From A5025, turn left onto B5110 (Llangefni). Continue straight on at crossroads. Site on right.

Special member rates mean you can save your membership subscription in less than a week. Visit our website to find out more.

General P Leisure

BRECON, Powys Map ref 1B3

★★★★
HOLIDAY, TOURING & CAMPING PARK

(60) £10.00–£14.00
(10) £10.00–£14.00
(40) £10.00–£14.00
110 touring pitches

Anchorage Caravan Park

Bronllys, Brecon LD3 0LD **t** (01874) 711246 **f** (01874) 711711 **w** anchoragecp.co.uk

High-standard family-run park. Panoramic views of the Brecon Beacons National Park. Ideal for touring and walking mid and south Wales.

open All year
payment Cash/cheques

General P Leisure

CAERNARFON, Gwynedd Map ref 1A1

Key to symbols

Open the back flap for a key to symbols.

COLWYN BAY, Conwy Map ref 1B1

★★★★★
TOURING PARK
(120) £14.00–£18.00
(10) £14.00–£18.00
130 touring pitches

Bron-Y-Wendon Touring Caravan Park

Wern Road, Llanddulas, Colwyn Bay LL22 8HG t (01492) 512903 f (01492) 512903
e stay@northwales-holidays.co.uk w northwales-holidays.co.uk

Award-winning park, all pitches overlooking the sea. Ideally situated for touring Snowdonia, Llandudno, Chester. Leave the A55 at Llanddulas, junction 23 (A547), and follow Tourist Information signs to the park.

open All year
payment Credit/debit cards, cash/cheques

General ▢⬚ P ◨ ⬚ ⬚ ⬚ ⬚ ⦿ ⬚⬚ ⬚ ☼ Leisure ⊡ ◕ ∪ ⏑

CONWY, Conwy Map ref 1B1

★★★
TOURING PARK
(320) £4.85–£17.30
(25) £4.85–£17.30
(50) £4.00–£17.30
320 touring pitches

Conwy Touring Park

Trefriw Road, Conwy LL32 8UX t (01492) 592856 f (01492) 580024

Set in spectacular scenery, the perfect location for touring Snowdonia and coastal resorts. Sheltered, wooded site with splendid views. Excellent children's facilities. Special offers. Storage available.

payment Credit/debit cards, cash/cheques

General P ◨ ⬚ ⬚ ⬚ ⦿ ⬚ ⬚ ☼ Leisure ⬚ ⬚ ⏑

CWMCARN, Newport Map ref 1B3

★★★
TOURING &
CAMPING PARK
(4) £8.50–£10.00
£8.50–£10.00
£6.00–£9.00
30 touring pitches

Cwmcarn Forest Drive and Campsite

Nantcarn Road, Cwmcarn, Newport NP11 7FA t (01495) 272001 f (01495) 271403
e cwmcarn-vc@caerphilly.gov.uk w caerphilly.gov.uk/visiting

Set amongst rolling hills and green forests, this quiet campsite is close to Cardiff, Newport and Brecon Beacons. Ideal base for touring. Mountain-bike trail, walking routes, visitor centre with new education rooms, changing rooms and lockers, cafe and gift shop on site.

open All year except Christmas and New Year
payment Credit/debit cards, cash/cheques

General P ◨ ⬚ ⬚ ⦿ ⬚ ✕ ⬚ ☼ Leisure ⏑

FISHGUARD, Pembrokeshire Map ref 1A2

★★★★
HOLIDAY, TOURING
& CAMPING PARK
£12.00–£14.00
£12.00–£14.00
(30) £11.00–£13.00
(14) £220.00–£460.00
20 touring pitches

Fishguard Bay Caravan & Camping Park

Garn Gelli, Fishguard SA65 9ET t (01348) 811415 f (01348) 811425 e enquiries@fishguardbay.com
w fishguardbay.com

Enjoy your stay on this beautiful stretch of Pembrokeshire National Park coastline. Ideal centre for walking and touring. Quiet, family-run park.

open All year except Christmas and New Year
payment Credit/debit cards, cash/cheques

General P ◨ ⬚ ⬚ ⬚ ⬚ ⬚ ⬚ ⬚ ☼ Leisure ⊡ ◕ ⬚ ∪

FISHGUARD, Pembrokeshire Map ref 1A2

★★★★
TOURING PARK
(19) £12.00–£13.00
(20) £12.00–£13.00
(8) £10.00–£11.50
28 touring pitches

Gwaun Vale Touring Park

Llanychaer, Fishguard SA65 9TA t (01348) 874698 e margaret.harries@talk21.com

Situated in the beautiful Gwaun Valley, overlooking Pembrokeshire National Park. Ideal for walking, sightseeing or just relaxing. Close to Irish ferry.

payment Cash/cheques

General ◨ ⬚ ⬚ ⬚ ⬚ ⬚ ⬚ ⬚

LLANDOVERY, Carmarthenshire Map ref 1B3

★★★★
HOLIDAY, TOURING
& CAMPING PARK

🚐(75) £10.00–£12.00
🚃(75) £10.00–£12.00
⛺(35) £10.00–£12.00
75 touring pitches

Erwlon Caravan & Camping

Brecon Road, Llandovery SA20 0RD **t** (01550) 721021 **e** peter@erwlon.fsnet.co.uk
w ukparks.com/erwlon

At the foothills of the Brecon Beacons, Erwlon provides an ideal base for touring south and west Wales and visiting the Brecon Beacons and the National Botanic Garden of Wales in particular.

open All year
payment Cash/cheques

General 🖥🛁P🔌🅿️🍴🖨📻☉📷🐾 🏇. Leisure ⛰⋃⤵🚴🏊

LLANGADOG, Carmarthenshire Map ref 1B3

★★★★
TOURING &
CAMPING PARK

🚐(60) £8.50–£10.50
🚃(60) £8.50–£10.50
⛺(28) £8.00–£10.50
88 touring pitches

Abermarlais Caravan Park

Llangadog SA19 9NG **t** (01550) 777868 & (01550) 777797 **w** ukparks.co.uk/abermarlais

payment Credit/debit cards, cash/cheques

A tranquil site in a beautiful woodland valley at the western end of the Brecon National Park, ideal for nature lovers and bird-watchers. The site's facilities are of the highest standard with excellent shower and toilet block. Camp shop and reception with comprehensive selection of groceries, gas, etc. Open March to November.

⊕ Situated on A40, 6 miles west of Llandovery or 6 miles east of Llandeilo. Signposted.

General 🖥🛁P🔌🅿️🍴📻☉📷🐾 🏇.☀ Leisure ⛰⋃⤵

LLIGWY BAY, Isle of Anglesey Map ref 1A1

★★★★★
HOLIDAY PARK

🏠(4) £140.00–£575.00

Minffordd Caravan Park

Lligwy, Dulas LL70 9HJ **t** (01248) 410678 **f** (01248) 410378 **e** enq@minffordd-holidays.com
w minffordd-holidays.com

Beautiful small garden park near Lligwy beach. Parking alongside each caravan, two of which are designed for physically disabled guests. Many local walks and cycle routes. Ideal countryside for bird-watchers. Open 1 April to 31 October.

payment Cash/cheques

General P🔌🍴📷🐾🏇.☀ Leisure ⛰⤵▸🚴🏊

LUDCHURCH, Pembrokeshire Map ref 1A3

★★★★★
HOLIDAY, TOURING
& CAMPING PARK

🚐   £15.00–£22.00
🚃   £15.00–£22.00
⛺(60) £14.00–£22.00
🏠(13) £300.00–£605.00
56 touring pitches

Little Kings Park

Amroth, Ludchurch SA67 8PG **t** (01834) 831330 **f** (01834) 831161 **e** littlekingspark@btconnect.com
w littlekings.co.uk

Quiet park with view across open land to sea. Beach 1.5 miles. Covered, heated pool; bar/restaurant; two toilet blocks; laundry; shop; mains hook-up; games room; children's play area; dog walk. Open March to January.

payment Credit/debit cards, cash/cheques

General P🔌🅿️🍴🖨📻☉📷🖨✕🐾🏇.☀ Leisure ⚓🍽🔍⛰⋃⤵▸

Check the maps

Colour maps at the front pinpoint all the places you will find accommodation entries in the regional sections. Pick your location and then refer to the place index at the back to find the page number.

NEWPORT, Newport Map ref 1B3

★★★★★
TOURING PARK

🚐 (80) £11.00–£24.00
🚎 (80) £11.00–£24.00
⛺ on application
80 touring pitches

See Ad on inside back cover

Tredegar House Country Park Caravan Club Site

Coedkernew, Newport NP10 8TW t (01633) 815600 w caravanclub.co.uk

open All year
payment Credit/debit cards, cash/cheques

High-standard site within the park, bordering one of the ornamental lakes. Just off the M4, seven miles from Cardiff. Non-members welcome.

⊕ M4 jct 28 via slip road. At roundabout turn onto A48 (signposted Tredegar House). Roundabout 0.25 miles, turn left. Next roundabout, turn left into Tredegar House.

♥ Special member rates mean you can save your membership subscription in less than a week. Visit our website to find out more.

General P 🚐 🔌 ⚙ ☎ ⊙ 🗑 🐕 ☀ Leisure ◭ ⌡ ►

ST DAVIDS, Pembrokeshire Map ref 1A3

★★★★
HOLIDAY, TOURING & CAMPING PARK

🚐 (28) £11.00–£15.50
🚎 (15) £9.00–£15.50
⛺ (77) £9.00–£12.50
🏠 (8) £190.00–£395.00
120 touring pitches

Caerfai Bay Caravan and Tent Park

St Davids, Haverfordwest SA62 6QT t (01437) 720274 f (01437) 720577 e info@caerfaibay.co.uk
w caerfaibay.co.uk

A quiet, family-run park. Turn off A487 (Haverfordwest to St Davids) in St Davids at Visitor Centre. The park is at road end, 1 mile, on the right. Signposted. Open April to mid-November.

payment Credit/debit cards, cash/cheques

General ⛓ P 🚐 🔌 ☎ ⚙ ☎ ⊙ 🗑 🐕 ☀ Leisure ⌡ ► ⛵

ST DAVIDS, Pembrokeshire Map ref 1A3

★★★★
TOURING PARK

🚐 (120) £11.00–£24.00
🚎 (120) £11.00–£24.00
120 touring pitches

See Ad on inside back cover

Lleithyr Meadow Caravan Club Site

Whitesands, St Davids SA62 6PR t (01437) 720401 w caravanclub.co.uk

payment Credit/debit cards, cash/cheques

Set on a peninsula, surrounded by the Pembrokeshire Coast National Park with its wonderful walks, wild coves and sandy bays. Visit the picturesque harbour village of Solva. Open March to October.

⊕ M4 to Carmarthen, A40 to Haverfordwest, A487 towards St Davids. Before entering St Davids turn right onto B4583, crossroads. Turn sharp right opposite entrance to St Davids golf club. Signposted.

♥ Special member rates mean you can save your membership subscription in less than a week. Visit our website to find out more.

General P 🚐 🔌 ☎ ⚙ ⊙ 🗑 🐕 Leisure ◭ ⌡ ►

enjoyEngland.com

★★★
TOURING PARK

British Graded
Holiday Parks Scheme

On the following pages you will find an exclusive listing of every park in England assessed under the British Graded Holiday Parks Scheme.

The information includes brief contact details together with its star rating and designator. The listing also shows if an establishment has a National Accessible rating or participates in the Walkers and Cyclists Welcome schemes (see the front of the guide for further information). Parks are listed by region and then alphabetically by place name. They may be located in, or a short distance from, the places in the blue bands.

More detailed information on all the places shown in black can be found in the regional sections (where parks have paid to have their details included). To find these entries please refer to the park index at the back of this guide.

The list which follows was compiled slightly later than the regional sections. For this reason you may find that, in a few instances, a star rating may differ between the two sections. This list contains the most up-to-date information and was correct at the time of going to press. Please note that it does not include parks in Scotland and Wales.

Holiday Villages

At the end of this section you will find details of quality-assessed holiday villages.

ENGLAND'S NORTHWEST

AINSDALE
Merseyside

Willowbank Holiday Home and Touring Park ★★★★★
Holiday & Touring Park
Coastal Road, Ainsdale,
Southport PR8 3ST
t (01704) 571566

ALLONBY
Cumbria

Manor House Caravan Park ★★★
Holiday, Touring & Camping Park
Edderside Road, Allonby,
Maryport CA15 6RA
t (01900) 881236
e holidays@manorhousepark.co.uk
w manorhousepark.co.uk

Spring Lea Caravan Park ★★★★
Holiday, Touring & Camping Park
Main Road, Allonby, Maryport
CA15 6QF
t (01900) 881331

AMBLESIDE
Cumbria

Greenhowe Caravan Park ★★★★
Holiday Park
Great Langdale, Ambleside
LA22 9JU
t (015394) 37231

Skelwith Fold Caravan Park ★★★★★
Holiday & Touring Park
Skelwith Fold, Ambleside
LA22 0HX
t (015394) 32277
e info@skelwith.com
w skelwith.com

APPLEBY-IN-WESTMORLAND
Cumbria

Wild Rose Park ★★★★★
Holiday, Touring & Camping Park
Ormside, Appleby-in-Westmorland CA16 6EJ
t (01768) 351077

ARMATHWAITE
Cumbria

Englethwaite Hall Caravan Club Site ★★★★
Touring Park
Armathwaite, Carlisle CA4 9SY
t (01228) 560202
w caravanclub.co.uk

BASSENTHWAITE
Cumbria

Bassenthwaite Lakeside Lodges ★★★★★
Holiday Park
Scarness, Keswick CA12 4QZ
t (01768) 776641
e enquiries@bll.ac
w bll.ac

BLACKPOOL
Lancashire

Marton Mere Holiday Village ★★★★
Holiday & Touring Park
Mythop Road, Blackpool
FY4 4XN
t (01253) 767544
w martonmere-park.co.uk

Newton Hall Caravan Park ★★★★
Holiday & Touring Park
Staining Road, Blackpool
FY3 0AX
t (01253) 882512
e reception@newtonhall.net
w partingtons.com

Windy Harbour Holiday Centre ★★★
Holiday, Touring & Camping Park
Windy Harbour Road,
Singleton, Poulton le Fylde
FY6 8NB
t (01253) 883064
e info@windyharbour.net
w windyharbour.net

BOTHEL
Cumbria

Skiddaw View Holiday Park ★★★★
Holiday Park
Bassenthwaite, Keswick
CA7 2JG
t (01697) 320919
e office@skiddawview.com
w skiddawview.co.uk

BOUTH
Cumbria

Black Beck Caravan Park ★★★★★ ROSE AWARD
Holiday & Touring Park
Bouth, Ulverston LA12 8JN
t (01229) 861274
e reception@blackbeck.com

BRAMPTON
Cumbria

Cairndale Caravan Park ★★★
Holiday & Touring Park
Cumwhitton, Headsnook,
Brampton CA8 9BZ
t (01768) 896280

BRAYSTONES
Cumbria

Tarnside Caravan Park ★★★★
Holiday & Touring Park
Braystones, Beckermet,
Egremont CA21 2YL
t (01946) 841308
w ukparks.co.uk/tarnside

BURY
Greater Manchester

Burrs Country Park Caravan Club Site ★★★★★
Touring Park
Woodhill Road, Bury BL8 1BN
t (0161) 761 0489
w caravanclub.co.uk

CABUS
Lancashire

Claylands Caravan Park ★★★★
Holiday, Touring & Camping Park
Claylands Farm, Preston
PR3 1AJ
t (01524) 791242
e alan@claylands-caravan-park.co.uk
w claylands-caravan-park.co.uk

CAPERNWRAY
Lancashire

Old Hall Caravan Park ★★★★★
Holiday & Touring Park
Carnforth LA6 1AD
t (01524) 733276

CARLISLE
Cumbria

Dalston Hall Caravan Park ★★★★
Holiday, Touring & Camping Park
Dalston Hall, Dalston, Carlisle
CA5 7JX
t (01228) 710165
w dalstonhall.co.uk

Dandy Dinmont Caravan and Camping Site ★★★★
Touring & Camping Park
Blackford, Carlisle CA6 4EA
t (01228) 674611
e dandydinmont@btopenworld.com
w caravan-camping-carlisle.itgo.com

CARNFORTH
Lancashire

Netherbeck Holiday Home Park ★★★★★
Holiday Park
North Road, Carnforth
LA5 9NG
t (01524) 735133
e info@netherbeck.co.uk
w netherbeck.co.uk

Redwell Fisheries ★★★
Touring & Camping Park
Kirkby Lonsdale Road,
Carnforth LA6 1BQ
t (01524) 221979
e kenanddiane@redwellfisheries.co.uk
w redwellfisheries.co.uk

CHESTER
Cheshire

Chester Fairoaks Caravan Club Site ★★★★★
Touring & Camping Park
Rake Lane, Little Stanney,
Chester CH2 4HS
t (0151) 355 1600
e firtrees@chester-holidays.co.uk
w chester-holidays.co.uk

CHRISTLETON
Cheshire

Park Fields Farm
Rating Applied For
Holiday, Touring & Camping Park
Parkfields Farm, Plough Lane,
Chester CH3 7BA
t (01244) 335002

CLITHEROE
Lancashire

The Camping and Caravanning Club Site Clitheroe ★★★★
Touring & Camping Park
Edisford Road, Clitheroe
BB7 3LA
t (01200) 425294
w campingandcaravanningclub.co.uk

COCKERHAM
Lancashire

Moss Wood Caravan Park ★★★★★
Holiday & Touring Park
Crimbles Lane, Lancaster
LA2 0ES
t (01524) 791041

COCKERMOUTH
Cumbria

Violet Bank Holiday Home Park ★★★★
Holiday Park
Simonscales Lane,
Cockermouth CA13 9TG
t (01900) 822169
w violetbank.co.uk

CODDINGTON
Cheshire

Manor Wood Country Caravan Park ★★★★
Touring & Camping Park
Manor Wood, Coddington,
Chester CH3 9EN
t (01829) 782990
e info@manorwoodcaravans.co.uk

CONISTON
Cumbria

Crake Valley Holiday Park ★★★★★ ROSE AWARD
Holiday Park
Lake Bank, Water Yeat,
Ulverston LA12 8DL
t (01229) 885203
e crakevalley@coniston1.fslife.co.uk
w crakevalley.co.uk

Park Coppice Caravan Club Site ★★★★★
Touring Park
Park Gate, Coniston LA21 8LA
t (015394) 41555
w caravanclub.co.uk

ENDMOOR
Cumbria

Gatebeck Park ★★★★★
Holiday Park
Gatebeck Road, Endmoor,
Kendal LA8 0HL
t (015395) 67875

ESKDALE
Cumbria

Fisherground Farm Campsite ★★★
Camping Park
Eskdale CA19 1TF
t (01946) 723349
e camping@
fishergroundcampsite.co.uk
w fishergroundcampsite.co.uk

FLEETWOOD
Lancashire

Cala Gran ★★★★
Holiday Park
Fleetwood Road, Fleetwood
FY7 8JX
t (01253) 872555
e enquiries@british-holidays.
co.uk
w british-holidays.co.uk

FLOOKBURGH
Cumbria

Lakeland Leisure Park ★★★★
Holiday, Touring & Camping Park
Moor Lane, Flookburgh,
Grange-over-Sands LA11 7LT
t (015395) 58556
w lakeland-park.co.uk

FRODSHAM
Cheshire

Ridgeway Country Holiday Park ★★★★
Holiday Park
The Ridgeway, Frodsham
WA6 6XQ
t (01928) 734981
e sue@ridgewaypark.com
w ridgewaypark.com

GILCRUX
Cumbria

The Beeches Caravan Park ★★★★
Holiday Park
Gilcrux, Wigton, Cockermouth
CA7 2QX
t (01697) 321555
e holiday@
thebeechescaravanpark.com
w thebeechescaravanpark.com

GRANGE-OVER-SANDS
Cumbria

Greaves Farm Caravan Park ★★★★ ROSE AWARD
Holiday & Touring Park
Field Broughton, Grange-over-
Sands LA11 6HR
t (015395) 36329 &
(015395) 36587

Meathop Fell Caravan Club Site ★★★★★
Touring Park
Meathop, Grange-over-Sands
LA11 6RB
t (015395) 32912
w caravanclub.co.uk

HAWKSHEAD
Cumbria

The Croft Caravan and Camp Site ★★★★
Holiday, Touring & Camping Park
North Lonsdale Road,
Hawkshead, Ambleside
LA22 0NX
t (015394) 36374
e enquiries@hawkshead-croft.
com
w hawkshead-croft.com

HEYSHAM
Lancashire

Ocean Edge Leisure Park ★★★
Holiday, Touring & Camping Park
Moneyclose Lane, Morecambe
LA3 2XA
t (01524) 781695

HEYWOOD
Greater Manchester

Gelder Wood Country Park ★★★★★
Touring & Camping Park
Oak Leigh Cottage, Ashworth
Road, Rochdale OL11 5UP
t (01706) 364858

HOLMROOK
Cumbria

Seven Acres Caravan Park
Rating Applied For
Holiday & Touring Park
Holmrook, Ravenglass
CA19 1YD
t (01946) 822777
e reception@seacote.com
w sevenacres.info

KENDAL
Cumbria

Camping & Caravanning Club – Kendal ★★★★
Touring Park
Millcrest, Shap Road, Kendal
LA9 6NY
t 0845 130 7633
w campingandcaravanning
club.co.uk

Low Park Wood Caravan Club Site ★★★★
Touring Park
Sedgwick, Kendal LA8 0JZ
t (015395) 60186
w caravanclub.co.uk

Waters Edge Caravan Park ★★★★
Holiday, Touring & Camping Park
Crooklands, Milnthorpe
LA7 7NN
t (015395) 67708
w watersedgecaravanpark.co.
uk

KESWICK
Cumbria

Camping & Caravanning Club – Derwentwater ★★★★
Touring & Camping Park
Crow Park Road, Keswick
CA12 5EN
t 0845 130 7633
w campingandcaravanning
club.co.uk

Camping & Caravanning Club – Keswick ★★★★
Holiday & Touring Park
Crow Park Road, Keswick
CA12 5EP
t 0845 130 7633
w campingandcaravanning
club.co.uk

Castlerigg Farm Camping & Caravan Site ★★★★
Touring & Camping Park
Castlerigg, Keswick CA12 4TE
t (017687) 72479
e info@castleriggfarm.com
w castleriggfarm.com

Castlerigg Hall Caravan & Camping Park ★★★★
Holiday, Touring & Camping Park
Castlerigg Hall, Keswick
CA12 4TE
t (017687) 74499
e info@castlerigg.co.uk
w castlerigg.co.uk

Low Briery Holiday Village ★★★★
Holiday Park
Low Briery Village, Keswick
CA12 4RN
t (01768) 772044
e lowbriery@wyrenet.co.uk
w keswick.uk.com

Scotgate Holiday Park ★★★★
Holiday, Touring & Camping Park
Braithwaite, Keswick CA12 5TF
t (01768) 778343
e info@scotgateholidaypark.
co.uk
w scotgateholidaypark.co.uk

KIRKBY LONSDALE
Cumbria

Woodclose Caravan Park ★★★★★
Holiday, Touring & Camping Park
Kirkby Lonsdale LA6 2SE
t (01524) 271597
e info@woodclosepark.com
w woodclosepark.com

KIRKBY STEPHEN
Cumbria

Pennine View Caravan Park ★★★★★
Touring & Camping Park
Station Road, Kirkby Stephen
CA17 4SZ
t (017683) 71717
e pennineviewcaravanpark@
googlemail.com

KIRKHAM
Lancashire

Mowbreck Holiday and Residential Park ★★★★★
Holiday Park
Mowbreck Lane, Preston
PR4 3HA
t (01772) 682494

LAMPLUGH
Cumbria

Dockray Meadow Caravan Club Site ★★★★
Touring Park
Lamplugh CA14 4SH
t (01946) 861357
w caravanclub.co.uk

Inglenook Caravan Park ★★★★
Holiday, Touring & Camping Park
Lamplugh, Workington
CA14 4SH
t (01946) 861240

LANCASTER
Lancashire

New Parkside Farm Caravan Park ★★★
Touring & Camping Park
Denny Beck, Lancaster
LA2 9HH
t (01524) 770723
w ukparks.co.uk/newparkside

LONGRIDGE
Lancashire

Beacon Fell View ★★★
Holiday, Touring & Camping Park
Higher Road, Longridge,
Preston PR3 2TF
t (01772) 783233

LOUGHRIGG
Cumbria

Neaum Crag ★★★★★
Holiday Park
Loughrigg, Ambleside
LA22 9HG
t (015394) 33221
e neaumcrag@ktdbroadband.
com
w neaumcrag.co.uk

LYTHAM ST ANNES
Lancashire

Eastham Hall Caravan Park ★★★★
Holiday & Touring Park
Saltcotes Road, Lytham St
Annes FY8 4LS
t (01253) 737907

MILNTHORPE
Cumbria

Fell End Caravan Park ★★★★★
Holiday, Touring & Camping Park
Slack Head Road, Hale,
Milnthorpe LA7 7BS
t (015395) 62122
e enquiries@southlakeland-
caravans.co.uk
w southlakeland-caravans.co.
uk

MORECAMBE
Lancashire

Regent Leisure Park ★★★★
Holiday Park
Westgate, Morecambe
LA3 3DF
t (01524) 781695

Venture Caravan Park
★★★★
Holiday, Touring & Camping Park
Langridge Way, Westgate, Morecambe LA4 4TQ
t (01524) 412986

Westgate Caravan Park
★★★★
Holiday & Touring Park
Westgate, Morecambe
LA3 3DE
t (01524) 411448

NETHER KELLET
Lancashire

The Hawthorns Caravan Park ★★★★★
Holiday Park
Nether Kellet, Carnforth
LA6 1EA
t (01524) 732079

NEW HUTTON
Cumbria

Ashes Exclusively Adult Caravan Park ★★★★★
Touring Park
New Hutton, Kendal LA8 0AS
t (015397) 31833
e info@ashescaravanpark.co.uk
w ashescaravanpark.co.uk

NEWBY BRIDGE
Cumbria

Newby Bridge Country Caravan Park ★★★★★
ROSE AWARD
Holiday Park
Canny Hill, Newby Bridge
LA12 8NF
t (015395) 31030
e info@cumbriancaravans.co.uk
w cumbriancaravans.co.uk

NEWLANDS
Cumbria

Low Manesty Caravan Club Site ★★★★
Holiday & Camping Park
Manesty, Keswick CA12 5UG
t (01768) 777275
w caravanclub.co.uk

ORTON
Cumbria

Westmorland Caravan Site
★★★★
Holiday & Touring Park
Orton, Penrith CA10 3SB
t (01539) 711322
e caravans@westmorland.com
w tebaycaravanpark.co.uk

PENRITH
Cumbria

Flusco Wood Caravan Park
★★★★★
Holiday & Touring Park
Flusco, Penrith CA11 0JB
t (017684) 80020
e admin@fluscowood.co.uk
w fluscowood.co.uk

Lowther Holiday Park
★★★★★
Holiday, Touring & Camping Park
Eamont Bridge, Penrith
CA10 2JB
t (01768) 863631
e info@lowther-holidaypark.co.uk
w lowther-holidaypark.co.uk

Troutbeck Head Caravan Club Site ★★★★★
Touring Park
Troutbeck, Penrith CA11 0SS
t (01768) 483521
w caravanclub.co.uk

PILLING
Lancashire

Fold House Caravan Park
★★★★★
Holiday Park
Head Dyke Lane, Pilling, Preston PR3 6SJ
t (01253) 790267

PLANTATION BRIDGE
Cumbria

Camping & Caravanning Club – Windermere
★★★★★
Holiday, Touring & Camping Park
Ashes Lane, Staveley, Windermere LA8 9JS
t 0845 130 7633
w campingandcaravanningclub.co.uk

POOLEY BRIDGE
Cumbria

Waterside House Campsite
★★★★
Camping Park
Waterside House, Howtown, Penrith CA10 2NA
t (017684) 86332
e enquire@watersidefarm-campsite.co.uk
w watersidefarm-campsite.co.uk

RIMINGTON
Lancashire

Rimington Caravan Park
★★★★★
Holiday, Touring & Camping Park
Hardacre Lane, Gisburn, N Clitheroe BB7 4EE
t (01200) 445355

ROCHDALE
Greater Manchester

Hollingworth Lake Caravan Park ★★★
Holiday, Touring & Camping Park
Roundhouse Farm, Hollingworth Lake, Littleborough OL15 0AT
t (01706) 378661

ST BEES
Cumbria

Seacote Park Caravan & Camping ★★★★
Holiday, Touring & Camping Park
The Beach, St Bees CA27 0ET
t (01946) 822777
e reception@seacote.com
w seacote.com

ST MICHAEL'S ON WYRE
Lancashire

Wyreside Farm Park ★★★
Holiday, Touring & Camping Park
Allotment Lane, St Michaels, Preston PR3 0TZ
t (01524) 792093
e penny.wyresidefarm@freenet.co.uk
w riverparks.co.uk

SCARISBRICK
Lancashire

Hurlston Hall Country Caravan Park ★★★★
Holiday & Touring Park
Southport Road, Ormskirk L40 8HB
t (01704) 841064

SILLOTH
Cumbria

Seacote Caravan Park
★★★★
Holiday & Touring Park
Skinburness Road, Silloth CA7 4QJ
t (01697) 331121

Solway Holiday Village ★★
Holiday & Touring Park
Skinburness Drive, Silloth, Wigton CA7 4QQ
t (016973) 31236
e solway@hagansleisure.co.uk
w hagansleisure.co.uk

Stanwix Park Holiday Centre
★★★★★
Holiday, Touring & Camping Park
Greenrow, Silloth CA7 4HH
t (01697) 332666
e enquiries@stanwix.com
w stanwix.com

Tanglewood Caravan Park
★★★
Holiday, Touring & Camping Park
Causewayhead, Silloth CA7 4PE
t (01697) 331253
e tanglewoodcaravanpar@hotmail.com
w tanglewoodcaravanpark.co.uk

SILVERDALE
Lancashire

Far Arnside Caravan Park
★★★★★
Holiday Park
Holgates Caravan Parks Ltd, Middlebarrow Plain, Carnforth LA5 0SH
t (01524) 701508
e caravan@holgates.co.uk
w holgates.co.uk

Holgates Caravan Park
★★★★★
Holiday, Touring & Camping Park
Cove Road, Silverdale, Carnforth LA5 0SH
t (01524) 701508
e caravan@holgates.co.uk
w holgates.co.uk

SKELTON
Cumbria

Upfront Caravans
Rating Applied For
Touring & Camping Park
Unthank, Nr Hutton-in-The - Forest, Penrith CA11 9TG
t (01768) 484538
e john.f.parkinson@btinternet.com
w up-front.com

THURSTASTON
Merseyside

Wirral Country Park Caravan Club Site ★★★★
Touring & Camping Park
Station Road, Wirral CH61 0HN
t (0151) 648 5228
w caravanclub.co.uk

TOSSIDE
Lancashire

Crowtrees Park ★★★★★
Holiday Park
Tosside, Skipton BD23 4SD
t (01729) 840278
e hol@crowtreespark.co.uk
w crowtreespark.co.uk

ULLSWATER
Cumbria

Quiet Site Caravan Park
★★★★★
Holiday, Touring & Camping Park
Ullswater, Penrith CA11 0LS
t (01768) 486337
e info@thequietsite.fsnet.co.uk
w thequietsite.co.uk

Waterfoot Caravan Park
★★★★★
Holiday & Touring Park
Pooley Bridge, Ullswater, Penrith CA11 0JF
t (017684) 86302
e enquiries@waterfootpark.co.uk
w waterfootpark.co.uk

ULVERSTON
Cumbria

Bardsea Leisure Park
★★★★
Holiday & Touring Park
Priory Road, Ulverston
LA12 9QE
t (01229) 584712

WARRINGTON
Cheshire

Holly Bank Caravan Park
★★★★
Touring Park
Warburton Bridge Road,
Rixton, Warrington WA3 6HL
t (0161) 775 2842

WASDALE
Cumbria

Church Stile Holiday Park
★★★★
Holiday, Touring & Camping Park
Church Stile Farm, Wasdale
CA20 1ET
t (01946) 726252
e churchstile@campfarm.fsnet.co.uk
w churchstile.com

WATERMILLOCK
Cumbria

Cove Caravan And Camping Park ★★★★★
Holiday, Touring & Camping Park
Watermillock, Ullswater
CA11 0LS
t (01768) 486549
e info@cove-park.co.uk
w cove-park.co.uk

WEST BRADFORD
Lancashire

Three Rivers Woodland Park
★★★
Holiday, Touring & Camping Park
Eaves Hall Lane, Clitheroe
BB7 3JG
t (01200) 423523
e enquiries@threeriverspark.co.uk
w threeriverspark.co.uk

WHITEGATE
Cheshire

Lamb Cottage Caravan Park
★★★★★
Touring Park
Dalefords Lane, Northwich
CW8 2BN
t (01606) 882302

WINDERMERE
Cumbria

Braithwaite Fold Caravan Club Site ★★★★
Touring Park
Glebe Road, Bowness-on-Windermere, Windermere
LA23 3GZ
t (015394) 42177
w caravanclub.co.uk

Fallbarrow Park ★★★★★
Holiday & Touring Park
Rayrigg Road, Bowness-on-Windermere, Windermere
LA23 3DL
t (015394) 44422
e enquiries@southlakeland-caravans.co.uk
w southlakeland-caravans.co.uk

Hill of Oaks and Blakeholme Caravans ★★★★★
Holiday & Touring Park
Tower Wood, Windermere
LA23 3PJ
t (015395) 31578
e enquiries@hillofoaks.co.uk
w hillofoaks.co.uk

Limefitt Park ★★★★★
Holiday, Touring & Camping Park
Patterdale Road, Windermere
LA23 1PA
t (015394) 32300
e enquiries@southlakeland-caravans.co.uk
w southlakeland-caravans.co.uk

Park Cliffe Caravan and Camping Estate ★★★★★
Holiday, Touring & Camping Park
Birks Road, Windermere
LA23 3PG
t (015395) 31344
e info@parkcliffe.co.uk
w parkcliffe.co.uk

White Cross Bay Holiday Park and Marina ★★★★★
Holiday & Touring Park
Ambleside Road, Troutbeck Bridge, Windermere LA23 1LF
t (015394) 43937
e enquiries@southlakeland-caravans.co.uk
w southlakeland-caravans.co.uk

WINSFORD
Cheshire

Elm Cottage Caravan Park
★★★
Touring & Camping Park
Chester Lane, Little Budworth,
Winsford CW7 2QJ
t (01829) 760544
e chris@elmcottagecp.co.uk
w elmcottagecp.co.uk

Lakeside Caravan Park
★★★★
Holiday Park
Stocks Hill, Winsford CW7 4EF
t (01606) 861043
e enquiries@thornleyleisure.co.uk

NORTH EAST ENGLAND

ALNWICK
Northumberland

Alnwick Rugby Football Club ★
Touring & Camping Park
Greensfield, Alnwick
NE66 1BG
t (01665) 602342

ASHINGTON
Northumberland

Wansbeck Riverside Park Caravan and Camp Site ★★
Touring & Camping Park
Wansbeck Riverside Park,
Ashington NE63 8TX
t (01670) 812323
e traceyproudlock@fsmail.net
w wansbeck.gov.uk

BAMBURGH
Northumberland

Bradford Kaims Caravan Park ★★
Holiday, Touring & Camping Park
Bradford House, Bamburgh
NE70 7JT
t (01668) 213432
e lwrob@tiscali.co.uk
w bradford-leisure.co.uk

Glororum Caravan Park
★★★
Holiday, Touring & Camping Park
Glororum, Bamburgh
NE69 7AW
t (01668) 214457
e info@glororum-caravanpark.co.uk
w glororum-caravanpark.co.uk

Meadowhead's Waren Caravan and Camping Park ★★★★ ROSE AWARD
Holiday, Touring & Camping Park
Waren Mill, Belford NE70 7EE
t (01668) 214366
e waren@meadowhead.co.uk
w meadowhead.co.uk

BARDON MILL
Northumberland

Winshields Camp Site ★★★
Camping Park
Bardon Mill, Hexham
NE47 7AN
t (01434) 344243

BEADNELL
Northumberland

The Camping And Caravanning Site Beadnell Bay ★★
Touring & Camping Park
The Camping and Caravanning Club Site, Chathill NE67 5BX
t (01665) 720586
w campingandcaravanning club.co.uk

BEAL
Northumberland

Haggerston Castle ★★★★★
Holiday, Touring & Camping Park
Haggerston, Berwick-upon-Tweed TD15 2PA
t (01289) 381333
e enquiries@british-holidays.co.uk
w haggerstoncastle-park.co.uk

BEAMISH
County Durham

Bobby Shafto Caravan Park
★★★★
Holiday, Touring & Camping Park
Money Hills, Stanley DH9 0RY
t (01913) 701776
e jeffharlepeel@hotmail.com
w ukparks.co.uk/bobbyshafto

BELFORD
Northumberland

South Meadows Caravan Park ★★★★★
Holiday, Touring & Camping Park
South Meadows, Belford
NE70 7DP
t (01668) 213326
e G.McL@btinternet.com
w southmeadows.co.uk

BELLINGHAM
Northumberland

Brown Rigg Caravan & Camping Park ★★★★
Touring & Camping Park
Tweed House, Hexham
NE48 2JY
t (01434) 220175
e enquiries@northumberlandcaravanparks.com
w northumberlandcaravanparks.com

Demesne Farm Campsite
★★
Touring & Camping Park
Demesne Farm, Hexham
NE48 2BS
t (01434) 220258
e stay@demesnefarmcampsite.co.uk
w demesnefarmcampsite.co.uk

BERWICK-UPON-TWEED
Northumberland

Beachcomber Campsite ★★
Touring & Camping Park
Goswick, Berwick-upon-Tweed
TD15 2RW
t (01289) 381217
e johngregson@micro-plus-web.net

Berwick Holiday Park
★★★★★
Holiday Park
Magdalene Fields, Berwick-upon-Tweed TD15 1NE
t (01289) 307113
e berwick@bourne-leisure.co.uk
w british-holidays.co.uk

Seaview Caravan Club Site
★★★★★
Touring & Camping Park
Billendean Road, Spittal,
Berwick-upon-Tweed
TD15 1QU
t (01289) 305198
w caravanclub.co.uk

BLACKHALL COLLIERY
County Durham

Crimdon Dene Holiday Park
★★
Holiday & Touring Park
Coast Road, Hartlepool
TS27 4BN
t (01429) 267801
w park-resorts.com

CASTLESIDE
County Durham

Manor Park Caravan Park
★★
Holiday, Touring & Camping Park
Broadmeadows, Rippon Burn,
Consett DH8 9HD
t (01207) 501000

CORBRIDGE
Northumberland

**Well House Farm –
Corbridge ★★★**
Touring & Camping Park
Newton, Stocksfield NE43 7UY
t (01661) 842193
e info@wellhousefarm.co.uk
w wellhousefarm.co.uk

COTHERSTONE
County Durham

Doe Park Caravan Site
★★★★
Touring & Camping Park
Cotherstone, Barnard Castle
DL12 9UQ
t (01833) 650302

CRASTER
Northumberland

Proctors Stead Caravan Site
★★★
Holiday, Touring & Camping Park
Dunstan Village, Dunstan,
Alnwick NE66 3TF
t (01665) 576613

CRESSWELL
Northumberland

**Cresswell Towers Holiday
Park ★★★**
Holiday Park
Cresswell, Morpeth NE61 5JT
t 0870 442 9311
e holidaysales.
cresswelltowers@
gbholidayparks.co.uk
w gbholidayparks.co.uk

Golden Sands Holiday Park
★★★★★
Holiday Park
Beach Road, Morpeth
NE61 5LF
t (01670) 860256
e enquiries@
northumbrianleisure.co.uk
w northumbrianleisure.co.uk

DARLINGTON
Tees Valley

**Newbus Grange Country
Park ★★★★**
Touring & Camping Park
Hurworth Road, Darlington
DL2 1PE
t (01325) 720973

DUNSTAN
Northumberland

**Camping and Caravan Club
Site Dunstan Hill ★★★★**
Touring & Camping Park
Dunstan, Alnwick NE66 3TQ
t (01665) 576310
w campingandcaravanning
club.co.uk

DURHAM
County Durham

**Finchale Abbey Caravan
Park ★★★**
Touring Park
Finchale Abbey Farm, Finchale
Abbey, Durham DH1 5SH
t (0191) 386528
e godricawatson@hotmail.com
w finchaleabbey.co.uk

Grange Caravan Club Site
★★★★★
Touring & Camping Park
Meadow Lane, Durham
DH1 1TL
t (0191) 384 4778
w caravanclub.co.uk

**Strawberry Hill Farm
Camping & Caravanning
Park ★★★★ ROSE AWARD**
*Holiday, Touring & Camping
Park*
Running Waters, Old Cassop,
Durham DH6 4QA
t (0191) 372 3457
e howarddunkerley@
strawberryhillfarm.freeserve.
co.uk
w strawberry-hill-farm.co.uk

EAST ORD
Northumberland

Ord House Country Park
★★★★★
*Holiday, Touring & Camping
Park*
East Ord, Berwick-upon-Tweed
TD15 2NS
t (01289) 305288
e enquiries@ordhouse.co.uk
w ordhouse.co.uk

EBCHESTER
County Durham

Byreside Caravan Site
★★★★
Touring & Camping Park
Hamsterley Colliery, Newcastle
upon Tyne NE17 7RT
t (01207) 560280

FELTON
Northumberland

Bockenfield Country Park
Rating Applied For
Holiday & Touring Park
Bockenfield, Felton, Morpeth
NE65 9QJ
t (01670) 786010
e bockenfieldpark@aol.com
w bockenfieldcountrypark.co.
uk

FIR TREE
County Durham

**Harperley 'Prisoner of War'
Caravan Site ★★**
Holiday & Camping Park
Fir Tree, Crook DL15 8DX
t (01388) 767098
e info@powcamp.com
w powcamp.com

GREENHEAD
Northumberland

Roam-n-Rest Caravan Park
★★★
Touring & Camping Park
Raylton House, Greenhead,
Brampton CA8 7HA
t (01697) 747213

HALTWHISTLE
Northumberland

**Camping & Caravanning
Club Site Haltwhistle**
★★★★
Touring & Camping Park
Burnfoot Park Village,
Haltwhistle NE49 0JP
t (01434) 320106
w campingandcaravanning
club.co.uk

HAYDON BRIDGE
Northumberland

**Poplars Riverside Caravan
Park ★★★★**
*Holiday, Touring & Camping
Park*
East Lands East, Hexham
NE47 6BY
t (01434) 684427

HEXHAM
Northumberland

**Fallowfield Dene Caravan
and Camping Park ★★★★**
Touring & Camping Park
Acomb, Hexham NE46 4RP
t (01434) 603553
e den@fallowfielddene.co.uk
w fallowfielddene.co.uk

**Hexham Racecourse
Caravan Site ★★★**
Touring & Camping Park
Yarridge Road, High Yarridge,
Hexham NE46 2JP
t (01434) 606847
e hexrace@aol.com
w hexham-racecourse.co.uk

KIELDER
Northumberland

**Kielder Caravan & Camping
Site ★★★**
Touring & Camping Park
Kielder Campsite, Kielder,
Hexham NE48 1EJ
t (01434) 250291
e kielder.campsite@
btopenworld.com
w kieldervillage.co.uk

**Kielder Water Caravan Club
Site ★★★★**
Touring & Camping Park
Leaplish Waterside Park,
Falstone, Hexham NE48 1AX
t (01434) 250278
w caravanclub.co.uk

LARTINGTON
County Durham

**Camping and Caravanning
Club Site Barnard Castle**
★★★★
Touring & Camping Park
Dockenflats Lane, Barnard
Castle DL12 9DG
t (01833) 630228
w campingandcaravanning
club.co.uk

LONGHORSLEY
Northumberland

Forget-Me-Not Holiday Park
★★★★
*Holiday, Touring & Camping
Park*
Croftside, Morpeth NE65 8QY
t (01670) 788364
e info@forget-me-
notholidaypark.co.uk
w forget-me-notholidaypark.
co.uk

LOWICK
Northumberland

Barmoor South Moor ★★★
Holiday Park
Lowick, Berwick-upon-Tweed
TD15 2QF
t (01289) 388205
e barryandanngold@aol.com

North East England/Yorkshire

MELKRIDGE
Northumberland

Hadrian's Wall Caravan and Camping Site ★★★
Touring & Camping Park
Melkridge Tilery, Haltwhistle
NE49 9PG
t (01434) 320495
e info@romanwallcamping.co.uk
w romanwallcamping.co.uk

NEWBIGGIN-BY-THE-SEA
Northumberland

Church Point Holiday Park ★★
Holiday & Touring Park
Newbiggin-by-the-Sea
NE64 6DP
t (01670) 817443
w park-resorts.com

NEWTON-BY-THE-SEA
Northumberland

Newton Hall Caravan Park ★★★★
Holiday & Touring Park
Newton-by-the-Sea, Alnwick
NE66 3DZ
t (01665) 576239
e ianpatterson@newtonholidays.co.uk
w newtonholidays.co.uk

NORTH SEATON
Northumberland

Sandy Bay Holiday Park ★★
Holiday, Touring & Camping Park
Ashington NE63 9YD
t 0870 442 9310
e holidaysales.sandybay@park-resorts.com
w park-resorts.com

OTTERBURN
Northumberland

Border Forest Caravan Park ★★★★
Holiday, Touring & Camping Park
Cottonshopeburnfoot,
Rochester, Otterburn NE19 1TF
t (01830) 520259
w borderforest.com

OVINGHAM
Northumberland

The High Hermitage Caravan Park ★★★
Holiday & Touring Park
The Hermitage, Main Road,
Ovingham, Prudhoe NE42 6HH
t (01661) 832250
e highhermitage@onetel.com

POWBURN
Northumberland

River Breamish Caravan Club Site ★★★★★
Touring & Camping Park
Powburn, Alnwick NE66 4HY
t (01665) 578320
w caravanclub.co.uk

RAMSHAW
County Durham

Craggwood Caravan Park ★★★
Holiday, Touring & Camping Park
Gordon Lane, Ramshaw,
Bishop Auckland DL14 0NS
t (01388) 835866
e billy6482@btopenworld.com
w craggwoodcaravanpark.co.uk

ROTHBURY
Northumberland

Coquetdale Caravan Park ★★★
Holiday & Touring Park
Whitton, Rothbury, Morpeth
NE65 7RU
t (01669) 620549
e enquiry@coquetdalecaravanpark.co.uk
w coquetdalecaravanpark.co.uk

Nunnykirk Caravan Club Site ★★★
Touring Park
Nunnykirk, Morpeth NE61 4PZ
t (01669) 620762
w caravanclub.co.uk

SEAHOUSES
Northumberland

Seafield Caravan Park ★★★★★ ROSE AWARD
Holiday & Touring Park
Seafield Road, Seahouses
NE68 7SP
t (01665) 720628
e info@seafieldpark.co.uk
w seafieldpark.co.uk

SOUTH SHIELDS
Tyne and Wear

Lizard Lane Camping & Caravan Site ★★★
Holiday, Touring & Camping Park
Lizard Lane, South Shields
NE34 7AB
t (01914) 544982

Sandhaven Caravan and Camping Park ★★★
Holiday, Touring & Camping Park
Bents Park Road, South Shields
NE33 2NL
t (01914) 247983

STOCKTON-ON-TEES
Tees Valley

White Water Caravan Club Park ★★★★★
Touring Park
Tees Barrage, Stockton-on-Tees TS18 2QW
t (01642) 634880
w caravanclub.co.uk

STONEHAUGH
Northumberland

Stonehaugh Campsite ★★★
Touring & Camping Park
Stonehaugh Shields,
Stonehaugh Village, Hexham
NE48 3BU
t (01434) 230798
e carole@stonehaugh.fsbusiness.co.uk
w stonehaugh.fsbusiness.co.uk

WHITLEY BAY
Tyne and Wear

Whitley Bay Holiday Park ★★★
Holiday Park
The Links, Whitley Bay
NE16 4BR
t 0871 664 9800
e holidaysales.whitleybay@park-resorts.com
w park-resorts.com

WINSTON
County Durham

Winston Caravan Park ★★★
Holiday, Touring & Camping Park
Front Street, Winston,
Darlington DL2 3RH
t (01325) 730228
e m.willetts@ic24.net
w touristnetuk.com/ne/winston

YORKSHIRE

ACASTER MALBIS
North Yorkshire

Chestnut Farm Holiday Park ★★★★★
Holiday, Touring & Camping Park
Moor End, York YO23 2UQ
t (01904) 704676
e enquiries@chestnutfarmholidaypark.co.uk
w chestnutfarmholidaypark.co.uk

Moor End Farm ★★★★
Holiday, Touring & Camping Park
Moor End, York YO23 2UQ
t (01904) 706727
e moorendfarm@acaster99.fsnet.co.uk
w ukparks.co.uk/moorend

ALLERSTON
North Yorkshire

Vale of Pickering Caravan Park ★★★★★
Touring & Camping Park
Pickering YO18 7PQ
t (01723) 859280
e tony@valeofpickering.co.uk
w valeofpickering.co.uk

BARDSEY
West Yorkshire

Haighfield Caravan Park ★★★★
Holiday Park
5 Blackmoor Lane, Leeds
LS17 9DY
t (01937) 574658

BARMSTON
East Riding of Yorkshire

Barmston Beach Holiday Park ★★★★
Holiday Park
Sands Lane, Driffield YO25 8PJ
t (01442) 830100
e yvonne.balsamo@park-resorts.com
w park-resorts.com

BEDALE
North Yorkshire

Pembroke Caravan Park ★★★★
Touring & Camping Park
19 Low Street, Leeming Bar,
Northallerton DL7 9BW
t (01677) 422652

BEVERLEY
East Riding of Yorkshire

Barmston Farm Caravan Park ★★★★★
Holiday Park
Barmston Farm, Barmston
Lane, Woodmansey, Beverley
HU17 0TP
t (01482) 863566 & 07970 042587
e enquiry@barmstonfarm.co.uk
w barmstonfarm.co.uk

BOLTON ABBEY
North Yorkshire

Howgill Lodge ★★★★★
Holiday, Touring & Camping Park
Barden, Skipton BD23 6DJ
t (01756) 720655
e info@howgill-lodge.co.uk
w howgill-lodge.co.uk

**Strid Wood Caravan Club
Site ★★★★★**
Touring Park
Skipton BD23 6AN
t (01756) 710433
w caravanclub.co.uk

Dacre Lakeside Park ★★★★
Holiday & Touring Park
Leven Road, Driffield
YO25 8RT
t 0800 180 4556
e chalets@dacrepark.co.uk
w dacrepark.co.uk

**Fosse Hill Caravan Park
★★★**
Touring & Camping Park
Catwick Lane, Driffield
YO25 8SB
t (01964) 542608
e tony@fossehill.co.uk
w fossehill.co.uk

**North Bay Leisure Limited
★★★★**
Holiday Park
Lime Kiln Lane, Bridlington
YO16 6TG
t (01262) 673733
e enquiries@northbayleisure.
co.uk
w northbayleisure.co.uk

**The Poplars Touring Park
★★★★**
Touring & Camping Park
45 Jewison Lane, Bridlington
YO15 1DX
t (01262) 677251
w the-poplars.co.uk

**South Cliff Caravan Park
★★★★**
*Holiday, Touring & Camping
Park*
Wilsthorpe, Bridlington
YO15 3QN
t (01262) 671051
e southcliff@eastriding.gov.uk
w southcliff.co.uk

**Gallaber Farm Caravan Park
★★★★**
*Holiday, Touring & Camping
Park*
Gallaber Farm, Burton in
Lonsdale, Carnforth LA6 3LU
t (01524) 261361
e gallaber@btopenworld.com
w gallaber.btinternet.co.uk

**Cayton Bay Holiday Park
★★★★**
Holiday Park
Mill Lane, Scarborough
YO11 3NJ
t (01442) 830100
e yvonne.balsamo@park-
resorts.com

**Cliff Farm Caravan Park
★★★★★**
Holiday Park
Mill Lane, Cayton Bay,
Scarborough YO11 3NN
t (01723) 582239

Giffords
Rating Applied For
Holiday & Touring Park
Lancaster LA2 8ET
t (01524) 251277

**Constable Burton Hall
Caravan Park ★★★★★**
Touring & Camping Park
Leyburn DL8 5LJ
t (01677) 450428

The Hollicarrs ★★★★★
Holiday Park
Riccall Road, York YO19 6EA
t 0800 980 8070
e sales@thehollicarrs.com
w thehollicarrs.com

**Kingfisher Caravan and
Camping Park ★★★★**
*Holiday, Touring & Camping
Park*
Low Moor Lane, Scotton,
Harrogate HG5 9JB
t (01423) 869411

**Filey Brigg Caravan &
Country Park ★★★★**
Touring & Camping Park
Church Cliff Drive, North Cliff,
Arndale, Filey YO14 9ET
t (01723) 513852
e fileybrigg@scarborough.gov.
uk
w scarborough.gov.uk

**Orchard Farm Holiday
Village ★★★★★**
Holiday Park
Stonegate, Hunmanby, Filey
YO14 0PU
t (01723) 891582

**Primrose Valley Holiday
Park ★★★★**
Holiday & Touring Park
Filey YO14 9RF
t (01442) 830100
e yvonne.balsamo@park-
resorts.com
w havenholidays.com

**Thornwick & Sea Farm
Holiday Centre ★★★★**
*Holiday, Touring & Camping
Park*
North Marine Road, Bridlington
YO15 1AU
t (01262) 850369
e enquiries@thornwickbay.co.
uk
w thornwickbay.co.uk

**Great Yorkshire
Showground Caravan Club
Site ★★★★**
Touring Park
Wetherby Road, Harrogate
HG3 1TZ
t (01423) 560470
w caravanclub.co.uk

**Hargill House Caravan Club
Site ★★★★**
Touring Park
Richmond DL10 5LJ
t (01342) 336732
w caravanclub.co.uk

**Blue Dolphin Holiday Park
★★★★**
*Holiday, Touring & Camping
Park*
Gristhorpe Bay, Filey
YO14 9PU
t (01442) 830100
e yvonne.balsamo@park-
resorts.com
w havenholidays.co.uk

**Harden & Bingley Holiday
Park ★★★★**
Holiday & Touring Park
Goit Stock Private Estate, Goit
Stock Lane, Bingley BD16 1DF
t (01535) 273810
e pauldavisdunham@tiscali.co.
uk
w ukparks.co.uk/harden

**Lower Wensleydale Caravan
Club Site ★★★**
Touring & Camping Park
Harmby, Leyburn DL8 5NU
t (01969) 623366
w caravanclub.co.uk

**High Moor Farm Park
★★★★★**
Holiday & Touring Park
Skipton Road, Felliscliffe,
Harrogate HG3 2LT
t (01423) 563637
e highmoorfarmpark@
btconnect.com

**Ripley Caravan Park
★★★★★**
*Holiday, Touring & Camping
Park*
Knaresborough Road,
Harrogate HG3 3AU
t (01423) 770050
e info@ripleycaravanpark.com
w ripleycaravanpark.com

**Rudding Holiday Park
★★★★★ ROSE AWARD**
*Holiday, Touring & Camping
Park*
Follifoot, Harrogate HG3 1JH
t (01423) 870439
e holiday-park@ruddingpark.
com
w ruddingpark.com

**Warren Forest Caravan Park
★★★★★**
Holiday Park
Warsill, Harrogate HG3 3LH
t (01765) 620683
e enquiries@
warrenforestpark.co.uk
w warrenforestpark.co.uk

Hatfield Water Park ★★★
Touring & Camping Park
Old Thorn Road, Doncaster
DN7 6EQ
t (01302) 841572

**Bainbridge Ings Caravan and
Camping Site ★★**
*Holiday, Touring & Camping
Park*
Hawes DL8 3NU
t (01969) 667354
e janet@bainbridge-ings.co.uk
w bainbridge-ings.co.uk

**Honeycott Caravan Park
★★★★**
*Holiday, Touring & Camping
Park*
Ingleton Road, Hawes DL8 3LH
t (01969) 667310
e info@honeycott.co.uk
w honeycott.co.uk

**Upwood Holiday Park
★★★★**
*Holiday, Touring & Camping
Park*
Blackmoor Road, Oxenhope,
Haworth, Keighley BD22 9SS
t (01535) 644242
e caravans@
upwoodholidaypark.fsnet.co.uk
w upwoodholidaypark.fsnet.
co.uk

**Lower Clough Foot Caravan
Club Site ★★★★**
Touring Park
Cragg Vale, Hebden Bridge
HX7 5RU
t (01422) 882531
w caravanclub.co.uk

**Foxholme Touring Caravan
Park ★★★★★**
Touring & Camping Park
Harome, Helmsley YO62 5JG
t (01439) 771241

Golden Square Caravan and Camping Park ★★★★★
Touring & Camping Park
Oswaldkirk, Helmsley, York
YO62 5YQ
t (01439) 788269
e barbara@
goldensquarecaravanpark.
freeserve.co.uk
w goldensquarecaravanpark.
com

HINDERWELL
North Yorkshire

Serenity Touring Caravan & Camping Park ★★★★
Touring & Camping Park
Saltburn-by-the-Sea TS13 5JH
t (01947) 841122

HOLMFIRTH
West Yorkshire

Holme Valley Camping and Caravan Park ★★★★
Touring & Camping Park
Thongsbridge, Huddersfield
HD9 7TD
t (01484) 665819
e enquiries@
homevalleycamping.com
w holmevalleycamping.com

HUTTON-LE-HOLE
North Yorkshire

Hutton le Hole Caravan Park ★★★★
Touring & Camping Park
Westfield Lodge, Hutton-le-Hole, York YO62 6UG
t (01751) 417261
e rwstrickland@
farmersweekly.net
w westfieldlodge.co.uk

INGLETON
North Yorkshire

Parkfoot Holiday Homes ★★★★★
Holiday Park
Bentham Road, Carnforth
LA6 3HR
t (01524) 261833
e Parkfoot.Ingleton@virgin.net
w parkfoot.co.uk

KEARBY WITH NETHERBY
North Yorkshire

Maustin Park Ltd ★★★★★
Holiday, Touring & Camping Park
Wharfe Lane, Kearby,
Wetherby LS22 4DA
t (0113) 288 6234
e info@maustin.co.uk
w maustin.co.uk

KEIGHLEY
West Yorkshire

Bronte Caravan Park ★★★★★
Holiday, Touring & Camping Park
Off Halifax Road, Keighley
BD21 5QF
t (01535) 649111
e bronte@brontecaravanpark.co.uk
w brontecaravanpark.co.uk

KILNSEA
East Riding of Yorkshire

Sandy Beaches Caravan Site ★★
Holiday Park
Kilnsea Road, Hull HU12 0UB
t (01964) 650372
e sandybeacheskiln@aol.com
w sandybeaches.co.uk

KNARESBOROUGH
North Yorkshire

Knaresborough Caravan Club Site ★★★★★
Touring Park
New Road, Catterick Garrison
HG5 9HH
t (01342) 336732
w caravanclub.co.uk

LANGTHORPE
North Yorkshire

Old Hall Holiday Park ★★★★
Holiday & Touring Park
Skelton Road, Langthorpe,
York YO51 9BZ
t (01423) 323190
e phil.brierley@which.net
w yhcparks.info

LEEDS
West Yorkshire

St Helena's Caravan Site ★★★★
Holiday, Touring & Camping Park
Otley Old Road, Leeds
LS18 5HZ
t (0113) 284 1142

LITTLE WEIGHTON
East Riding of Yorkshire

Croft Park ★★★★★
Touring & Camping Park
55 Rowley Road, Cottingham
HU20 3XJ
t (01482) 840600
e steve@croftpark.fsnet.co.uk
w croftpark.net

LOFTHOUSE
North Yorkshire

Studfold Farm Caravan and Camping Park ★★★
Holiday, Touring & Camping Park
Studfold Farm, Harrogate
HG3 5SG
t (01423) 755210
e ianwalker@studfold.fsnet.co.uk
w studfoldfarm.co.uk

LONG PRESTON
North Yorkshire

Gallaber Park ★★★★
Holiday & Touring Park
Skipton BD23 4QF
t (01756) 795621
e info@gallaberpark.com
w gallaberpark.com

MALTON
North Yorkshire

Wolds Way Caravan and Camping ★★★★
Touring & Camping Park
West Farm, West Knapton,
Malton YO17 8JE
t (01944) 728463
e knapton.wold.farms@
farming.co.uk
w ryedalesbest.co.uk

MARKINGTON
North Yorkshire

J S Brayshaw Caravans Limited ★★★★
Holiday, Touring & Camping Park
High Street, Harrogate
HG3 3NR
t (01765) 677327
e yorkshirehussar@yahoo.co.uk

MASHAM
North Yorkshire

Black Swan Holiday Park ★★★
Holiday, Touring & Camping Park
Rear Black Swan Hotel, Ripon
HG4 4NF
t (01765) 689477
e info@blackswanholiday.co.uk
w blackswanholiday.co.uk

NAWTON
North Yorkshire

Wrens of Ryedale Caravan and Camp Site ★★★★
Touring & Camping Park
Gale Lane, York YO62 7SD
t (01439) 771260
e dave@wrensofryedale.fsnet.co.uk
w wrensofryedale.fsnet.co.uk

NEWTON-LE-WILLOWS
North Yorkshire

Lindale Holiday Park ★★★
Holiday & Camping Park
Bedale DL8 1TA
t (01677) 450842
e info@lindalepark.co.uk
w lindalepark.co.uk

NORTHALLERTON
North Yorkshire

Cote Ghyll Caravan & Camping Park ★★★★
Holiday, Touring & Camping Park
Osmotherley, Northallerton
DL6 3AH
t (01609) 883425
e hills@coteghyll.com
w coteghyll.com

NOSTELL
West Yorkshire

Nostell Priory Holiday Home Park ★★★★★
Holiday, Touring & Camping Park
Nostell Priory Estate, Wakefield
WF4 1QE
t (01924) 863938
e info@
nostellprioryholidaypark.co.uk
w nostellprioryholidaypark.co.uk

PATRINGTON
East Riding of Yorkshire

Patrington Haven Leisure Park Ltd ★★★★★
Holiday Park
Patrington Haven, Hull
HU12 0PT
t (01964) 630071
e guy@phlp.co.uk
w phlp.co.uk

PICKERING
North Yorkshire

Upper Carr Chalet and Touring Park ★★★★
Holiday, Touring & Camping Park
Upper Carr Lane, Malton Road,
Pickering YO18 7JP
t (01751) 473115
e harker@uppercarr.demon.co.uk
w upercarr.demon.co.uk

Wayside Caravan Park ★★★★
Holiday, Touring & Camping Park
Pickering YO18 8PG
t (01723) 512373
e waysideparks@freenet.co.uk
w waysideparks.co.uk

REIGHTON GAP
North Yorkshire

Reighton Sands Holiday Park ★★★
Holiday, Touring & Camping Park
Reighton Gap, Filey YO14 9RF
t (01442) 830100
e yvonne.balsamo@park-resorts.com

RICHMOND
North Yorkshire

Brompton Caravan Park ★★★★
Holiday, Touring & Camping Park
Easby, Richmond DL10 7EZ
t (01748) 824629
e brompton.caravanpark@
btinternet.com
w bromptoncaravanpark.co.uk

RIPON
North Yorkshire

River Laver Holiday Park ★★★★★
Holiday & Touring Park
Studley Road, Ripon HG4 2QR
t (01765) 690508
e riverlaver@lineone.net
w riverlaver.co.uk

Sleningford Watermill Caravan & Camping ★★★★
Touring & Camping Park
North Stainley, Ripon
HG4 3HQ
t (01765) 635201
e sleningford@hotmail.co.uk
w ukparks.co.uk/sleningford

Woodhouse Farm Caravan & Camping Park ★★★★
Holiday, Touring & Camping Park
Winksley, Ripon HG4 3PG
t (01765) 658309
e woodhouse.farm@talk21.com
w woodhousewinksley.com

Camping & Caravanning Club Boroughbridge ★★★★★
Touring Park
Bar Lane, Roecliffe, York
YO51 9LS
t (024) 475318
w campingandcaravanning club.co.uk

**Sand-le-Mere Caravan & Leisure Park ★★★★
ROSE AWARD**
Holiday, Touring & Camping Park
Seaside Lane, Tunstall, Hull
HU12 0JQ
t (01964) 670403
e info@sand-le-mere.co.uk
w sand-le-mere.co.uk

Thorpe Hall Caravan and Camping Site ★★★★
Touring & Camping Park
Thorpe Hall, Driffield YO25 4JE
t (01262) 420393
e caravansite@thorpehall.co.uk
w thorpehall.co.uk

Whitby Holiday Park ★★★★
Holiday, Touring & Camping Park
Whitby YO22 4JX
t (01947) 602664
e info@whitbyholidaypark.co.uk

Cayton Village Caravan Park ★★★★★
Touring & Camping Park
Mill Lane, Cayton Bay,
Scarborough YO11 3NN
t (01723) 583171
e info@caytontouring.co.uk
w caytontouring.co.uk

Crows Nest Caravan Park ★★★★ ROSE AWARD
Holiday, Touring & Camping Park
Gristhorpe, Filey YO14 9PS
t (01723) 582206
e enquiries@crowsnestcaravanpark.com
w crowsnestcaravanpark.com

**Flower of May Holiday Parks Ltd ★★★★★
ROSE AWARD**
Holiday, Touring & Camping Park
Lebberston, Scarborough
YO11 3NU
t (01723) 584311
e info@flowerofmay.com
w flowerofmay.com

Lebberston Touring Park ★★★★★
Touring Park
Lebberston, Scarborough
YO11 3PE
t (01723) 585723
e info@lebberstontouring.co.uk
w lebberstontouring.co.uk

Scalby Close Park ★★★★
Holiday, Touring & Camping Park
Burniston Road, Scarborough
YO13 0DA
t (01723) 365908
e info@scalbyclose.co.uk
w scalbyclosepark.co.uk

Scalby Manor Touring Caravan & Camp Park ★★★★★
Touring Park
Burniston Road, Scarborough
YO13 0DA
t (01723) 366212
w campingandcaravanning club.co.uk

Langcliffe Caravan Park ★★★★
Holiday, Touring & Camping Park
Settle BD24 9LX
t (01729) 822387
e info@langcliffe.fsbusiness.co.uk
w langcliffe.com

Camping & Caravanning Club Sheriff Hutton ★★★★
Touring & Camping Park
Bracken Hill, York YO60 6QG
t (024) 475318
w campingandcaravanning club.co.uk

Far Grange Park Ltd ★★★★★
Holiday Park
Hornsea Road, Driffield
YO25 8SY
t (01262) 468010
e enquiries@fargrangepark.co.uk
w fargrangepark.co.uk

Skipsea Sands Holiday Village ★★★★
Holiday, Touring & Camping Park
Mill Lane, Driffield YO25 8TZ
t (01262) 468210
e info@skipseasands.co.uk

Skirlington Leisure Park ★★★★★
Holiday, Touring & Camping Park
Hornsea Road, Driffield
YO25 8SY
t (01262) 468213
e enquiries@skirlington.com
w skirlington.com

Burton Constable Holiday Park & Arboretum ★★★★★
Holiday, Touring & Camping Park
The Old Lodges, Hull
HU11 4LN
t (01964) 562508
e info@burtonconstable.co.uk
w burtonconstable.co.uk

Camping & Caravanning Club Site Slingsby ★★★★★
Touring & Camping Park
Railway Street, York YO62 4AA
t (024) 475318
w campingandcaravanning club.co.uk

**Robin Hood Caravan & Camping Park ★★★★★
ROSE AWARD**
Holiday, Touring & Camping Park
Green Dyke Lane, Slingsby,
York YO62 4AP
t (01653) 628391
e info@robinhoodcaravanpark.co.uk
w robinhoodcaravanpark.co.uk

Jasmine Park ★★★★★
Holiday, Touring & Camping Park
Cross Lane, Snainton,
Scarborough YO13 9BE
t (01723) 859240
e info@jasminepark.co.uk
w jasminepark.co.uk

Low Moor Caravan Club Site ★★★★
Touring Park
Sneaton, Whitby YO22 5JE
t (01947) 810505
w caravanclub.co.uk

Otterington Park ★★★★
Holiday & Touring Park
Station Farm, Northallerton
DL7 9JB
t (01609) 780656
e info@otteringtonpark.com
w otteringtonpark.com

Knight Stainforth Hall Caravan and Camping Park ★★★★
Holiday, Touring & Camping Park
Little Stainforth, Settle
BD24 0DP
t (01729) 822200
e info@knightstainforth.co.uk
w knightstainforth.co.uk

Moorside Caravan Park ★★★★★
Touring Park
Lords Moor Lane, York
YO32 5XJ
t (01904) 491208
w moorsidecaravanpark.co.uk

Thirsk Racecourse Caravan Club Site ★★
Touring & Camping Park
Station Road, Thirsk YO7 1QL
t (01845) 525266
w caravanclub.co.uk

York House Caravan Park ★★★★
Holiday, Touring & Camping Park
Balk YO7 2AQ
t (01845) 597495
e yorkhouse@yhlparks.co.uk
w yhlparks.co.uk

Elder House Touring Park ★★★★
Touring Park
Elder House Farm, Crow Tree
Bank, Doncaster DN8 5TD
t (01405) 813173

Overbrook Caravan Park ★★★★
Touring Park
Maltongate, Pickering
YO18 7SE
t (01751) 474417
e overbrook@breathe.com
w overbrookcaravanpark.co.uk

Long Ashes Park ★★★★
Holiday Park
Threshfield, Skipton BD23 5PN
t (01756) 752261
e info@longashespark.co.uk
w longashespark.co.uk

Wood Nook Caravan Park ★★★★
Holiday, Touring & Camping Park
Skirethorns, Skipton BD23 5NU
t (01756) 752412
e enquiries@woodnook.net
w woodnook.net

WHITBY
North Yorkshire

Flask Holiday Home Park
★★★★ ROSE AWARD
Holiday Park
Robin Hood's Bay, Fylingdales,
Whitby YO22 4QH
t (01947) 880592
e flaskinn@aol.com
w flaskinn.com

Ladycross Plantation
Caravan Park ★★★★★
Touring & Camping Park
Whitby YO21 1UA
t (01947) 895502
e enquiries@
ladycrossplantation.co.uk
w ladycrossplantation.co.uk

Middlewood Farm Holiday
Park ★★★★★
ROSE AWARD
*Holiday, Touring & Camping
Park*
Middlewood Lane,
Fylingthorpe, Robin Hood's
Bay, Whitby YO22 4UF
t (01947) 880414
e info@middlewoodfarm.
fsnet.co.uk
w middlewoodfarm.com

Northcliffe & Seaview
Holiday Parks ★★★★★
*Holiday, Touring & Camping
Park*
Bottoms Lane, Whitby
YO22 4LL
t (01947) 880477
e enquiries@northcliffe-
seaview.com
w northcliffe-seaview.com

Partridge Nest Farm Holiday
Caravans ★★★
Holiday Park
Eskdaleside, Whitby YO22 5ES
t (01947) 810450
e barbara@partridgenestfarm.
com
w partridgenestfarm.com

Sandfield House Farm
Caravan Park ★★★★★
Touring Park
Sandsend Road, Whitby
YO21 3SR
t (01947) 602660
e info@sandfieldhousefarm.
co.uk
w sandfieldhousefarm.co.uk

WILSTHORPE
East Riding of Yorkshire

The White House Caravan
Park ★★★★★
Holiday Park
Wilsthorpe, Bridlington
YO15 3QN
t (01262) 673894

WITHERNSEA
East Riding of Yorkshire

Willows Holiday Park
★★★★
*Holiday, Touring & Camping
Park*
Hollym Road, Withernsea
HU19 2PN
t (01964) 612233
e info@highfield.caravans.co.
uk
w highfield-caravans.co.uk

Withernsea Holiday Village
★★★
Holiday Park
North Road, Withernsea
HU19 2BS
t (01964) 612189
e jjones@gbholidayparks.co.
uk

WOMBLETON
North Yorkshire

Wombleton Caravan Park
★★★★★
Touring & Camping Park
Moorfield Lane, York
YO62 7RY
t (01751) 431684
e info@
wombletoncaravanpark.co.uk
w wombletoncaravanpark.co.
uk

YORK
North Yorkshire

Alders Caravan Park
★★★★★
Touring & Camping Park
Home Farm, Monk Green,
Alne, York YO61 1RY
t (01347) 838722
e enquiries@homefarmalne.
co.uk
w alderscaravanpark.co.uk

Allerton Park Caravan Park
★★★★ ROSE AWARD
*Holiday, Touring & Camping
Park*
Allerton Park, Knaresborough
HG5 0SE
t (01423) 330569
e enquiries@
yorkshireholidayparks.co.uk
w yorkshireholidayparks.co.uk

Beechwood Grange Caravan
Club Site ★★★★★
Touring Park
Malton Road, York YO32 9TH
t (01904) 424637
w caravanclub.co.uk

Castle Howard Lakeside
Holiday Park ★★★
*Holiday, Touring & Camping
Park*
Coneysthorpe YO60 7DD
t (01653) 648316
e lakeside@castlehoward.co.
uk
w castlehoward.co.uk

Cawood Holiday Park
★★★★★
*Holiday, Touring & Camping
Park*
Ryther Road, Vale of York,
York YO8 3TT
t (01757) 268450
e info@cawoodpark.com
w cawoodpark.com

Goosewood Holiday Park
★★★★★
*Holiday, Touring & Camping
Park*
Goose Lane, York YO61 1ET
t (01347) 810829
e enquiries@goosewood.co.
uk
w goosewood.co.uk

Mount Pleasant Holiday
Park and Park Home Estate
★★★★
Holiday Park
Mount Pleasant Holiday Park
and Park Hom, York YO23 2UA
t (01904) 707078
w holgates.com

Rowntree Park Caravan Club
Site ★★★★★
Touring & Camping Park
Terry Avenue, York YO23 1JQ
t (01904) 658997
w caravanclub.co.uk

Weir Caravan Park ★★★★
ROSE AWARD
Holiday & Touring Park
Buttercrambe Road, Stamford
Bridge, York YO41 1AN
t (01759) 371377
e enquiries@
yorkshireholidayparks.co.uk
w yorkshireholidayparks.co.uk

York Touring Caravan Site
★★★★
Touring & Camping Park
Towthorpe Lane, Towthorpe,
York YO32 9ST
t (01904) 499275
e info@yorkcaravansite.co.uk
w yorkcaravansite.co.uk

HEART OF ENGLAND

ALREWAS
Staffordshire

Kingfisher Holiday Park
★★★★★
Holiday Park
Fradley Junction, Alrewas,
Burton-on-Trent DE13 7DN
t (01283) 790407
e mail@kingfisherholidaypark.
com
w kingfisherholidaypark.com

ASTON CANTLOW
Warwickshire

Island Meadow Caravan
Park ★★★
*Holiday, Touring & Camping
Park*
The Mill House, Aston Cantlow
B95 6JP
t (01789) 488273
e holiday@
islandmeadowcaravanpark.co.
uk
w islandmeadowcaravanpark.
co.uk

BIRMINGHAM
West Midlands

Chapel Lane Caravan Club
Site ★★★★★
Touring Park
Chapel Lane, Wythall,
Birmingham B47 6JX
t (01564) 826483
w caravanclub.co.uk

BLACKSHAW MOOR
Staffordshire

Blackshaw Moor Caravan
Club Site ★★★★★
Touring Park
Buxton Road, Blackshaw Moor,
Leek ST13 8TW
t (01538) 300203
w caravanclub.co.uk

BODYMOOR HEATH
West Midlands

Kingsbury Camping &
Caravan Club ★★★★★
Touring & Camping Park
Bodymoor Heath Lane,
Bodymoor Heath, Sutton
Coldfield B76 0DY
t (01827) 874101
w campingandcaravanning
club.co.uk

BREWOOD
Staffordshire

Homestead Caravan Park
★★★★
Holiday Park
Shutt Green, Nr Brewood,
Abbots Langley ST19 9LX
t (01902) 851302
e david@caravanpark.
fsbusiness.co.uk
w caravanparkstaffordshire.co.
uk

BRIDGNORTH
Shropshire

Park Grange Holidays
★★★★
Holiday Park
Park Grange, Morville,
Bridgnorth WV16 4RN
t (01746) 714285
e info@parkgrangeholidays.
co.uk
w parkgrangeholidays.co.uk

Stanmore Hall Touring Park
★★★★★
Holiday & Touring Park
Stourbridge Road, Bridgnorth
WV15 6DT
t (01746) 761761
e stanmore@morris-leisure.co.uk
w morris-leisure.co.uk

BROMYARD
Herefordshire

Bromyard Downs Caravan Club Site ★★★★
Holiday & Camping Park
Brockhampton, Bringsty,
Worcester WR6 5TE
t (01885) 482607
w caravanclub.co.uk

CHEDDLETON
Staffordshire

Glencote Caravan Park
★★★★★
Holiday, Touring & Camping Park
Station Road, Cheddleton,
Leek ST13 7EE
t (01538) 360745
w glencote.co.uk

EARDISLAND
Herefordshire

Arrow Bank Holiday Park
★★★★
Holiday, Touring & Camping Park
Nun House Farm, Eardisland,
Leominster HR6 9BG
t (01544) 388312
e enquiries@arrowbankholidaypark.co.uk
w arrowbankholidaypark.co.uk

ELLESMERE
Shropshire

Fernwood Caravan Park
★★★★★
Holiday & Touring Park
Lyneal, Ellesmere SY12 0QF
t (01948) 710221
e enquiries@fernwoodpark.co.uk
w fernwoodpark.co.uk

EVESHAM
Worcestershire

The Ranch Caravan Park
★★★★★
Holiday & Touring Park
Station Road, Honeybourne,
Evesham WR11 7PR
t (01386) 830744
e enquiries@ranch.co.uk
w ranch.co.uk

HANLEY SWAN
Worcestershire

Blackmore Camping and Caravanning Club Site
★★★★★
Touring & Camping Park
Camp Site No 2, Hanley Swan,
Worcester WR8 0EE
t (01684) 310280
w campingandcaravanning
club.co.uk

HAUGHTON
Shropshire

Ebury Hill Camping & Caravanning Club Site
★★★★
Touring & Camping Park
Ebury Hill, Haughton, Telford
TF6 6BU
t (01743) 709334
w stmem.com/eburyhill/

HEREFORD
Herefordshire

Lucksall Caravan and Camping Park ★★★★★
ROSE AWARD
Holiday & Touring Park
Mordiford, Hereford HR1 4LP
t (01432) 870213
e enquiries@lucksallpark.co.uk
w lucksallpark.co.uk

HOPTON HEATH
Shropshire

Ashlea Pools Country Park-Log Cabins ★★★★★
Holiday Park
Hopton Heath, Craven Arms
SY7 0QD
t (01547) 530430
e ashleapools@surfbay.dircon.co.uk
w ashleapools.co.uk

LEEK
Staffordshire

The Camping and Caravanning Club Site Leek
★★★★★
Touring & Camping Park
Blackshaw Grange, Blackshaw
Moor, Leek ST13 8TL
t (01538) 300285
w campingandcaravanning
club.co.uk

LEOMINSTER
Herefordshire

Fairview Caravan Park ★★★
Holiday Park
c/o The Willows, Hatfield,
Leominster HR6 0SF
t (01568) 760428
e fairviewcaravanpark@
supanet.com

LITTLE TARRINGTON
Herefordshire

The Millpond ★★★★★
Touring & Camping Park
Little Tarrington, Hereford
HR1 4JA
t (01432) 890243
e enquiries@millpond.co.uk
w millpond.co.uk

LUDLOW
Shropshire

Orleton Rise Holiday Home Park ★★★★★
Holiday & Touring Park
Green Lane, Orleton, Ludlow
SY8 4JE
t (01584) 831617

MERIDEN
West Midlands

Somers Wood Caravan Park
★★★★★
Touring Park
Somers Road, Meriden
CV7 7PL
t (01676) 522978
e enquiries@somerswood.co.uk
w somerswood.co.uk

PEMBRIDGE
Herefordshire

Townsend Touring Park
★★★★★
Touring & Camping Park
Townsend Farm, Pembridge,
Leominster HR6 9HB
t (01544) 388527
e info@townsend-farm.co.uk
w townsend-farm.co.uk

PETERCHURCH
Herefordshire

Poston Mill Park ★★★★★
Holiday & Touring Park
Goldon Valley, Hereford
HR2 0SF
t (01981) 550225
e Enquiries@poston-mill.co.uk

PRESTHOPE
Shropshire

Presthope Caravan Club Site
★★★
Touring & Camping Park
Stretton Road, Much Wenlock
TF13 6DQ
t (01746) 785234
w caravanclub.co.uk

ROMSLEY
Worcestershire

Camping and Caravanning Club Site, Clent Hills
★★★★★
Touring Park
Fieldhouse Lane, Romsley,
Halesowen B62 0NH
t (01562) 710015
w campingandcaravanning
club.co.uk

ROSS-ON-WYE
Herefordshire

Broadmeadow Caravan Park
★★★★★
Touring & Camping Park
Broadmeadows, Ross-on-Wye
HR9 7BH
t (01989) 768076

RUGELEY
Staffordshire

Camping and Caravanning Club Site Cannock Chase
★★★★
Touring & Camping Park
Old Youth Hostel, Wandon,
Rugeley WS15 1QW
t (01889) 582166
w campingandcaravanning
club.co.uk

Silver Trees Caravan Park
★★★★ ROSE AWARD
Holiday Park
Stafford Brook Road, Penkridge
Bank, Rugeley WS15 2TX
t (01889) 582185
e enquiries@
silvertreescaravanpark.co.uk
w silvertreescaravanpark.co.uk

SHOBDON
Herefordshire

Pearl Lake Leisure Park Ltd
★★★★★
Holiday Park
Shobdon, Leominster
HR6 9NQ
t (01568) 708326
e info@pearllake.co.uk
w bestparks.co.uk

SHREWSBURY
Shropshire

Beaconsfield Farm Caravan Park ★★★★★
Holiday & Touring Park
Upper Battlefield, Shrewsbury
SY4 4AA
t (01939) 210370
e mail@beaconsfield-farm.co.uk
w beaconsfield-farm.co.uk

Oxon Hall Touring Park
★★★★★
Holiday & Touring Park
Welshpool Road, Bicton Heath,
Shrewsbury SY3 5FB
t (01743) 340868
e oxon@morris-leisure.co.uk
w morris-leisure.co.uk

STOKE-ON-TRENT
Staffordshire

The Star Caravan and Camping Park ★★★★★
ROSE AWARD
Holiday, Touring & Camping Park
Star Road, Cotton, Stoke-on-Trent ST10 3DW
t (01538) 702219
w starcaravanpark.co.uk

STOURPORT-ON-SEVERN
Worcestershire

Lickhill Manor Caravan Park
★★★★★
Holiday Park
Lickhill, Stourport-on-Severn
DY13 8RL
t (01299) 871041
e excellent@lickhillmanor.co.uk
w lickhillmanor.co.uk

STRATFORD-UPON-AVON
Warwickshire

Dodwell Park ★★★
Touring & Camping Park
Evesham Rd, Stratford-upon-Avon CV37 9SR
t (01789) 204957
e enquiries@dodwellpark.co.uk
w dodwellpark.co.uk

SYMONDS YAT WEST
Herefordshire

Sterretts Caravan Park ★★★★
Holiday & Touring Park
Symonds Yat West, Ross-on-
Wye HR9 6BY
t (01594) 833162

TITTON
Worcestershire

Lincomb Lock Caravan Park ★★★
Holiday & Touring Park
Worcester Road, Titton,
Stourport-on-Severn
DY13 9QR
t (01299) 823836
e lincomb@hillandale.co.uk
w hillandale.co.uk

Severnside Park ★★
Holiday Park
Sandy Lane, Stourport-on-
Severn DY13 9PS
t (01299) 824976

UTTOXETER
Staffordshire

Uttoxeter Racecourse Caravan Club Site ★★
Touring Park
Wood Lane, Uttoxeter
ST14 8BD
t (01889) 564172
w caravanclub.co.uk

WARWICK
Warwickshire

Warwick Racecourse ★★★
Holiday & Touring Park
Hampton Street, Warwick
CV34 6HN
t (01926) 495448
e enquiries@caravanclub.co.uk
w caravanclub.co.uk

WOLVERLEY
Worcestershire

Wolverley Camping and Caravanning Club Site ★★★
Touring & Camping Park
Brown Westhead Park,
Wolverley, Kidderminster
DY10 3PX
t (01562) 850909
w campingandcaravanning
club.co.uk

WYRE PIDDLE
Worcestershire

Rivermead Holiday Home Park ★★★★★
Holiday Park
Church Street, Wyre Piddle,
Pershore WR10 2JF
t (01386) 561250
e enquiries@
rivermeadcaravanpark.co.uk
w rivermeadcaravanpark.co.uk

EAST MIDLANDS

ALSOP-EN-LE-DALE
Derbyshire

Rivendale Caravan and Leisure Park ★★★★
Holiday, Touring & Camping Park
Buxton Road, Alsop en le Dale,
Ashbourne DE6 1QU
t (01335) 310311
e greg@rivendalecaravanpark.co.uk
w rivendalecaravanpark.co.uk

AMBERGATE
Derbyshire

The Firs Farm Caravan and Camping Park ★★★★
Touring & Camping Park
Crich Lane, Nether Heage,
Belper DE56 2JH
t (01773) 852913
w thefirsfarmcaravanpark.btinternet.co.uk

ANDERBY CREEK
Lincolnshire

Anderby Springs Caravan Estate ★★★
Holiday Park
Sea Road, Anderby Creek,
Skegness PE24 5XW
t (01754) 872265

ASHBOURNE
Derbyshire

Blackwall Plantation Caravan Club Site ★★★★
Touring Park
Kirk Ireton, Ashbourne DE6 3JL
t (01335) 370903
w caravanclub.co.uk

Callow Top Holiday Park ★★★★
Holiday, Touring & Camping Park
Buxton Road, Sandybrook,
Ashbourne DE6 2AQ
t (01335) 344020
e enquiries@callowtop.co.uk
w callowtop.co.uk

BAKEWELL
Derbyshire

Chatsworth Park Caravan Club Site ★★★★★
Touring Park
Chatsworth, Bakewell
DE45 1PN
t (01246) 582226
w caravanclub.co.uk

BARTON-UPON-HUMBER
Lincolnshire

Silver Birches Tourist Park ★★★
Touring & Camping Park
Waterside Road, Barton-upon-
Humber DN18 5BA
t (01652) 632509

BELPER
Derbyshire

Broadhouse Lane Caravan Park ★★★
Touring Park
Broadholme Lane, Belper
DE56 2JF
t (01773) 823517
w broadhouse-caravanpark.co.uk

BOSTON
Lincolnshire

Orchard Caravan Park ★★★
Holiday, Touring & Camping Park
Frampton Lane, Hubberts
Bridge, Boston PE20 3QU
t (01205) 290328
e DavidMay@
orchardholidaypark.fsnet.co.uk
w orchardpark.co.uk

BURGH-LE-MARSH
Lincolnshire

Sycamore Lakes Touring Site ★★★★
Touring & Camping Park
Skegness Road, Burgh le
Marsh PE24 5LN
t (01754) 811411
w sycamorelakes.co.uk

BUXTON
Derbyshire

Cottage Farm Caravan Park ★★★
Touring & Camping Park
Beech Croft, Blackwell, Buxton
SK17 9TQ
t (01298) 85330
e mail@cottagefarmsite.co.uk
w cottagefarmsite.co.uk

Grin Low Caravan Club Site ★★★★★
Touring & Camping Park
Grin Low Road, Ladmanlow,
Buxton SK17 6UJ
t (01298) 77735
w caravanclub.co.uk

Lime Tree Park ★★★★ ROSE AWARD
Holiday, Touring & Camping Park
Dukes Drive, Buxton SK17 9RP
t (01298) 22988
e info@limetreeparkbuxton.co.uk
w limetreeparkbuxton.co.uk

Longnor Wood Caravan Park ★★★★
Holiday, Touring & Camping Park
Longnor, Buxton SK17 0NG
t (01298) 83648
e enquiries@longnorwood.co.uk
w longnorwood.co.uk

Newhaven Caravan and Camping Park ★★★
Holiday, Touring & Camping Park
Newhaven, Nr Buxton
SK17 0DT
t (01298) 84300
w newhavencaravanpark.co.uk

CASTLETON
Derbyshire

Losehill Caravan Club Site ★★★★★
Touring & Camping Park
Castleton, Hope Valley
S33 8WB
t (01433) 620636
w caravanclub.co.uk

CHAPEL ST LEONARDS
Lincolnshire

Tomlinsons Leisure Park ★★★★
Holiday Park
South Road, Chapel St
Leonards, Skegness PE24 5TL
t (01754) 872241
w tomlinsons-leisure.com

CROFT
Lincolnshire

Pine Trees Leisure Park ★★★
Touring Park
Croft Bank, Croft, Skegness
PE24 4RE
t (01754) 762949
e holidays@pine148.fsnet.co.uk
w pinetreesholidays.co.uk

DERBY
Derbyshire

Elvaston Castle Caravan Club Site ★★★
Touring Park
Elvaston Castle Country Park,
Borrowash Road, Derby
DE72 3EP
t (01332) 573735
w caravanclub.co.uk

EAST FIRSBY
Lincolnshire

Manor Farm Caravan and Camping Site ★★★
Touring & Camping Park
Manor Farm, East Firsby,
Market Rasen LN8 2DB
t (01673) 878258
e info@lincolnshire-lanes.com
w lincolnshire-lanes.com

FINESHADE
Northamptonshire

Top Lodge Caravan Club Site ★★★★
Holiday & Touring Park
Fineshade, Duddington, Corby
NN17 3BB
t (01780) 444617
w caravanclub.co.uk

FLAGG
Derbyshire

Pomeroy Caravan and Camping Park ★★
Touring & Camping Park
Street House Farm, Pomeroy,
Buxton SK17 9QG
t (01298) 83259

FLEET HARGATE
Lincolnshire

Delph Bank Touring Caravan & Camping Park – Just for Adults ★★★★
Touring & Camping Park
Old Main Road, Fleet Hargate,
Spalding PE12 8LL
t (01406) 422910
e enquiries@delphbank.co.uk
w delphbank.co.uk

FOLKINGHAM
Lincolnshire

Low Farm Touring Park ★★★
Touring Park
Spring Lane, Folkingham
NG34 0SJ
t (01529) 497322

HADFIELD
Derbyshire

Camping and Caravanning Club Site Crowden ★★★
Touring & Camping Park
Crowden, Glossop SK13 1HZ
t (01457) 866057
w campingandcaravanning club.co.uk

HAYFIELD
Derbyshire

Camping and Caravanning Club Site Hayfield ★★★
Camping Park
Kinder Road, Hayfield, High
Peak SK22 2LE
t (01663) 745394
w campingandcaravanning club.co.uk

HOLBEACH
Lincolnshire

Heron Cottage Camping and Caravanning ★★★
Touring & Camping Park
Frostley Gate, Spalding
PE12 8SR
t (01406) 540435

HORNCASTLE
Lincolnshire

Ashby Park ★★★★
Holiday, Touring & Camping Park
Horncastle, West Ashby
LN9 5PP
t (01507) 527966
e ashbyparklakes@aol.com
w ukparks.co.uk/ashby

Elmhirst Lakes Caravan Park ★★★★
Holiday Park
Elmhirst Road, Horncastle
LN9 5LU
t (01507) 527533
w elmhirstlakes.co.uk

HUMBERSTON
North East Lincolnshire

Thorpe Park Holiday Centre ★★★★
Holiday, Touring & Camping Park
Grimsby DN35 0PW
t (01442) 868325
e theresa.ludlow@bourne-leisure.co.uk
w british-holidays.co.uk

INGOLDMELLS
Lincolnshire

Coastfield Caravan Park ★★★
Holiday Park
Vickers Point, Roman Bank,
Ingoldmells, Skegness
PE25 1JU
t (01754) 872592

Country Meadows Touring Park ★★★★
Holiday & Touring Park
Anchor Lane, Ingoldmells,
Skegness PE25 1LZ
t (01754) 874455
e bookings@countrymeadows.co.uk
w countrymeadows.co.uk

Golden Beach Holiday Park ★★★★
Holiday Park
Roman Bank, Ingoldmells,
Skegness PE25 1LT
t (01754) 873000

Ingoldale Park ★★★
Holiday Park
Beach Estate, Roman Bank,
Skegness PE25 1LL
t (01754) 872335

Kingfisher Park ★★★
Holiday Park
Sea Lane, Ingoldmells
PE25 1PG
t (01754) 872465
e kingfisherpark@e-lindsey.gov.uk

KIRKBY-ON-BAIN
Lincolnshire

Camping and Caravanning Club Site Woodhall Spa ★★★★★
Touring & Camping Park
Wellsyke Lane, Kirkby-on-Bain,
Woodhall Spa LN10 6YU
t (01526) 352911
w campingandcaravanning club.co.uk

LINCOLN
Lincolnshire

Hartsholme Country Park ★★★
Touring Park
Skellingthorpe Road, Lincoln
LN6 0EY
t (01522) 873578
e hartsholmecp@lincoln.gov.uk
w lincoln.gov.uk

MABLETHORPE
Lincolnshire

Camping and Caravanning Club Site Mablethorpe ★★★★
Touring & Camping Park
Highfield, 120 Church Lane,
Mablethorpe LN12 2NU
t (01507) 472374
w campingandcaravanning club.co.uk

Golden Sands Holiday Park ★★★
Holiday & Touring Park
Quebec Road, Mablethorpe
LN12 1QJ
t (01507) 477871

Holivans Ltd ★★★
Touring Park
Dept G, Quebec Road,
Mablethorpe LN12 1QH
t (01507) 473327
e holivans@enterprise.net
w holivans.co.uk

Trusthorpe Springs Leisure Park ★★
Holiday & Touring Park
Mile Lane, Trusthorpe,
Mablethorpe LN12 2QQ
t (01507) 441384
e d.brailsford@ukonline.co.uk

MARKET BOSWORTH
Leicestershire

Bosworth Water Trust ★★★
Touring & Camping Park
Wellesborough Road, Market
Bosworth CV13 6PD
t (01455) 291876
e info@bosworthwatertrust.co.uk
w bosworthwatertrust.co.uk

MARKET HARBOROUGH
Leicestershire

Brook Meadow ★★
Holiday & Camping Park
Welford Road, Sibbertoft,
Market Harborough LE16 9UJ
t (01858) 880886
e brookmeadow@farmline.com
w brookmeadow.co.uk

MEDBOURNE
Leicestershire

Innarla Caravan & Camping Park ★
Holiday, Touring & Camping Park
Hallaton Road, Medbourne,
Market Harborough LE16 8DR
t (01858) 565478
e innarla@jgalway.freeserve.co.uk
w jgalway.freeserve.co.uk

MUMBY
Lincolnshire

Inglenook Caravan Park ★★★
Touring Park
Hogsthorpe Road, Mumby,
Alford LN13 9SE
t (01507) 490365

NEWARK
Nottinghamshire

Milestone Caravan Park ★★★★★
Touring Park
Great North Road, Cromwell,
Newark NG23 6JE
t (01636) 821244
e enquiries@experiencenottinghamshire.com

NORMANBY
Lincolnshire

Normanby Hall Country Park ★★★
Touring Park
Scunthorpe DN15 9HU
t (01724) 720588
e normanby.hall@northlincs.gov.uk
w northlincs.gov.uk/normanby

RIPLEY
Derbyshire

Golden Valley Caravan & Camping ★★★
Touring & Camping Park
The Tanyard, Coach Road,
Golden Valley, Ripley DE5 3QU
t (01773) 513881 &
07971 283643
e enquiries@goldenvalleycaravanpark.co.uk
w goldenvalleycaravanpark.co.uk

SALTFLEET
Lincolnshire

Sunnydale Holiday Park ★★★
Holiday Park
Sea Lane, Saltfleet, Louth
LN11 7RP
t (01507) 338100
w gbholidayparks.co.uk

SCUNTHORPE
Lincolnshire

Brookside Caravan Park ★★★★★
Touring Park
Stather Road, Burton upon
Stather, Scunthorpe
DN15 9DH
t (01724) 721369
e brookside@aol.com
w brooksidecaravanpark.co.uk

SKEGNESS
Lincolnshire

Manor Farm Caravan Park ★★
Touring & Camping Park
Sea Road, Anderby PE24 5YB
t (01507) 490372
e skegnessinfo@e-lindsey.gov.uk

Richmond Holiday Centre
★★★
Holiday & Touring Park
Richmond Drive, Skegness
PE25 3TQ
t (01754) 762097
e sales@richmondholidays.
com
w richmondholidays.com

**Skegness Water Leisure
Park** ★★★
*Holiday, Touring & Camping
Park*
Walls Lane, Ingoldmells,
Skegness PE25 1JF
t (01754) 899400
e enquiries@
skegnesswaterleisurepark.co.
uk

Walsh's Holiday Park ★★★
Holiday Park
Roman Bank, Skegness
PE25 1QP
t (01754) 764485

SUTTON-ON-SEA
Lincolnshire

Cherry Tree Site ★★★★
Touring Park
Huttoft Road, Sutton on Sea
LN12 2RU
t (01507) 441626
e info@cherrytreesite.co.uk
w cherrytreesite.co.uk

SUTTON ST EDMUND
Lincolnshire

**Orchard View Caravan &
Camping Park** ★★★
*Holiday, Touring & Camping
Park*
102 Broadgate, Sutton St
Edmund, Spalding PE12 0LT
t (01945) 700482
e raymariaorchardview@
btinternet.com

SUTTON ST JAMES
Lincolnshire

**Foreman's Bridge Caravan
Park** ★★★★
*Holiday, Touring & Camping
Park*
Sutton Road, Sutton St James,
Spalding PE12 0HU
t (01945) 440346
e info@foremans-bridge.co.uk
w foremans-bridge.co.uk

SWADLINCOTE
Derbyshire

**Beehive Farm Woodland
Lakes Camping &** ★★★
Touring & Camping Park
Rosliston, Swadlincote
DE12 8HZ
t (01283) 763981
w beehivefarm-
woodlandlakes.co.uk

TANSLEY
Derbyshire

Lickpenny Caravan Park
★★★★
Holiday & Touring Park
Lickpenny Lane, Tansley,
Matlock DE4 5GF
t (01629) 583040
e lickpenny@btinternet.com
w lickpennycaravanpark.co.uk

Packhorse Farm Bungalow
★★★★
Touring Park
Chesterfield Road, Tansley,
Matlock DE4 5LF
t (01629) 582781

TRUSTHORPE
Lincolnshire

Seacroft Holiday Estate Ltd
★★★★
Holiday & Touring Park
Sutton Road, Trusthorpe,
Mablethorpe LN12 2PN
t (01507) 472421
e info@seacroftcaravanpark.
co.uk
w seacroftcaravanpark.co.uk

**Sutton Springs Holiday
Estate** ★★★
Holiday Park
Sutton Road, Trusthorpe,
Mablethorpe LN12 2PZ
t (01507) 441333
e d.brailsford@ukonline.co.uk

WHATSTANDWELL
Derbyshire

**Birchwood Farm Caravan
Park** ★★
*Holiday, Touring & Camping
Park*
Wirksworth Road,
Whatstandwell, Matlock
DE4 5HS
t (01629) 822280
w birchwoodfcp.co.uk

WHISSENDINE
Rutland

**Greendale Farm Caravan &
Camping Park** ★★★★
Touring & Camping Park
Pickwell Lane, Whissendine,
Oakham LE15 7LB
t (01664) 474516
e enq@rutlandgreendale.co.
uk
w rutlandgreendale.co.uk

WOODHALL SPA
Lincolnshire

Bainland Country Park Ltd
★★★★★
*Holiday, Touring & Camping
Park*
Horncastle Road, Roughton
Moor, Woodhall Spa LN10 6UX
t (01526) 352903
e bookings@bainland.com
w bainland.com

WORKSOP
Nottinghamshire

**Clumber Park Caravan Club
Site** ★★★★
Touring Park
Limetree Avenue, Clumber
Park, Worksop S80 3AE
t (01909) 484758
w caravanclub.co.uk

YOULGREAVE
Derbyshire

**Camping and Caravanning
Club Site** ★★★
Touring & Camping Park
c/o Hopping Farm, Youlgrave,
Bakewell DE45 1NA
t (01629) 636555
w campingandcaravanning
club.co.uk

EAST OF ENGLAND

ASHILL
Norfolk

**Brick Kiln Farm Caravan &
Camping Park** ★★★
Touring & Camping Park
Swaffham Road, Ashill,
Thetford IP25 7BT
t (01760) 441300

ATTLEBOROUGH
Norfolk

Oak Tree Caravan Park
★★★★
Touring Park
Norwich Road, Attleborough
NR17 2JX
t (01953) 455565

BACTON-ON-SEA
Norfolk

Cable Gap Holiday Park
★★★★★
Holiday Park
Coast Road, Bacton, Norwich
NR12 0EW
t (01692) 650667

BANHAM
Norfolk

**Applewood Caravan and
Camping Park** ★★★★
Touring Park
The Grove, Kenninghall Road,
Banham, Norwich NR16 2HE
t (01953) 888370

BAWBURGH
Norfolk

**Norfolk Showground
Caravan Club Site** ★★★★
Touring Park
Royal Norfolk Showground,
Long Lane, Bawburgh, Norwich
NR9 3LX
t (01603) 742708
w caravanclub.co.uk

BELTON
Norfolk

Wild Duck Holiday Park
★★★★
Holiday Park
Howards Common, Belton,
Great Yarmouth NR31 9NE
t (01493) 780268

BENHALL
Suffolk

**Whitearch (Touring
Caravan) Park** ★★★
Holiday Park
Main Road, Benhall,
Saxmundham IP17 1NA
t (01728) 604646

BRENTWOOD
Essex

**Camping and Caravanning
Club Site Kelvedon Hatch**
★★★
Holiday Park
Warren Lane, Doddinghurst,
Brentwood CM15 0JG
t (01277) 372773
w campingandcaravanning
club.co.uk

BUCKLESHAM
Suffolk

The Oaks Caravan Park
★★★★
Holiday & Touring Park
Chapel Road, Bucklesham,
Ipswich IP10 0BT
t (01394) 448837

BUNGAY
Suffolk

**Outney Meadow Caravan
Park** ★★★
Touring & Camping Park
Outney Meadow, Bungay
NR35 1HG
t (01986) 892338

BURGH CASTLE
Norfolk

**Burgh Castle Marina and
Caravan Park** ★★★★
*Holiday, Touring & Camping
Park*
Butt Lane, Burgh Castle, Great
Yarmouth NR31 9PZ
t (01493) 780331

BURGH ST PETER
Norfolk

Waveney River Centre
★★★★
Holiday Park
Staithe Road, Burgh St Peter,
Beccles NR34 0BT
t (01502) 677343

BURNHAM DEEPDALE
Norfolk

Deepdale Camping ★★★★
Camping Park
Deepdale Farms, Burnham
Deepdale, King's Lynn
PE31 8DD
t (01485) 210256
e info@deepdalefarm.co.uk
w deepdalefarm.co.uk

CAISTER-ON-SEA
Norfolk

**Caister Beach Holiday Park
★★★★★**
Holiday Park
Branford Road, Caister-on-Sea,
Great Yarmouth NR30 5NE
t (01493) 720278

Caister Holiday Park ★★★
Holiday Park
Ormesby Road, Caister-on-Sea,
Great Yarmouth NR30 5NQ
t (01493) 728931

**Eastern Beach Caravan Park
★★★★**
Holiday Park
Manor Road, Caister-on-Sea,
Great Yarmouth NR30 5HH
t (01493) 720367

**Elm Beach Caravan Park
★★★★**
Holiday Park
Manor Road, Caister-on-Sea,
Great Yarmouth NR30 5HG
t (01493) 721630

Wentworth Holidays ★★★
Holiday Park
9 Bultitudes Loke, Caister-on-
Sea, Great Yarmouth
NR30 5DH
t (01493) 720382

CALIFORNIA
Norfolk

**Wakefield Court T/A
Beachside Holidays ★★★★**
Holiday Park
California, Scratby, Great
Yarmouth NR29 3QT
t (01493) 730279

CAMBRIDGE
Cambridgeshire

Appleacre Park ★★
Touring Park
London Road, Fowlmere,
Royston SG8 7RU
t (01763) 208229

**Cherry Hinton Caravan Club
Site ★★★★★**
Touring & Camping Park
Lime Kiln Road, Cherry Hinton,
Cambridge CB1 8NQ
t (01223) 244088
w caravanclub.co.uk

**Highfield Farm Touring Park
★★★★★**
Touring & Camping Park
Long Road, Comberton,
Cambridge CB3 7DG
t (01223) 262308
e enquiries@
highfieldfarmtouringpark.co.uk
w highfieldfarmtouringpark.co.
uk

CAWSTON
Norfolk

**Haveringland Hall Park
★★★**
Holiday & Touring Park
Haveringland, Norwich
NR10 4PN
t (01603) 871302

CLACTON-ON-SEA
Essex

**Highfield Holiday Park
★★★**
Holiday Park
London Road, Clacton-on-Sea
CO16 9QY
t (01255) 424244

**Valley Farm Holiday Park
★★★★**
Holiday Park
Valley Road, Clacton-on-Sea
CO15 6LY
t (01255) 422484

CLIPPESBY
Norfolk

Clippesby Hall ★★★★
Holiday Park
Hall Lane, Clippesby, Great
Yarmouth NR29 3BL
t (01493) 367800

CORTON
Suffolk

**Broadland Sands Holiday
Park ★★★★**
Holiday Park
Coast Road, Corton, Lowestoft
NR32 5LG
t (01502) 730939
e admin@broadlandsands.co.
uk
w broadlandsands.co.uk

CROMER
Norfolk

**Forest Park Caravan Site
★★★**
Touring & Camping Park
Northrepps Road, Northrepps,
Cromer NR27 0JR
t (01263) 513290

Seacroft Caravan Club Site
Rating Applied For
Touring & Camping Park
Runton Road, Cromer
NR27 9NH
t (01263) 514938
w caravanclub.co.uk

DUNWICH
Suffolk

**Cliff House Holiday Park
★★★★**
Holiday Park
Minsmere Road, Dunwich,
Saxmundham IP17 3DQ
t (01728) 648282

EAST HARLING
Norfolk

**The Dower House Touring
Park ★★★★**
Touring & Camping Park
Thetford Forest, East Harling,
Norwich NR16 2SE
t (01953) 717314

EAST MERSEA
Essex

**Coopers Beach Holiday Park
★★★**
Holiday Park
East Mersea, Colchester
CO5 8TN
t (01206) 383236

**Cosway Holiday Home Park
★★★★★**
Holiday Park
Fen Lane, East Mersea,
Colchester CO5 8UA
t (01206) 383252

**Fen Farm Caravan and
Camping Site ★★★★**
Holiday Park
East Mersea, Colchester
CO5 8UA
t (01206) 383275

EAST RUNTON
Norfolk

Woodhill Park ★★★★
*Holiday, Touring & Camping
Park*
Cromer Road, East Runton,
Cromer NR27 9PX
t (01263) 512242

FAKENHAM
Norfolk

Fakenham Racecourse ★★★
Touring Park
The Racecourse, Fakenham
NR21 7NY
t (01328) 862388
e caravan@
fakenhamracecourse.co.uk
w fakenhamracecourse.co.uk

**The Old Brick Kilns
★★★★★**
Touring & Camping Park
Little Barney Lane, Barney,
Fakenham NR21 0NL
t (01328) 878305

FELIXSTOWE
Suffolk

**Peewit Caravan Park
★★★★**
Touring & Camping Park
Walton Avenue, Felixstowe
IP11 2HB
t (01394) 284511

FOXHALL
Suffolk

**Low House Touring Caravan
Centre ★★★★**
Holiday Park
Low House, Bucklesham Road,
Foxhall, Ipswich IP10 0AU
t (01473) 659437

GOLDHANGER
Essex

Osea Leisure Park ★★★★
Holiday Park
Goldhanger Road, Heybridge,
Maldon CM9 4SA
t (01621) 854695

GRAFHAM
Cambridgeshire

**Old Manor Caravan Park
★★★★**
Touring & Camping Park
Church Road, Grafham,
Huntingdon PE28 0BB
t (01480) 810264

GREAT SHELFORD
Cambridgeshire

**Camping and Caravanning
Club Site Cambridge
★★★★**
Touring Park
19 Cabbage Moor, Great
Shelford, Cambridge CB2 5NB
t (01223) 841185
w campingandcaravanning
club.co.uk

GREAT YARMOUTH
Norfolk

**Breydon Water Holiday Park
(Bure Village) ★★★**
*Holiday, Touring & Camping
Park*
Butt Lane, Burgh Castle, Great
Yarmouth NR31 9PY
t (01493) 780481

**Cherry Tree Holiday Park
★★★★**
Holiday Park
Burgh Castle, Great Yarmouth
NR31 9QR
t 0870 420 2997
e enquiries@
parkdeanholidays.co.uk
w parkdeanholidays.co.uk

**The Grange Touring Park
★★★★**
Holiday Park
Yarmouth Road, Ormesby St
Margaret, Great Yarmouth
NR29 3QG
t (01493) 730306

**Grasmere Caravan Park
★★★**
Touring Park
Bultitudes Loke, Yarmouth
Road, Caister-on-Sea, Great
Yarmouth NR30 5DH
t (01493) 720382
w grasmere-wentworth.co.uk

**Great Yarmouth Caravan
Club Site ★★★★**
Holiday Park
Great Yarmouth Racecourse,
Jellicoe Road, Great Yarmouth
NR30 4AU
t (01493) 855223
w caravanclub.co.uk

**Hopton Holiday Village
★★★★**
Holiday Park
Warren Lane, Hopton, Great
Yarmouth NR31 9BW
t (01502) 730214

Liffens Holiday Park ★★★★
Holiday Park
Butt Lane, Burgh Castle, Great
Yarmouth NR31 9QB
t (01493) 780357

Seacroft (Hemsby) Ltd Summerfields Holiday Village ★★★★
Holiday Park
Beach Road, Scratby, Great Yarmouth NR29 3NW
t (01493) 731419

Seashore Holiday Park ★★★
Holiday Park
North Denes, Great Yarmouth NR30 4HG
t (01493) 851131

Vauxhall Holiday Park ★★★★★
Holiday & Touring Park
Acle New Road, Great Yarmouth NR30 1TB
t (01493) 857231

HADLEIGH
Suffolk

Polstead Touring Park ★★★★
Touring & Camping Park
Holt Road, Polstead, Colchester CO6 5BZ
t (01787) 211969

HANWORTH
Norfolk

Deer's Glade Caravan & Camping Park ★★★★★
Touring & Camping Park
White Post Road, Hanworth, Norwich NR11 7HN
t (01263) 768633

HEACHAM
Norfolk

Heacham Beach Holiday Park ★★★
Holiday Park
South Beach Road, Heacham, King's Lynn PE31 7BD
t (01485) 570270

HEMEL HEMPSTEAD
Hertfordshire

Breakspear Way Caravan Club Site
Rating Applied For
Touring Park
Buncefield Lane, Breakspear Way, Hemel Hempstead HP2 4TZ
t (01442) 268466
w caravanclub.co.uk

HEMINGFORD ABBOTS
Cambridgeshire

Quiet Waters Caravan Park ★★★★
Holiday, Touring & Camping Park
Hemingford Abbots, Huntingdon PE28 9AJ
t (01480) 463405
e quietwaters.park@btopenworld.com
w quietwaterscaravanpark.co.uk

HEMSBY
Norfolk

Newport Caravan Park (Norfolk) Ltd ★★★
Holiday, Touring & Camping Park
Newport Road, Hemsby, Great Yarmouth NR29 4NW
t (01493) 730405

HERTFORD
Hertfordshire

Camping and Caravanning Club Site Hertford ★★★★
Touring & Camping Park
Mangrove Road, Hertford SG13 8QF
t (01992) 586696
w campingandcaravanning club.co.uk

HEYBRIDGE
Essex

Barrow Marsh Caravan and Chalet Park ★★
Holiday Park
Goldhanger Road, Heybridge, Maldon CM9 4RA
t (01621) 852859

HODDESDON
Hertfordshire

Lee Valley Caravan Park ★★★★
Touring & Camping Park
Essex Road, Hoddesdon EN11 0AS
t (01992) 462090

HUNSTANTON
Norfolk

Manor Park Holiday Village ★★★★
Holiday & Touring Park
Manor Road, Hunstanton PE36 5AZ
t (01485) 532300

Searles Leisure Resort ★★★★★ ROSE AWARD
Holiday, Touring & Camping Park
South Beach Road, Hunstanton PE36 5BB
t (01485) 534211
e bookings@searles.co.uk
w searles.co.uk

HUNTINGDON
Cambridgeshire

Houghton Mill Caravan Club Site ★★★★
Touring Park
Mill Street, Houghton, Huntingdon PE28 2AZ
t (01480) 466716
w caravanclub.co.uk

JAYWICK
Essex

Martello Beach Holiday Park ★★
Holiday, Touring & Camping Park
Belsize Avenue, Clacton-on-Sea CO15 2LF
t (01255) 820372
w park-resorts.com

Tower Holiday Park ★★
Holiday, Touring & Camping Park
Belsize Avenue, Jaywick, Clacton-on-Sea CO15 2LF
t (01255) 820372

KESSINGLAND
Suffolk

Alandale Park ★★
Holiday Park
Bethel Drive, Kessingland, Lowestoft NR33 7SD
t (01502) 740610

Camping and Caravanning Club Site Kessingland ★★★★
Touring & Camping Park
Whites Lane, Kessingland, Lowestoft NR33 7TF
t (01502) 742040
w campingandcaravanning club.co.uk

Heathland Beach Caravan Park ★★★★★
Holiday, Touring & Camping Park
London Road, Kessingland, Lowestoft NR33 7PJ
t (01502) 740337

Kessingland Beach Holiday Park ★★★
Holiday, Touring & Camping Park
Beach Road, Kessingland, Lowestoft NR33 7RW
t (01502) 740636

LITTLE CORNARD
Suffolk

Willowmere Caravan Park ★★★
Touring & Camping Park
Bures Road, Little Cornard, Sudbury CO10 0NN
t (01787) 375559

LOUGHTON
Essex

Debden House Camp Site ★★
Holiday Park
Debden Green, Loughton IG10 2NZ
t (020) 8508 3008

LOWESTOFT
Suffolk

Beach Farm Residential and Holiday Park Limited ★★★
Holiday Park
Arbor Lane, Pakefield, Lowestoft NR33 7BD
t (01502) 572794

MARCH
Cambridgeshire

Floods Ferry Marina Park ★★★
Touring & Camping Park
Staffurths Bridge, Floods Ferry Road, March PE15 0YP
t (01354) 677302

MERSEA ISLAND
Essex

Waldegraves Holiday Park ★★★
Holiday, Touring & Camping Park
Waldegraves Lane, Mersea Island, Colchester CO5 8SE
t (01206) 382898

MILDENHALL
Suffolk

Round Plantation Caravan Club Site ★★★★
Holiday Park
Brandon Road, Mildenhall, Bury St Edmunds IP28 7JE
t (01638) 713089
w caravanclub.co.uk

MUNDESLEY
Norfolk

Sandy Gulls Cliff Top Touring Park ★★★
Holiday & Touring Park
Cromer Road, Mundesley, Norwich NR11 8DF
t (01263) 720513

MUTFORD
Suffolk

Beulah Hall Caravan Park ★★★
Touring & Camping Park
Beulah Hall, Dairy Lane, Beccles NR34 7QJ
t (01502) 476609

NORTH RUNCTON
Norfolk

Kings Lynn Caravan & Camping Park ★★★
Touring & Camping Park
New Road, North Runcton, King's Lynn PE33 0RA
t (01553) 840004

NORTH WALSHAM
Norfolk

North Walsham Caravan and Chalet Park ★★★
Holiday Park
Bacton Road, North Walsham NR28 0RA
t (01692) 501070

Two Mills Touring Park ★★★★★
Touring Park
Yarmouth Road, North Walsham NR28 9NA
t (01692) 405829

NORWICH
Norfolk

Camping and Caravanning Club Site Norwich ★★★
Holiday Park
Martineau Lane, Norwich NR1 2HX
t (01603) 620060
w campingandcaravanning club.co.uk

Reedham Ferry Touring and Camping Park ★★★
Holiday, Touring & Camping Park
Ferry Road, Reedham, Norwich NR13 3HA
t (01493) 700999

OULTON BROAD
Suffolk

Broadland Holiday Village ★★★★★
Holiday Park
Marsh Road, Oulton Broad, Lowestoft NR33 9JY
t (01502) 573033

OVERSTRAND
Norfolk

Ivy Farm Holiday Park
★★★★
Holiday, Touring & Camping Park
Overstrand, Cromer NR27 0AB
t (01263) 579239

PAKEFIELD
Suffolk

Pakefield Caravan Park
★★★
Holiday Park
Arbor Lane, Pakefield,
Lowestoft NR33 7BQ
t (01502) 561136

PENTNEY
Norfolk

Pentney Park Caravan Site
★★★★
Touring & Camping Park
Main Road, Pentney, King's
Lynn PE32 1HU
t (01760) 337479

PETERBOROUGH
Cambridgeshire

Ferry Meadows Caravan Club Site ★★★★★
Holiday Park
Ham Lane, Peterborough
PE2 5UU
t (01733) 233526
w caravanclub.co.uk
🅰🐕🎫

ROYDON
Essex

Roydon Mill Leisure Park
★★★
Holiday Park
Roydon Mill Park, Roydon,
Harlow CM19 5EJ
t (01279) 792777

SAHAM HILLS
Norfolk

Lowe Caravan Park ★★★★
Touring & Camping Park
Ashdale, Hills Road, Saham
Hills, Thetford IP25 7EZ
t (01953) 881051

ST NEOTS
Cambridgeshire

Camping and Caravanning Club Site St Neots ★★★★
Touring Park
Hardwick Road, Eynesbury, St
Neots PE19 2PR
t (01480) 474404
w campingandcaravanning
club.co.uk

ST OSYTH
Essex

The Orchards Holiday Village ★★★★
Holiday Park
Point Clear, Clacton-on-Sea
CO16 8LJ
t (01255) 820651

SANDRINGHAM
Norfolk

Camping and Caravanning Club Site Sandringham
★★★★★
Touring Park
Northgate Precinct,
Hunstanton PE36 6EA
t (01485) 542555
w campingandcaravanning
club.co.uk

The Sandringham Estate Caravan Club Site ★★★★★
Touring Park
Glucksburgh Woods,
Sandringham PE35 6EZ
t (01553) 631614
w caravanclub.co.uk

SCRATBY
Norfolk

California Cliffs Holiday Park ★★★★
Holiday Park
Rottenstone Lane, Scratby,
Great Yarmouth NR29 3QU
t (01493) 730584

Green Farm Caravan Park
★★★★★
Holiday & Touring Park
Beach Road, Scratby, Great
Yarmouth NR29 3NW
t (01493) 730440

Scratby Hall Caravan Park
★★★★
Touring & Camping Park
Thoroughfare Lane, Scratby,
Great Yarmouth NR29 3PH
t (01493) 730283

SEA PALLING
Norfolk

Golden Beach Holiday Centre ★★★
Holiday & Touring Park
Beach Road, Sea Palling,
Norwich NR12 0AL
t (01692) 598269

SNETTISHAM
Norfolk

Diglea Caravan and Camping Park ★★★
Holiday, Touring & Camping Park
Beach Road, Snettisham, King's
Lynn PE31 7RA
t (01485) 541367

SOUTHMINSTER
Essex

Eastland Meadows Country Park ★★★
Holiday Park
East End Road, Bradwell-on-
Sea, Southminster CM0 7PP
t (01621) 776577

Waterside Holiday Park ★★
Holiday & Touring Park
Main Road, St Lawrence Bay,
Southminster CM0 7LY
t (01621) 779248

STANHOE
Norfolk

The Rickels Caravan and Camping Park ★★★★
Touring Park
Bircham Road, Stanhoe, King's
Lynn PE31 8PU
t (01485) 518671

SWAFFHAM
Norfolk

The Covert Caravan Club Site ★★★★
Touring Park
High Ash, Hilborough,
Thetford IP26 5BZ
t (01842) 878356
w caravanclub.co.uk
🐕🎫

TATTERSETT
Norfolk

Manor Park Touring Caravans ★★★
Touring Park
Manor Farm, Tattersett, King's
Lynn PE31 8RS
t (01485) 528310

UPPER SHERINGHAM
Norfolk

Woodlands Caravan Park
★★★★
Holiday & Touring Park
Holt Road, Upper Sheringham,
Sheringham NR26 8TU
t (01263) 823802

WALTHAM CROSS
Hertfordshire

Camping and Caravanning Club Site Theobalds Park
★★★
Holiday Park
Bulls Cross Ride, Waltham
Cross EN7 5HS
t (01992) 620604
w campingandcaravanning
club.co.uk

WALTON-ON-THE-NAZE
Essex

Naze Marine Holiday Park
★★
Holiday Park
Hall Lane, Walton on the Naze
CO14 8HL
t 0870 442 9292

WEELEY
Essex

Homestead Lake Park ★★★
Holiday Park
Thorpe Road, Weeley, Clacton-
on-Sea CO16 9JN
t (01255) 833492

Weeley Bridge Holiday Park
★★★
Holiday Park
Clacton Road, Weeley,
Clacton-on-Sea CO16 9DH
t (01255) 830403

WELLS-NEXT-THE-SEA
Norfolk

Pinewoods Holiday Park
★★★★
Holiday Park
Beach Road, Wells-next-the-
Sea NR23 1DR
t (01328) 710439

WEST ROW
Suffolk

The Willows ★★★
Touring & Camping Park
Hurdle Drove, West Row, Bury
St Edmunds IP28 8RB
t (01638) 715963

WEST RUNTON
Norfolk

Laburnum Caravan Park
★★★
Holiday Park
Water Lane, West Runton,
Cromer NR27 9QP
t (01263) 837473

WEYBOURNE
Norfolk

Kelling Heath Holiday Park
★★★★★
Holiday, Touring & Camping Park
Sandy Hill Lane, Weybourne,
Holt NR25 7HW
t (01263) 588181

WISBECH
Cambridgeshire

Virginia Lake Caravan Park
★★★★
Holiday Park
Smeeth Road, St Johns Fen
End, Wisbech PE14 8JF
t (01945) 430585

WOODBRIDGE
Suffolk

Forest Camping ★★★
Touring & Camping Park
Tangham Campsite,
Rendlesham Forest Centre,
Woodbridge IP12 3NF
t (01394) 450707

WORTWELL
Norfolk

Little Lakeland Caravan Park
★★★★
Holiday & Touring Park
Wortwell, Harleston IP20 0EL
t (01986) 788646

WYTON
Cambridgeshire

Wyton Lakes Holiday Park
★★★★
Holiday Park
Banks End, Wyton,
Huntingdon PE28 2AA
t (01480) 412715
e loupeter@supanet.com
w wytonlakes.com

LONDON

INNER LONDON

E4

Lee Valley Campsite ★★★★
Touring Park
Sewardstone Road, Chingford,
London E4 7RA
t (020) 8529 5689
e scs@leevalleypark.org.uk
w leevalleypark.org.uk

N9

Lee Valley Leisure Centre Camping and Caravan Park ★★★★
Touring & Camping Park
Picketts Lock Lane, London
N9 0AS
t (020) 8803 6900
e leisurecentre@leevalleypark.org.uk
w leevalleypark.com

SE2

Abbey Wood Caravan Club Site ★★★★★
Touring & Camping Park
Federation Road, Abbey
Wood, London SE2 0LS
t (020) 8311 7708
w caravanclub.co.uk

SE19

Crystal Palace Caravan Club Site ★★★★★
Touring & Camping Park
Crystal Palace Parade, London
SE19 1UF
t (020) 8778 7155
w caravanclub.co.uk

SOUTH EAST ENGLAND

ALBURY
Surrey

Edgeley Holiday Park ★★★
Touring Park
Farley Green, Albury, Guildford
GU5 9DW
t (01483) 202129
e edgeley@haulfryn.co.uk

ANDOVER
Hampshire

Wyke Down Touring Caravan & Camping Park ★★★
Touring & Camping Park
Picket Piece, Andover
SP11 6LX
t (01264) 352048
e wykedown@wykedown.co.uk
w wykedown.co.uk

APSE HEATH
Isle of Wight

Old Barn Touring Park ★★★★
Touring & Camping Park
Cheverton Farm, Newport
Road, Sandown PO36 9PJ
t (01983) 866414

Village Way Caravan & Camping Site ★★★
Holiday, Touring & Camping Park
Newport Road, Sandown
PO36 9PJ
t (01983) 863279

ARRETON
Isle of Wight

Perreton Farm ★★
Holiday Park
East Lane, Arreton, Newport
PO30 3DL
t (01983) 865218
e roger.perreton@virgin.net

ASHFORD
Kent

Broadhembury Caravan & Camping Park ★★★★★
Holiday, Touring & Camping Park
Steeds Lane, Kingsnorth,
Ashford TN26 1NQ
t (01233) 620859
e holidays@broadhembury.co.uk
w broadhembury.co.uk

ASHURST
Kent

Manor Court Farm ★★★
Touring & Camping Park
Ashurst Road, Ashurst,
Tunbridge Wells TN3 9TB
t (01892) 740279
e jsoyke@jsoyke.freeserve.co.uk
w manorcourtfarm.co.uk

ATHERFIELD BAY
Isle of Wight

Chine Farm Camping Site ★★
Touring & Camping Park
Military Road, Atherfield
PO38 2JH
t (01983) 740228
e info@chine-farm.co.uk
w chine-farm.co.uk

BANBURY
Oxfordshire

Bo-Peep Caravan Park ★★★★
Holiday & Touring Park
Aynho Road, Adderbury,
Banbury OX17 3NP
t (01295) 810605
e warden@bo-peep.co.uk
w bo-peep.co.uk

BATTLE
East Sussex

**Crowhurst Park ★★★★★
ROSE AWARD**
Holiday Park
Telham Lane, Battle TN33 0SL
t (01424) 773344
e enquiries@crowhurstpark.co.uk
w crowhurstpark.co.uk

Normanhurst Court Caravan Club Site ★★★★★
Touring Park
Stevens Crouch, Battle
TN33 9LR
t (01424) 773808
w caravanclub.co.uk

BEACONSFIELD
Buckinghamshire

Highclere Farm Country Touring Park ★★★★
Touring & Camping Park
Newbarn Lane, Seer Green,
Beaconsfield HP9 2QZ
t (01494) 874505
e highclerepark@aol.com
w highclerepark.co.uk

BEMBRIDGE
Isle of Wight

Sandhills Caravan Park ★★★
Holiday Park
Whitecliff Bay, Bembridge
PO35 5QB
t (01983) 872277

Whitecliff Bay Holiday Park ★★★★
Holiday Park
Hillway Road, Bembridge
PO35 5PL
t (01983) 872671
e holiday@whitecliff-bay.com
w whitecliff-bay.com

BEXHILL-ON-SEA
East Sussex

Cobbs Hill Farm Caravan & Camping Park ★★★★
Holiday, Touring & Camping Park
Watermill Lane, Sidley, Bexhill-on-Sea TN39 5JA
t (01424) 213460
e cobbshillfarmuk@hotmail.com
w cobbshillfarm.co.uk

Kloofs Caravan Park ★★★★★
Touring & Camping Park
Sandhurst Lane, Bexhill-on-Sea
TN39 4RG
t (01424) 842839
e camping@kloofs.com

BIDDENDEN

Woodlands Park ★★★★
Touring & Camping Park
Biddenden, Ashford TN27 8BT
t (01580) 291216
e woodlandsp@aol.com
w campingsite.co.uk

BIRCHINGTON
Kent

Quex Caravan Park ★★★★★
Holiday & Touring Park
Park Road, Birchington
CT7 0BL
t (01843) 841273
e info@keatfarm.co.uk
w keatfarm.co.uk

Two Chimneys Holiday Park ★★★★★
Holiday, Touring & Camping Park
Shottendane Road, Birchington
CT7 0HD
t (01843) 841068
e info@twochimneys.co.uk
w twochimneys.co.uk

BOGNOR REGIS
West Sussex

Copthorne Caravans ★★★★
Holiday Park
Rose Green Road, Bognor
Regis PO21 3ER
t (01243) 262408
e copthornecaravans@dsl.pipex.com

The Lillies Caravan Park ★★★
Touring Park
Yapton Road, Barnham, Bognor
Regis PO22 0AY
t (01243) 552081
e thelillies@hotmail.com
w lilliescaravanpark.co.uk

Riverside Caravan Centre (Bognor) Ltd ★★★★★
Holiday Park
Shripney Road, Bognor Regis
PO22 9NE
t (01243) 865823
e info@rivcentre.co.uk
w rivcentre.co.uk

Rowan Park Caravan Club Site ★★★★
Holiday Park
Rowan Way, Bognor Regis
PO22 9RP
t (01243) 828515
w caravanclub.co.uk

BRIGHSTONE
Isle of Wight

Grange Farm Brighstone Bay ★★★
Holiday & Touring Park
Military Road, Brighstone,
Newport PO30 4DA
t (01983) 740296

Lower Sutton Farm ★★★
Holiday Park
Military Road, Newport
PO30 4PG
t (01983) 740401
e info@dinosaur-farm-
holidays.co.uk
w dinosaur-farm-holidays.co.
uk

BRIGHTON & HOVE
East Sussex

**Sheepcote Valley Caravan
Club Site ★★★★★**
Touring & Camping Park
East Brighton Park, Brighton
BN2 5TS
t (01273) 626546
w caravanclub.co.uk

BROOK
Isle of Wight

Compton Farm ★★
Holiday Park
Military Road, Brook, Newport,
Isle of Wight PO30 4HF
t (01983) 740215

BURFORD
Oxfordshire

Burford Caravan Club Site
★★★★★
Touring Park
Bradwell Grove, Burford
OX18 4JJ
t (01993) 823080
w caravanclub.co.uk

CAMBER
East Sussex

**Camber Sands Holiday Park
★★★★**
Holiday Park
New Lydd Road, Camber, Rye
TN31 7RT
t 0871 664 9718
e holidaysales.cambersands@
park-resorts.com
w park-resorts.com

CANTERBURY
Kent

**Camping & Caravanning
Club Site Canterbury
★★★★**
Touring & Camping Park
Bekesbourne Lane, Canterbury
CT3 4AB
t (01227) 463216
w campingandcaravanning
club.co.uk

Yew Tree Park ★★★★
*Holiday, Touring & Camping
Park*
Stone Street, Petham,
Canterbury CT4 5PL
t (01227) 700306
e info@yewtreepark.com
w yewtreepark.com

CAPEL LE FERNE
Kent

**Little Satmar Holiday Park
★★★★**
*Holiday, Touring & Camping
Park*
Winehouse Lane, Capel-le-
Ferne, Folkestone CT18 7JF
t (01303) 251188
w katefarm.co.uk

**Varne Ridge Holiday Park
★★★★★**
Holiday & Touring Park
Old Dover Road, Capel-le-
Ferne, Folkestone CT18 7HX
t (01303) 251765
e vrcp@varne-ridge.freeserve.
co.uk
w varne-ridge.co.uk

CHADLINGTON
Oxfordshire

**Camping & Caravanning
Club Site Chipping Norton
★★★★**
Touring & Camping Park
Chipping Norton Road,
Chadlington, Chipping Norton
OX7 3PE
t (01608) 641993
w campingandcaravanning
club.co.uk

CHALE
Isle of Wight

Atherfield Bay Holidays ★
Holiday Park
Shepherds Chine, Military
Road, Ventnor PO38 2JD
t (01983) 740307
e aly@atherfieldbay.co.uk
w atherfieldbay.co.uk

CHERTSEY
Surrey

**Camping and Caravanning
Club Site, Chertsey ★★★★**
Camping Park
Bridge Road, Chertsey
KT16 8JX
t (024) 7685 6787
w campingandcaravanning
club.co.uk

CHICHESTER
West Sussex

Bell Caravan Park ★
Holiday & Touring Park
Bell Lane, Birdham, Chichester
PO20 7HY
t (01243) 512264

**Wicks Farm Holiday Park
★★★★★**
Holiday & Camping Park
Redlands Lane, West
Wittering, Chichester
PO20 8QE
t (01243) 513116
e wicks.farm@virgin.net
w wicksfarm.co.uk

COLWELL BAY
Isle of Wight

**Colwell Bay Caravan Park
★★★★**
Holiday & Camping Park
Madeira Lane, Colwell,
Freshwater PO40 9SR
t (01983) 752403
e james.bishop1@tinyworld.
co.uk
w isleofwight-colwellbay.co.uk

COWES
Isle of Wight

**Sunnycott Caravan Park
★★★★**
Holiday Park
Rew Street, Gurnard
PO31 8NN
t (01983) 292859
e info@sunnycottcaravanpark.
co.uk
w sunnycottcaravanpark.co.uk

CROWBOROUGH
East Sussex

**Camping & Caravanning
Club Site ★★★★**
Touring & Camping Park
Pevensey BN24 6PR
t (01323) 761190
w campingandcaravanning
club.co.uk

CROWMARSH GIFFORD
Oxfordshire

**Bridge Villa Caravan &
Camping Park**
Rating Applied For
Holiday & Touring Park
The Street, Crowmarsh Gifford,
Wallingford OX10 8HB
t (01491) 836860
e bridge.villa@btinternet.com

DORNEY REACH
Berkshire

**Amerden Caravan &
Camping Park ★★★★**
Touring & Camping Park
Old Marsh Lane, Dorney
Reach, Maidenhead SL6 0EE
t (01628) 627461

DOVER
Kent

**Hawthorn Farm Caravan &
Camping Park ★★★★★**
*Holiday, Touring & Camping
Park*
Station Road, Martin Mill,
Dover CT15 5LA
t (01304) 852658
e info@keatfarm.co.uk
w keatfarm.co.uk

**Sutton Vale Country Club &
Caravan Park ★★★★**
Holiday & Touring Park
Vale Road, Sutton-by-Dover,
Dover CT15 5DH
t (01304) 374155
e office@sutton-vale.co.uk
w sutton-vale.co.uk

DYMCHURCH
Kent

**Dymchurch Caravan Park
★★★★**
Holiday Park
St Marys Road, Dymchurch,
Romney Marsh TN29 0PW
t (01303) 872303

**E & J Piper Caravan Park
★★★★**
Holiday Park
St Marys Road, Dymchurch,
Romney Marsh TN29 0PN
t (01303) 872103

**New Beach Holiday Village
★★★★**
Holiday Park
Hythe Road, Dymchurch,
Romney Marsh TN29 0JX
t (01303) 872233 &
(01303) 872234
e newbeachholiday@aol.com

**New Beach Holiday Village
Touring Park ★★★★**
Touring & Camping Park
Hythe Road, Dymchurch,
Romney Marsh TN29 0JX
t (01303) 872234
e newbeachholiday@aol.com

EAST COWES
Isle of Wight

**Waverley Park Holiday
Centre ★★★★**
*Holiday, Touring & Camping
Park*
51 Old Road, East Cowes
PO32 6AW
t (01983) 293452
e holidays@waverley-park.co.
uk
w waverley-park.co.uk

EAST HORSLEY
Surrey

**Camping and Caravanning
Club Site, Horsley ★★★★**
Touring & Camping Park
Ockham Road North, East
Horsley KT24 6PE
t (024) 7685 6787
w campingandcaravanning
club.co.uk

EASTBOURNE
East Sussex

**Fairfields Farm Caravan &
Camping Park ★★★★**
Touring & Camping Park
Eastbourne Road, Westham,
Pevensey BN24 5NG
t (01323) 763165
e enquiries@fairfieldsfarm.
com
w fairfieldsfarm.com

EASTCHURCH
Kent

**Ashcroft Coast Holiday Park
★★★★★**
Holiday Park
Plough Road, Eastchurch,
Sheerness ME12 4JH
t 0871 664 9701
e holidaysales.ashcroftcoast@
park-resorts.com
w park-resorts.com

**Copperfields Holiday Park
★★★★**
Holiday Park
Fourth Avenue, Eastchurch,
Sheerness ME12 4EW
t (01795) 880080
e copperfields@
palmtreemanagement.co.uk
w palmtreemanagement.co.uk

Palm Trees Holiday Park
★★★
Holiday Park
Second Avenue, Warden Road,
Isle of Sheppey ME12 4ET
t (01795) 880080
e palmtrees@
palmtreemanagement.co.uk
w palmtreemanagement.co.uk

Shurland Dale Holiday Park
★★★★
Holiday Park
Warden Road, Eastchurch,
Sheerness ME12 4EN
t 0871 664 9769
e holidaysales.shurland@park-
resorts.com
w park-resorts.com

**Warden Springs Holiday
Park** ★★★
*Holiday, Touring & Camping
Park*
Thorn Hill Road, Eastchurch,
Sheerness ME12 4HF
t 0871 664 9790
e holidayparks.
wardensprings@park-resorts.
com
w park-resorts.com

FAREHAM
Hampshire

**Ellerslie Touring Caravan &
Camping Park** ★
Touring Park
Down End Road, Fareham
PO16 8TS
t (01329) 822248

FOLKESTONE
Kent

**Black Horse Farm Caravan
Club Site** ★★★★★
Touring & Camping Park
385 Canterbury Road, Densole,
Folkestone CT18 7BG
t (01303) 892665
w caravanclub.co.uk

**Camping & Caravanning
Club Site Folkestone** ★★★★
Touring & Camping Park
The Warren, Folkestone
CT19 6NQ
t (01303) 255093
w campingandcaravanning
club.co.uk

FORDINGBRIDGE
Hampshire

Sandy Balls Holiday Centre
★★★★★
Holiday Park
Godshill, Fordingbridge
SP6 2JZ
t (01425) 653042
e post@sandy-balls.co.uk
w sandy-balls.co.uk

FRESHWATER
Isle of Wight

**Heathfield Farm Camping
Site** ★★★★
Touring & Camping Park
Heathfield Road, Freshwater
PO40 9SH
t (01983) 756756
e web@heathfieldcamping.co.
uk
w heathfieldcamping.co.uk

GOSPORT
Hampshire

Kingfisher Caravan Park
★★★
*Holiday, Touring & Camping
Park*
Browndown Road, Stokes
Road, Gosport, Lee-on-the-
Solent PO13 9BG
t (023) 9250 2611
e info@kingfisher-caravan-
park.co.uk
w kingfisher-caravan-park.co.
uk

GRAFFHAM
West Sussex

**Camping & Caravanning
Club Site** ★★★★
Touring & Camping Park
Great Bury, Graffham,
Petworth GU28 0QJ
t (024) 7685 6787
w campingandcaravanning
club.co.uk

GURNARD
Isle of Wight

**Gurnard Pines Holiday
Village** ★★★★★
Holiday Park
Cockleton Lane, Cowes
PO31 8QE
t (01983) 292395
e info@gurnardpines.co.uk

HAILSHAM
East Sussex

**Peel House Farm Caravan
Park** ★★★★
*Holiday, Touring & Camping
Park*
Sayerland Lane, Polegate
BN26 6QX
t (01323) 845629
e peelhocp@tesco.net

HAMBLE
Hampshire

Riverside Park ★★★
*Holiday, Touring & Camping
Park*
Satchell Lane, Hamble,
Southampton SO31 4HR
t (023) 8045 3220
e enquiries@riversideholidays.
co.uk
w riversideholidays.co.uk

HASTINGS
East Sussex

Combe Haven Holiday Park
★★★★★
Holiday Park
Harley Shute Road, St
Leonards-on-Sea TN38 8BZ
t (01424) 427891

Rocklands Holiday Park
★★★★
Holiday Park
Rocklands Lane, East Hill,
Hastings TN35 5DY
t (01424) 423097

Shear Barn Holiday Park
★★★★★
*Holiday, Touring & Camping
Park*
Barley Lane, Hastings
TN35 5DX
t (01424) 423583

**Stalkhurst Camping &
Caravan Park** ★★★
*Holiday, Touring & Camping
Park*
Ivyhouse Lane, Hastings
TN35 4NN
t (01424) 439015
e stalkhurstpark@btinternet.
com

HAYLING ISLAND
Hampshire

**Fishery Creek Caravan &
Camping Park** ★★★
Touring & Camping Park
Fishery Lane, Hayling Island
PO11 9NR
t (023) 9246 2164
e camping@fisherycreek.
fsnet.co.uk
w keyparks.co.uk

**Mill Rythe Entertainment
Resort and Holiday Village**
Rating Applied For
Holiday & Touring Park
Mill Rythe Holiday Village,
16 Havant Road, Hayling Island
PO11 0PB
t (023) 9246 3805
w hollybushhotels.co.uk

HENFIELD
West Sussex

Downsview Caravan Park
★★★
*Holiday, Touring & Camping
Park*
Bramlands Lane,
Woodmancote, Henfield
BN5 9TG
t (01273) 492801
e phr.peter@lineone.net

HERSTMONCEUX
East Sussex

Orchard View Park
★★★★★
Holiday Park
Victoria Road, Herstmonceux,
Hailsham BN27 4SY
t (01323) 832335

HORAM
East Sussex

Horam Manor Touring Park
★★★★
Touring & Camping Park
Horam, Heathfield TN21 0YD
t (01435) 813662
e camp@horam-manor.co.uk
w horam-manor.co.uk

HORSHAM
West Sussex

Honeybridge Park ★★★★
Holiday Park
Honeybridge Lane, Dial Post,
Nr Horsham RH13 8NX
t (01403) 710923
e enquiries@
honeybridgepark.co.uk
w honeybridgepark.co.uk

**Sumners Ponds Fishery &
Campsite** ★★★★
Touring Park
Slaughterford Farm, Chapel
Road, Barns Green, Horsham
RH13 0PR
t (01403) 732539
e sumnersponds@dsl.pipex.
com
w sumnersponds.co.uk

HURLEY
Berkshire

Hurley Riverside Park
★★★★
Holiday Park
Hurley, Maidenhead SL6 5NE
t (01628) 824493
e info@hurleyriversidepark.co.
uk
w hurleyriversidepark.co.uk

Hurleyford Farm Ltd ★★★★
Holiday Park
Mill Lane, Hurley, Maidenhead
SL6 5ND
t (01628) 829009

KINGSDOWN
Kent

**Kingsdown Park Holiday
Village** ★★★★★
Holiday Park
Upper Street, Kingsdown, Deal
CT14 8AU
t (01304) 361205
e info@kingsdownpark.co.uk
w kingsdownpark.net

LINGFIELD
Surrey

**Long Acres Caravan &
Camping Park** ★★
Touring Park
Newchapel Road, Lingfield
RH7 6LE
t (01342) 833205
e longacrescamping@yahoo.
co.uk
w longacrescamping.co.uk

LYMINGTON
Hampshire

Hurst View Caravan Park
★★★
Camping Park
Lower Pennington Lane,
Pennington, Lymington
SO41 8AL
t (01590) 671648

LYMINSTER
West Sussex

Brookside Caravan Park
★★★
Holiday Park
Lyminster Road, Lyminster,
Littlehampton BN17 7QE
t (01903) 713292
e mark@brooksideuk.com
w brooksideuk.com

MAIDSTONE
Kent

Pine Lodge Touring Park
★★★★★
Touring & Camping Park
A20 Ashford Road,
Hollingbourne, Maidstone
ME17 1XH
t (01622) 730018
e booking@
pinelodgetouringpark.co.uk
w pinelodgetouringpark.co.uk

MARDEN
Kent

**Tanner Farm Touring
Caravan & Camping Park**
★★★★★
Touring & Camping Park
Goudhurst Road, Tonbridge
TN12 9ND
t (01622) 832399
e enquiries@tannerfarmpark.
co.uk
w tannerfarmpark.co.uk

MILFORD ON SEA
Hampshire

Carrington Park ★★★★★
Holiday Park
New Lane, Milford on Sea,
Lymington SO41 0UQ
t (01590) 642654

Downton Holiday Park
★★★★
Holiday Park
Shorefield Road, Milford on
Sea, Lymington SO41 0LH
t (01425) 476131 &
(01590) 642515
e info@downtonholidaypark.
co.uk

Lytton Lawn Touring Park
★★★★
Touring Park
Lymore Lane, Milford on Sea,
Lymington SO41 0TX
t (01590) 648331
e holidays@shorefield.co.uk
w shorefield.co.uk

Shorefield Country Park
★★★★★
Holiday Park
Shorefield Road, Milford on
Sea, Lymington SO41 0LH
t (01590) 648331
e holidays@shorefield.co.uk
w shorefield.co.uk

MINSTER-IN-SHEPPEY
Kent

Seacliff Holiday Estate Ltd
★★★
Holiday Park
Oak Lane, Minster on Sea,
Sheerness ME12 3QS
t (01795) 872262

Willow Trees Holiday Park
★★★
Holiday Park
Oak Lane, Minster on Sea,
Sheerness ME12 3QR
t (01795) 875833

MINSTER-IN-THANET
Kent

Wayside Caravan Park
★★★★★
Holiday Park
Way Hill, Minster, Ramsgate
CT12 4HW
t (01843) 821272
e lydia@scott9330.freeserve.
co.uk

MOLLINGTON
Oxfordshire

**Anita's Touring Caravan
Park ★★★★**
Touring & Camping Park
Church Farm, Mollington,
Banbury OX17 1AZ
t (01295) 750731
e anitagail@btopenworld.com

MONKTON
Kent

The Foxhunter Park
★★★★★
Holiday Park
Monkton Street, Monkton,
Ramsgate CT12 4JG
t (01843) 821311
e foxhunterpark@aol.com
w thefoxhunterpark.co.uk

NEW MILTON
Hampshire

Glen Orchard Holiday Park
★★★★
Holiday Park
Walkford Lane, New Milton
BH25 5NH
t (01425) 616463

Hoburne Bashley ★★★★
Holiday Park
Sway Road, New Milton
BH25 5QR
t (01425) 612340

Hoburne Naish ★★★★★
Holiday Park
Christchurch Road, New Milton
BH25 7RE
t (01425) 273586
e enquiries@hoburne.com
w hoburne.com

NEW ROMNEY
Kent

Romney Sands Holiday Park
★★★★
Holiday Park
The Parade, Greatstone, New
Romney TN28 8RN
t 0871 664 9760
e holidaysales.romneysands@
park-resorts.com
w park-resorts.com

NEWCHURCH
Isle of Wight

Southland Camping Park
★★★★★
Touring & Camping Park
Winford Road, Sandown
PO36 0LZ
t (01983) 865385
e info@southland.co.uk
w southland.co.uk

NEWCHURCH
Kent

**Norwood Farm Caravan &
Camping Park Ltd ★★★★**
Touring & Camping Park
Newchurch, Romney Marsh
TN29 0DU
t (01303) 873659
e jameswimble@farming.co.uk

NITON
Isle of Wight

Meadow View Caravan Site
★
Holiday Park
Newport Road, Niton
PO38 2NS
t (01983) 730015

NORTH BOARHUNT
Hampshire

South Hants Country Club
★★★★
Holiday Park
Blackhouse Lane, North
Boarhunt, Fareham PO17 6JS
t (01329) 832919
e info@naturistholidays.co.uk
w naturistholidays.co.uk

OLNEY
Buckinghamshire

Emberton Country Park ★★
Touring & Camping Park
Emberton, Olney MK46 5DB
t (01234) 711575
e embertonpark@milton-
keynes.gov.uk
w mkweb.co.uk/embertonpark

OWER
Hampshire

**Green Pastures Caravan
Park ★★★**
Touring Park
Whitemoor Lane, Ower,
Romsey SO51 6AJ
t (023) 8081 4444

OXFORD
Oxfordshire

**The Camping & Caravanning
Club Site Oxford ★★★**
Touring & Camping Park
426 Abingdon Road, Oxford
OX1 4XN
t (01865) 244088
w campingandcaravanning
club.co.uk

PAGHAM
West Sussex

Church Farm Holiday Village
★★★★
Holiday Park
Church Lane, Bognor Regis
PO21 4NR
t 0870 405 0151
e churchfarm@bourne-leisure.
co.uk
w churchfarm-park.co.uk

PEVENSEY
East Sussex

**Camping and Caravanning
Club Site Normans Bay**
★★★★
Touring & Camping Park
Pevensey BN24 6PR
t (01323) 761190
w campingandcaravanning
club.co.uk

PEVENSEY BAY
East Sussex

Bay View Park ★★★
*Holiday, Touring & Camping
Park*
Old Martello Road, Pevensey
Bay BN24 6DX
t (01323) 768688
e holidays@bay-view.co.uk
w bay-view.co.uk

Martello Beach Park
★★★★★
Holiday Park
Eastbourne Road, Pevensey
Bay, Pevensey BN24 6DH
t (01323) 761424
e m.smart@
martellobeachpark.fsbusiness.
co.uk
w ukparks.co.uk/martello

RAMSGATE
Kent

**Manston Caravan &
Camping Park ★★★★**
*Holiday, Touring & Camping
Park*
Manston Court Road, Manston,
Ramsgate CT12 5AU
t (01843) 823442

Nethercourt Touring Park
★★★
Touring & Camping Park
Nethercourt Hill, Ramsgate
CT11 0RX
t (01843) 595485

READING
Berkshire

Wellington Country Park
★★★★
Touring & Camping Park
Odiham Road, Riseley, Reading
RG7 1SP
t (0118) 932 6444
e info@wellington-country-
park.co.uk
w wellington-country-park.co.
uk

REDHILL
Surrey

**Alderstead Heath Caravan
Club Site ★★★★**
Touring Park
Dean Lane, Redhill RH1 3AH
t (01737) 644629
w caravanclub.co.uk

RINGWOOD
Hampshire

Red Shoot Camping Park
★★★
Camping Park
Linwood, Ringwood BH24 3QT
t (01425) 473789
e enquiries@redshoot-
campingpark.com
w redshoot-campingpark.com

Shamba Holidays ★★
Touring & Camping Park
230 Ringwood Road, St
Leonards, Ringwood BH24 2SB
t (01202) 873302
e enquiries@shamba.co.uk
w shambaholidays.co.uk

ROCHESTER
Kent

Allhallows Leisure Park
★★★★
Holiday Park
Allhallows-on-Sea, Rochester
ME3 9QD
t (01634) 270385
e enquiries@british-holidays.
co.uk
w british-holidays.co.uk

Woolmans Wood Caravan Park ★★★★
Touring & Camping Park
Rochester Road, Chatham
ME5 9SB
t (01634) 867685
e woolmans.wood@
currantbun.com
w woolmans-wood.co.uk

ROMSEY
Hampshire

Hill Farm Caravan Park
★★★★
Holiday, Touring & Camping Park
Branches Lane, Sherfield
English, Romsey SO51 6FH
t (01794) 340402
e gib@hillfarmpark.com
w hillfarmpark.com

ROOKLEY
Isle of Wight

Rookley Country Park – Island View Holidays
★★★★
Holiday Park
Rookley Country Park, Main
Road, Ventnor PO38 3LU
t (01983) 721606
e info@islandviewhols.co.uk
w islandviewhols.co.uk

RYDE
Isle of Wight

Beaper Farm ★★★
Touring Park
Brading Road, Ryde PO33 1QJ
t (01983) 615210
e beaper@btinternet.com

Pondwell Holiday Park
★★★
Holiday Park
Pondwell Hill, Ryde PO33 1QA
t (01983) 612100
e info@isleofwightselfcatering.
co.uk
w isleofwightselfcatering.co.uk

Roebeck Camping and Caravan Park ★★★
Touring & Camping Park
Gatehouse Road, Upton, Ryde
PO33 4BP
t (01522) 545088
e info@roebeck-farm.co.uk
w roebeck-farm.co.uk

ST HELENS
Isle of Wight

Carpenters Farm Campsite
★★★
Touring & Camping Park
Carpenters Road, St Helens,
Ryde PO33 1YL
t (01983) 874557
e info@carpentersfarm.co.uk
w carpentersfarm.co.uk

Field Lane Holiday Park
★★★★★ **ROSE AWARD**
Holiday Park
Field Lane, St Helens, Ryde
PO33 1UX
t (01983) 872779
e office@fieldlane.com
w fieldlane.com

Hillgrove Park ★★★★★
Holiday Park
Field Lane, St Helens
PO33 1UT
t (01983) 872802
e holidays@hillgrove.co.uk
w hillgrove.co.uk

Nodes Point Holiday Park
★★★★
Touring & Camping Park
Nodes Road, St Helens, Ryde
PO33 1YA
t (01983) 872401
w park-resorts.com

Old Mill Holiday Park
★★★★★
Holiday Park
Mill Road, St Helens PO33 1UE
t (01983) 872507
e web@oldmill.co.uk
w oldmill.co.uk

ST LAWRENCE
Isle of Wight

Undercliff Glen Caravan Park ★★★★★
Holiday Park
Undercliff Drive, St Lawrence
PO38 1XY
t (01983) 730261
e lee@morrisl9.freeserve.co.
uk

ST-MARGARETS-AT-CLIFFE
Kent

St Margarets Holiday Park
★★★★★
Holiday Park
Reach Road, St Margarets-at-
Cliffe, Dover CT15 6AE
t 0871 664 9772
e holidaysales.
stmargaretsbay@park-resorts.
com
w park-resorts.com

ST NICHOLAS AT WADE
Kent

St Nicholas Camping Site
★★
Touring & Camping Park
Court Road, St Nicholas at
Wade, Birchington CT7 0NH
t (01843) 847245

SANDOWN
Isle of Wight

Camping & Caravanning Club – Adgestone Club Site
★★★★
Holiday Park
Lower Adgestone Road,
Sandown PO36 0HL
t (01983) 403432
w campingandcaravanning
club.co.uk

Cheverton Copse Holiday Park ★★★★
Holiday, Touring & Camping Park
Scotchells Brook Lane,
Sandown PO36 0JP
t (01983) 403161
e holidays@cheverton-copse.
co.uk
w cheverton-copse.co.uk

Fairway Holiday Park ★★★
Holiday Park
The Fairway, Sandown
PO36 9PS
t (01983) 403462
e enquiries@
fairwayholidaypark.co.uk
w fairwayholidaypark.co.uk

Fort Holiday Park ★★★
Holiday Park
Avenue Road, Sandown
PO36 8BD
t (01983) 402858
e bookings@fortholidaypark.
co.uk
w fortholidaypark.co.uk

Fort Spinney Holiday Chalets ★★★★★
Holiday Park
Yaverland Road, Sandown
PO36 8QB
t (01983) 402360
e fortspinney@isle-of-wight.
uk.com
w isle-of-wight.uk.com/
spinney

Sandown Holiday Chalets
★★★★
Holiday Park
Avenue Road, Sandown
PO36 9AP
t (01983) 404025
e chalets@isle-of-wight.uk.
com
w isle-of-wight.uk.com/chalets

SANDWICH
Kent

Sandwich Leisure Park
★★★★★
Holiday, Touring & Camping Park
Woodnesborough Road,
Sandwich CT13 0AA
t (01304) 612681
e info@
coastandcountryleisure.com
w coastandcountryleisure.com

SEAFORD
East Sussex

Sunnyside Caravan Park
★★★★
Holiday Park
Marine Parade, Seaford
BN25 2QW
t (01323) 892825

SEAL
Kent

Camping & Caravanning Club Site Oldbury Hill
★★★★
Touring & Camping Park
Styants Bottom, Seal,
Sevenoaks TN15 0ET
t (01732) 762728
w campingandcaravanning
club.co.uk

SEASALTER
Kent

Homing Leisure Park
★★★★★
Holiday, Touring & Camping Park
Church Lane, Seasalter,
Whitstable CT5 4BU
t (01227) 771777
e info@homingpark.co.uk
w coastandcountryleisure.com

SEAVIEW
Isle of Wight

Salterns Holidays ★★★
Holiday Park
Salterns Road, Seaview
PO34 5AQ
t (01983) 612330
e info@isleofwightselfcatering.
co.uk
w isleofwightselfcatering.co.uk

Tollgate Holiday Park ★★★
Holiday Park
Duver Road, Seaview
PO34 5AJ
t (01983) 612107
e info@isleofwightselfcatering.
co.uk
w isleofwightselfcatering.co.uk

SELSEY
West Sussex

Bunn Leisure – Green Lawns Holiday Park ★★★★★
Holiday Park
Paddock Lane, Selsey,
Chichester PO20 9EJ
t (01243) 604121
e holidays@bunnleisure.co.uk
w bunnleisure.co.uk

Warner Farm Touring Park
★★★★★
Touring Park
Warners Lane, Selsey,
Chichester PO20 9EL
t (01243) 604499 &
(01243) 606080
e touring@bunnleisure.co.uk
w bunnleisure.co.uk

West Sands Holiday Park
★★★★
Holiday Park
Mill Lane, Selsey, Chichester
PO20 9BH
t (01243) 606080
e holidays@bunnleisure.co.uk
w bunnleisure.co.uk

White Horse Caravan Park
★★★★
Holiday Park
Paddock Lane, Selsey,
Chichester PO20 9EJ
t (01243) 606080
e holidays@bunnleisure.co.uk
w bunnleisure.co.uk

SHANKLIN
Isle of Wight

Landguard Camping Park
★★★★
Touring & Camping Park
Landguard Manor Road,
Shanklin PO37 7PH
t (01983) 867028
e landguard@weltinet.com
w landguard-camping.co.uk

**Landguard Holidays –
Davidson Leisure Resorts
Ltd** ★★★
Holiday Park
Landguard Manor Road,
Shanklin PO37 7PJ
t (01983) 863100
e enquiries@
landguardholidays.co.uk
w landguardholidays.co.uk

Lower Hyde Holiday Village
★★★★
*Holiday, Touring & Camping
Park*
Landguard Road, Shanklin
PO37 7LL
t 0871 664 9751
e holidaysales.lowerhyde@
park-resorts.com
w park-resorts.com

Ninham Country Holidays
★★★★
Holiday & Touring Park
Ninham Farm, Shanklin
PO37 7PL
t (01983) 864243
e info@ninham.fsnet.co.uk
w ninham-holidays.co.uk

SLINDON
West Sussex

**Camping & Caravanning
Club Site, Slindon** ★★
Touring Park
Slindon, Arundel BN18 0RG
t (01243) 814387
w campingandcaravanning
club.co.uk

SMALL DOLE
West Sussex

Southdown Caravan Park
★★★
Holiday & Touring Park
Henfield Road, Small Dole,
Henfield BN5 9XH
t (01903) 814323

SOUTHBOURNE
West Sussex

**Camping & Caravanning
Club Site** ★★★
Touring & Camping Park
Main Road, Southbourne,
Chichester PO10 8JH
t (01243) 373202
w campingandcaravanning
club.co.uk

SOUTHWATER
West Sussex

Raylands Park ★★★
*Holiday, Touring & Camping
Park*
Jackrells Lane, Southwater,
Horsham RH13 9DH
t (01403) 730218
e raylands@
roundstonecaravans.com
w roundstonecaravans.com

STANDLAKE
Oxfordshire

Hardwick Parks ★★★
*Holiday, Touring & Camping
Park*
The Downs, Standlake, Witney
OX29 7PZ
t (01865) 300501
e info@hardwickparks.co.uk
w hardwickparks.co.uk

Lincoln Farm Park Limited
★★★★★
Touring Park
High Street, Standlake, Witney
OX29 7RH
t (01865) 300239
e info@lincolnfarm.touristnet.
uk.com
w lincolnfarmpark.uk.com

THORNESS BAY
Isle of Wight

Thorness Bay Holiday Park
★★★★
*Holiday, Touring & Camping
Park*
Thorness Lane, Cowes
PO31 8NJ
t (01983) 523109
w park-resorts.com

UCKFIELD
East Sussex

Honeys Green Caravan Park
★★★
*Holiday, Touring & Camping
Park*
Easons Green, Framfield,
Uckfield TN22 5RE
t (01732) 860205

WALTON-ON-THAMES
Surrey

**Camping and Caravanning
Club Site (Walton on
Thames)** ★★★
Camping Park
Fieldcommon Lane, Walton-on-
Thames KT12 3QG
t (024) 669 4995
w campingandcaravanning
club.co.uk

WARSASH
Hampshire

Dibles Park Company Ltd
★★★★
Touring Park
Dibles Park, Dibles Road,
Warsash, Southampton
SO31 9SA
t (01489) 575232

WASHINGTON
West Sussex

**Washington Caravan &
Camping Park** ★★★★
Touring & Camping Park
London Road, Washington,
Pulborough RH20 4AJ
t (01903) 892869
e washcamp@amserve.com
w washcamp.com

WESTENHANGER
Kent

**Folkestone Racecourse
Caravan Club Site** ★★★
Holiday & Camping Park
Westenhanger, Hythe
CT21 4HX
t (01303) 261761
w caravanclub.co.uk
▶🚲

WINCHESTER
Hampshire

Morn Hill Caravan Club Site
★★★★
Touring & Camping Park
Morn Hill, Winchester
SO21 2PH
t (01962) 869877
w caravanclub.co.uk

WORTHING
West Sussex

**Northbrook Farm Caravan
Club Site** ★★★★
Touring Park
Titnore Way, Worthing
BN13 3RT
t (01903) 502962
w caravanclub.co.uk

WROTHAM HEATH
Kent

**Gate House Wood Touring
Park** ★★★★★
Touring Park
Ford Road, Wrotham Heath,
Sevenoaks TN15 7SD
t (01732) 843062
e gatehousewood@btinternet.
com

WROXALL
Isle of Wight

**Appuldurcombe Gardens
Holiday Park** ★★★★
Holiday & Touring Park
Appuldurcombe Road, Ventnor
PO38 3EP
t (01983) 852597
e info@
appuldurcombegardens.co.uk
w appuldurcombegardens.co.
uk

YARMOUTH
Isle of Wight

**The Orchards Holiday
Caravan & Camping Park**
★★★★★
Holiday & Touring Park
Main Road, Yarmouth
PO41 0TS
t (01983) 531331
e info@orchards-holiday-park.
co.uk
w orchards-holiday-park.co.uk

Silver Glades Caravan Park
★★★★
Holiday Park
Solent Road, Cranmore
PO41 0XZ
t (01983) 760172
e holiday@silvergladesiow.co.
uk
w silvergladesiow.co.uk

SOUTH WEST ENGLAND

ALDERHOLT
Dorset

**Hill Cottage Farm Touring
Caravan Park** ★★★★
Touring & Camping Park
Sandleheath Road, Alderholt,
Fordingbridge SP6 3EG
t (01425) 650513

ASHBURTON
Devon

Parkers Farm Holiday Park
★★★★
*Holiday, Touring & Camping
Park*
Higher Mead Farm, Alston
Cross, Ashburton, Newton
Abbot TQ13 7LJ
t (01364) 652598
e parkersfarm@btconnect.com
w parkersfarm.co.uk

River Dart Adventures
★★★★
Touring & Camping Park
Holne Park, Ashburton,
Newton Abbot TQ13 7NP
t (01364) 652511
e enquiries@riverdart.co.uk
w riverdart.co.uk

AXMINSTER
Devon

Andrewshayes Caravan Park
★★★★
Holiday Park
Dalwood, Axminster EX13 7DY
t (01404) 831225
e enquiries@andrewshayes.
co.uk
w andrewshayes.co.uk

Hunters Moon Country Estate ★★★★
Holiday, Touring & Camping Park
Hawkchurch, Axminster
EX13 5UL
t (01297) 678402
w ukparks.co.uk/huntersmoon

BARNSTAPLE
Devon

Kentisbury Grange Country Park ★★★★
Holiday, Touring & Camping Park
Kentisbury, Barnstaple
EX31 4NL
t (01271) 883454
e info@kentisburygrange.co.uk
w kentisburygrange.co.uk

BATH
Somerset

Newton Mill Camping ★★★★
Touring & Camping Park
Newton Road, Bath BA2 9JF
t (01225) 333909
e newtonmill@hotmail.com
w campinginbath.co.uk

BEETHAM
Somerset

Five Acres Caravan Club Site ★★★★
Touring Park
Beetham, Chard TA20 3QA
t (01460) 234519
w caravanclub.co.uk

BERE REGIS
Dorset

Rowlands Wait Touring Park ★★★
Touring & Camping Park
Rye Hill, Bere Regis, Wareham
BH20 7LP
t (01929) 472727
e bta@rowlandswait.co.uk
w rowlandswait.co.uk

BERRY HEAD
Devon

Landscove Holiday Village ★★★★
Holiday Park
Gillard Road, Brixham TQ5 9EP
t 0870 442 9750
e bookings@landscove.biz
w southdevonholidays.biz

BERRYNARBOR
Devon

Sandaway Beach Holiday Park ★★★★
Holiday Park
Berrynarbor, Ilfracombe
EX34 9ST
t (01271) 866766
e stay@johnfowlerholidays.com
w johnfowlerholidays.com

BICKINGTON
Devon

Lemonford Caravan Park ★★★★★
Holiday, Touring & Camping Park
Bickington, Newton Abbot
TQ12 6JR
t (01626) 821242
e mark@lemonford.co.uk
w lemonford.co.uk

BIDEFORD
Devon

Bideford Bay Holiday Park ★★★★
Holiday Park
Bucks Cross, Bideford
EX39 5DU
t (01237) 431331
e gm.bidefordbay@park-resorts.com
w park-resorts.com

BISHOP SUTTON
Somerset

Bath Chew Valley Caravan Park ★★★★★
Touring Park
Ham Lane, Bishop Sutton,
Bristol BS39 5TZ
t (01275) 332127

BLACKWATER
Cornwall

Trevarth Holiday Park ★★★★
Touring & Camping Park
Blackwater, Truro TR4 8HR
t (01872) 560266
e trevarth@lineone.net
w trevarth.co.uk

BLANDFORD FORUM
Dorset

The Inside Park ★★★★
Touring & Camping Park
Down House Estate, Blandford
St Mary, Blandford Forum
DT11 9AD
t (01258) 453719
e inspark@aol.com
w members.aol.com/inspark/inspark

BLUE ANCHOR
Somerset

Hoburne Blue Anchor ★★★★
Holiday & Touring Park
Blue Anchor (Hoburne),
Minehead TA24 6JT
t (01643) 821360
e enquiries@hoburne.co.uk
w hoburne.co.uk

BODMIN
Cornwall

Camping & Caravanning Club (Bodmin) ★★★★
Touring & Camping Park
Old Callywith Road, Bodmin
PL31 2DZ
t (01872) 501658
w campingandcaravanningclub.co.uk

Ruthern Valley Holidays ★★★★
Holiday, Touring & Camping Park
Ruthern Bridge, Bodmin
PL30 5LU
t (01208) 831395

BOURNEMOUTH
Dorset

Meadow Bank Holidays ★★★★★
Holiday, Touring & Camping Park
Stour Way, Christchurch
BH23 2PQ
t (01202) 483597
e enquiries@meadowbank-holidays.co.uk
w meadowbank-holiday.co.uk

St Leonards Farm Caravan and Camping Park ★★
Touring & Camping Park
Ringwood Road, West Moors,
Ferndown BH22 0AQ
t (01202) 872637
w stleonardsfarm.biz

BOVEY
Devon

Bovisand Lodge Estate Ltd ★★★★
Holiday Park
Bovisand Lodge, Bovisand,
Plymouth PL9 0AA
t (01752) 403554
e stay@bovisand.com
w bovisand.com

BRATTON FLEMING
Devon

Greenacres Farm Touring Caravan Park ★★★★
Touring Park
Bratton Fleming, Barnstaple
EX31 4SG
t (01598) 763334

BRAUNTON
Devon

Lobb Fields Caravan and Camping Park ★★★★
Touring & Camping Park
Saunton Road, Braunton
EX33 1EB
t (01271) 812090
e info@lobbfields.com
w lobbfields.com

BREAN
Somerset

Diamond Farm ★★★
Touring & Camping Park
Weston Road, Brean,
Burnham-on-Sea TA8 2RL
t (01278) 751263
e trevor@diamondfarm42.freeserve.co.uk
w diamondfarm.co.uk

Dolphin Caravan Park ★★★★★
Holiday Park
Coast Road, Brean, Burnham-on-Sea TA8 2QY
t (01278) 751258
w dolphincaravanpark.co.uk

Golden Sands Caravan Park ★★★
Holiday Park
South Road, Brean, Burnham-on-Sea TA8 2RF
t (01278) 752100
e admin@brean.com
w brean.com

Isis and Wyndham Park ★★★★
Holiday Park
Warren Road, Brean Sands,
Burnham-on-Sea TA8 2RP
t (01278) 751227
e enquiries@warren-farm.co.uk
w warren-farm.co.uk

Northam Farm Touring Park ★★★★
Holiday, Touring & Camping Park
Brean Sands, Burnham-on-Sea
TA8 2SE
t (01278) 751244
e enquiries@northamfarm.co.uk
w northamfarm.co.uk

Warren Farm Holiday Centre ★★★★
Holiday, Touring & Camping Park
Warren Road, Brean Sands,
Burnham-on-Sea TA8 2RP
t (01278) 751227
e enquiries@warren-farm.co.uk
w warren-farm.co.uk

BRIDESTOWE
Devon

Glebe Park ★★★
Holiday & Touring Park
Bridestowe, Okehampton
EX20 4ER
t (01837) 861261

BRIDGWATER
Somerset

Fairways International Touring Caravan and Camping Park ★★
Touring & Camping Park
Bath Road, Bawdrip,
Bridgwater TA7 8PP
t (01278) 685569
e fairwaysint@btinternet.com
w fairwaysint.btinternet.co.uk

BRIDPORT
Dorset

Binghams Farm Touring Caravan Park ★★★★
Touring & Camping Park
Binghams Farm, Melplash,
Bridport DT6 3TT
t (01308) 488234
e enquiries@binghamsfarm.co.uk
w binghamsfarm.co.uk

Eype House Caravan Park Ltd ★★★
Holiday, Touring & Camping Park
Eype, Bridport DT6 6AL
t (01308) 424903
e enquiries@eypehouse.co.uk
w eypehouse.co.uk

Freshwater Beach Holiday Park ★★★★
Holiday, Touring & Camping Park
Burton Bradstock, Bridport
DT6 4PT
t (01308) 897317
e office@freshwaterbeach.co.uk
w freshwaterbeach.co.uk

Golden Cap Holiday Park ★★★★★ ROSE AWARD
Holiday, Touring & Camping Park
Seatown, Chideock, Bridport
DT6 6JX
t (01308) 422139
e holidays@wdlh.co.uk
w wdlh.co.uk

Highlands End Holiday Park ★★★★★ ROSE AWARD
Holiday, Touring & Camping Park
Eype, Bridport DT6 6AR
t (01308) 422139
e holidays@wdlh.co.uk
w wdlh.co.uk

BRISTOL
City of Bristol

Baltic Wharf Caravan Club Site ★★★★
Touring Park
Cumberland Road, Bristol
BS1 6XG
t (0117) 926 8030
w caravanclub.co.uk

BRIXHAM
Devon

Brixham Holiday Park ★★★★
Holiday Park
Fishcombe Road, Brixham
TQ5 8RA
t (01803) 853324
e enquiries@brixhamholpk.fsnet.co.uk
w brixhamholidaypark.co.uk

Centry Touring Caravans & Tents ★★
Touring & Camping Park
Mudberry House, Centry Road,
Brixham TQ5 9EY
t (01803) 853215
e jlacentry.touring@talk21.com
w english-riviera.co.uk

Galmpton Touring Park ★★★★
Touring & Camping Park
Greenway Road, Galmpton,
Brixham TQ5 0EP
t (01803) 842066
e galmptontouringpark@hotmail.com
w galmptontouringpark.co.uk

Hillhead Holiday Park ★★★★★
Touring & Camping Park
Hillhead, Brixham TQ5 0HH
t (01803) 853204
w caravanclub.co.uk

Riviera Bay Holiday Centre ★★★★
Holiday Park
Mudstone Lane, Brixham
TQ5 9EJ
t (01803) 856335
e info@rivierabay.biz
w rivierabay.biz

BUDE
Cornwall

Bude Holiday Park ★★★
Holiday, Touring & Camping Park
Maer Lane, Bude EX23 9EE
t (01288) 355955
e enquiries@budeholidaypark.co.uk
w budeholidaypark.co.uk

Budemeadows Touring Holiday Park ★★★★★
Touring Park
Budemeadows, Bude
EX23 0NA
t (01288) 361646
e holiday@budemeadows.com
w budemeadows.com

Penhalt Farm Holiday Park ★★★
Touring & Camping Park
Widemouth Bay, Poundstock,
Bude EX23 0DG
t (01288) 361210
e den&jennie@penhaltfarm.fsnet.co.uk
w holidaybank.co.uk/penhaltfarmholidaypark

Sandymouth Bay Holiday Park ★★★★
Holiday & Touring Park
Sandymouth Bay, Bude
EX23 9HW
t (01288) 352563
e reception@sandymouthbay.co.uk
w dolphinholidays.co.uk

Upper Lynstone Caravan and Camping Site ★★★★
Holiday, Touring & Camping Park
Upton, Bude EX23 0LP
t (01288) 352017
e reception@upperlynstone.co.uk
w upperlynstone.co.uk

Wooda Farm Park ★★★★★
Holiday & Touring Park
Poughill, Bude EX23 9HJ
t (01288) 352069
e enquiries@wooda.co.uk
w wooda.co.uk

BURNHAM-ON-SEA
Somerset

Burnham-on-Sea Holiday Village ★★★★
Holiday, Touring & Camping Park
Marine Drive, Burnham-on-Sea
TA8 1LA
t (01278) 783391
e enquiries@british-holidays.co.uk
w british-holidays.co.uk

Home Farm Holiday Park ★★★★★
Holiday & Touring Park
Edithmead, Highbridge
TA9 4HD
t (01278) 788888
e office@homefarmholidaypark.co.uk
w homefarmholidaypark.co.uk

Lakeside Holiday Park ★★★★
Holiday & Touring Park
Westfield Road, Burnham-on-Sea TA8 2AE
t (01278) 792222
e enquiries@lakesideholidays.co.uk
w lakesideholidays.co.uk

The Retreat Caravan Park ★★★★★
Holiday Park
Berrow Road, Burnham-on-Sea
TA8 2ES
t (01458) 860504

BURTON BRADSTOCK
Dorset

Coastal Caravan Park ★★★
Holiday, Touring & Camping Park
Annings Lane, Burton
Bradstock, Bridport DT6 4QP
t (01308) 422139
e holidays@wdlh.co.uk
w wdlh.co.uk

CAMELFORD
Cornwall

Juliot's Well Holiday Park ★★★
Holiday, Touring & Camping Park
Camelford PL32 9RF
t (01840) 213302
e juliotswell@holidaysincornwall.net
w holidaysincornwall.net

CARNON DOWNS
Cornwall

Carnon Downs Caravan and Camping Park ★★★★★
Touring Park
Carnon Downs, Truro TR3 6JJ
t (01872) 862283

CHACEWATER
Cornwall

Chacewater Park ★★★★
Touring Park
Cox Hill, Chacewater, Truro
TR4 8LY
t (01209) 820762
e chacewaterpark@aol.com
w chacewaterpark.co.uk

Killiwerris Touring Park ★★★★
Touring Park
Penstraze, Chacewater, Truro
TR4 8PF
t (01872) 561356
e killiwerris@tiscali.co.uk
w killiwerris.co.uk

CHARD
Somerset

Alpine Grove Touring Park ★★★★
Touring Park
Forton, Chard TA20 4HD
t (01460) 63479
e stay@alpinegrovetouringpark.com
w alpinegrovetouringpark.com

CHARMOUTH
Dorset

The Camping and Caravanning Club Site Charmouth ★★★★★
Touring & Camping Park
Monkton Wylde Farm, Nr
Charmouth, Bridport DT6 6DB
t (01297) 32965
w campingandcaravanningclub.co.uk

Dolphins River Park ★★★★
Holiday Park
Berne Lane, Charmouth,
Bridport DT6 6RD
t 0800 074 6375
w dolphinsriverpark.co.uk

Manor Farm Holiday Centre ★★★
Holiday, Touring & Camping Park
The Street, Charmouth,
Bridport DT6 6QL
t (01297) 560226
e enq@manorfarmholidaycentre.co.uk
w manorfarmholidaycentre.co.uk

Monkton Wyld Farm Caravan & Camping Park ★★★★
Touring & Camping Park
Monkton Wyld, Bridport
DT6 6DB
t (01297) 34525
e simonkewley@mac.com
w monktonwyld.co.uk

Newlands Holidays ★★★★
Holiday, Touring & Camping Park
Charmouth, Bridport DT6 6RB
t (01297) 560259
e enq@newlandsholidays.co.uk
w newlandsholidays.co.uk

Seadown Holiday Park ★★★★★
Holiday, Touring & Camping Park
Bridge Road, Charmouth,
Bridport DT6 6QS
t (01297) 560154
w seadowncaravanpark.co.uk

Wood Farm Caravan and Camping Park ★★★★★ ROSE AWARD
Holiday, Touring & Camping Park
Charmouth, Bridport DT6 6BT
t (01297) 560697
e holidays@woodfarm.co.uk
w woodfarm.co.uk

CHEDDAR
Somerset

Broadway House Holiday Touring Caravan and Camping Park ★★★★
ROSE AWARD
Holiday, Touring & Camping Park
Axbridge Road, Cheddar
BS27 3DB
t (01934) 742610
e info@broadwayhouse.uk.com
w broadwayhouse.uk.com

Cheddar Bridge Touring Park ★★★★
Holiday & Touring Park
Draycott Road, Cheddar
BS27 3RJ
t (01934) 743048

Cheddar Touring Caravan and Camping Park ★★★
Touring & Camping Park
Gas House Lane, Off Draycott Road, Cheddar BS27 3RL
t (01934) 740207

Cheddar, Mendip Heights Camping and Caravanning Club Site ★★★★
Touring & Camping Park
Townsend, Priddy, Wells
BA5 3BP
t (01749) 870241
e cheddar@campingandcaravanning club.co.uk
w campingandcaravanning club.co.uk

CHELTENHAM
Gloucestershire

Briarfields Motel & Touring Park ★★★
Touring & Camping Park
Gloucester Road, Cheltenham
GL51 0SX
t (01242) 235324

Cheltenham Racecourse Caravan Club Site ★★
Touring & Camping Park
Prestbury Park, Evesham Road, Cheltenham GL50 4SH
t (01242) 523102
w caravanclub.co.uk

CHICKERELL
Dorset

Bagwell Farm Touring Park ★★★★
Touring & Camping Park
Knights in the Bottom, Chickerell, Weymouth
DT3 4EA
t (01305) 782575
e enquiries@bagwellfarm.co.uk
w bagwellfarm.co.uk

CHRISTCHURCH
Dorset

Beaulieu Gardens Holiday Park ★★★★★
Holiday Park
Beaulieu Avenue, Christchurch
BH23 2EB
t (01202) 486215
e enquiries@meadowbank-holidays.co.uk
w meadowbank-holidays.co.uk

Harrow Wood Farm Caravan Park ★★★
Camping Park
Poplar Lane, Bransgore, Christchurch BH23 8JE
t (01425) 672487
e harrowwood@caravan-sites.co.uk
w caravan-sites.co.uk

Hoburne Park ★★★★★
Touring & Camping Park
Hoburne Caravan Park, Hoburne Lane, Christchurch
BH23 4HU
t (01425) 273379
e enquiries@hoburne.com
w hoburne.com

CHUDLEIGH
Devon

Finlake Holiday Park ★★★★
Touring & Camping Park
Chudleigh, Newton Abbot
TQ13 0EJ
t (01626) 853833
e finlake.reception@haulfryn.co.uk
w finlake.co.uk

Holmans Wood Holiday Park ★★★★
Holiday, Touring & Camping Park
Harcombe Cross, Chudleigh, Newton Abbot TQ13 0DZ
t (01626) 853785
e enquiries@holmanswood.co.uk
w holmanswood.co.uk

COLYTON
Devon

Leacroft Touring Park ★★★★
Touring Park
Colyton Hill, Colyton EX24 6HY
t (01297) 552823

COMBE MARTIN
Devon

Stowford Farm Meadows ★★★★
Touring & Camping Park
Combe Martin, Ilfracombe
EX34 0PW
t (01271) 882476
e enquiries@stowford.co.uk
w stowford.co.uk

CONNOR DOWNS
Cornwall

Higher Trevaskis Park ★★★★
Touring & Camping Park
Gwinear Road, Connor Downs, Hayle TR27 5JQ
t (01209) 831736

COOMBE BISSETT
Wiltshire

Summerlands Caravan Park ★★★
Touring & Camping Park
College Farm, Rockbourne Road, Coombe Bissett, Salisbury SP5 4LP
t (01722) 718259
w summerlands-park.com

CORFE CASTLE
Dorset

Woodyhyde Farm Camping Park ★★
Camping Park
Afflington, Corfe Castle, Wareham BH20 5HT
t (01929) 480274
e camp@woodyhyde.fsnet.co.uk
w woodyhyde.co.uk

CORFE MULLEN
Dorset

Charris Camping & Caravan Park ★★★★
Touring & Camping Park
Candys Lane, Corfe Mullen, Wimborne BH21 3EF
t (01202) 885970
e jandjcharris@iclway.co.uk
w charris.co.uk

CRACKINGTON HAVEN
Cornwall

Hentervene Caravan & Camping Park ★★★
Holiday, Touring & Camping Park
Crackington Haven, Bude
EX23 0LF
t (01840) 230365
e contact@hentervene.co.uk
w hentervene.co.uk

CROWCOMBE
Somerset

Quantock Orchard Caravan Park ★★★★★
Touring & Camping Park
Crowcombe, Taunton
TA4 4AW
t (01984) 618618
e qocp@flaxpool.freeserve.co.uk
w quantockorchard.co.uk

CROYDE BAY
Devon

Ruda Holiday Park ★★★★
Holiday, Touring & Camping Park
Croyde Bay EX33 1NY
t 0870 420 2997
e enquiries@parkdeanholidays.co.uk
w parkdeanholidays.co.uk

DAWLISH
Devon

Cofton Country Holidays ★★★★
Holiday, Touring & Camping Park
Cofton, Starcross, Exeter
EX6 8RP
t (01626) 890111
e info@coftonholidays.co.uk
w coftonholidays.co.uk

Dawlish Sands Holiday Park ★★★★
Holiday Park
Warren Road, Dawlish Warren, Dawlish EX7 0PG
t (01626) 862038

Golden Sands Holiday Park ★★★★
Holiday, Touring & Camping Park
Week Lane, Dawlish Warren, Dawlish EX7 0LZ
t (01626) 863099
e info@goldensands.co.uk
w goldensands.co.uk

Ladys Mile Touring and Camping Park ★★★★
Holiday Park
Exeter Road, Dawlish EX7 0LX
t (01626) 863411
e info@ladysmile.co.uk
w ladysmile.co.uk

Leadstone Camping ★★★
Touring & Camping Park
Warren Road, Dawlish
EX7 0NG
t (01626) 864411
e info@leadstonecamping.co.uk
w leadstonecamping.co.uk

Oakcliff Holiday Park ★★★★
Holiday Park
Mount Pleasant Road, Dawlish Warren, Dawlish EX7 0ND
t (01626) 863347
e info@oakcliff.co.uk
w oakcliff.co.uk

Peppermint Park ★★★★
Holiday, Touring & Camping Park
Warren Road, Dawlish Warren, Dawlish EX7 0PQ
t (01626) 863436
e info@peppermintpark.co.uk
w peppermintpark.co.uk

Welcome Family Holiday Park ★★★★
Holiday Park
Welcome Family Holiday Park, Warren Road, Dawlish Warren, Dawlish EX7 0PH
t (01626) 862070
e fun@welcomefamily.co.uk
w welcomefamily.co.uk

DOBWALLS
Cornwall

Hoburne Doublebois ★★★★
Holiday Park
Doublebois, Dobwalls, Liskeard
PL14 6LD
t (01579) 320049

DONIFORD
Somerset

Doniford Bay Holiday Park ★★★★
Holiday Park
Doniford, Watchet TA23 0TJ
t (01984) 632423

Sunnybank Caravan Park
Rating Applied For
Holiday Park
Doniford, Watchet TA23 0UD
t (01984) 632237
e mail@sunnybankcp.co.uk
w sunnybankcp.co.uk

DORCHESTER
Dorset

Giants Head Caravan & Camping Park ★★
Touring & Camping Park
Old Sherborne Road, Dorchester DT2 7TR
t (01300) 341242
e holidays@giantshead.co.uk
w giantshead.co.uk

Morn Gate Caravan Park ★★★★
Holiday Park
Bridport Road, Dorchester DT2 9DS
t (01305) 889284
e morngate@ukonline.co.uk
w morngate.co.uk

DOUBLEBOIS
Cornwall

Pine Green Caravan Park ★★★★
Touring & Camping Park
Doublebois, Dobwalls, Liskeard PL14 6LE
t (01579) 320183
e mary.ruhleman@btinternet.com
w pinegreenpark.co.uk

DREWSTEIGNTON
Devon

Woodland Springs Touring Park ★★★
Touring & Camping Park
Venton, Drewsteignton, Exeter EX6 6PG
t (01647) 231695
e enquiries@woodlandsprings.co.uk
w woodlandsprings.co.uk

DULVERTON
Somerset

Exmoor House Caravan Club Site ★★★★
Touring Park
Dulverton TA22 9HL
t (01398) 323268
w caravanclub.co.uk

Lakeside Caravan Club Site ★★★★
Touring Park
Higher Grants, Exebridge, Dulverton TA22 9BE
t (01398) 324068
w caravanclub.co.uk

EAST WORLINGTON
Devon

Yeatheridge Farm Caravan Park ★★★★
Touring & Camping Park
East Worlington, Crediton EX17 4TN
t (01884) 860330

EXFORD
Somerset

Westermill Farm ★★
Camping Park
Exford, Minehead TA24 7NJ
t (01643) 831238
e BC@westermill.com
w westermill.com

EXMOUTH
Devon

Webbers Caravan & Camping Park ★★★★★
Touring Park
Castle Lane, Woodbury, Exeter EX5 1EA
t (01395) 232276
e reception@webberspark.co.uk
w webberspark.co.uk

FALMOUTH
Cornwall

Pennance Mill Farm ★★★
Holiday, Touring & Camping Park
Maenporth, Falmouth TR11 5HJ
t (01326) 317431
w pennancemill.co.uk

FIDDINGTON
Somerset

Mill Farm Caravan and Camping Park ★★★★
Touring Park
Bridgwater TA5 1JQ
t (01278) 732286

FOWEY
Cornwall

Penhale Caravan & Camping Park ★★★
Holiday, Touring & Camping Park
Fowey PL23 1JU
t (01726) 833425
e info@penhale.co.uk
w penhale-fowey.co.uk

Penmarlam Caravan & Camping Park ★★★★
Touring & Camping Park
Bodinnick by Fowey, Fowey PL23 1LZ
t (01726) 870088
e info@penmarlampark.co.uk
w penmarlampark.co.uk

GLASTONBURY
Somerset

The Old Oaks Touring Park ★★★★★
Holiday Park
Wick, Glastonbury BA6 8JS
t (01458) 831437
e info@theoldoaks.co.uk
w theoldoaks.co.uk

GOONHAVERN
Cornwall

Silverbow Park ★★★★★
Holiday Park
Perranwell, Goonhavern, Truro TR4 9NX
t (01872) 572347

GREAT TORRINGTON
Devon

Greenways Valley Holiday Park ★★★★
Holiday Park
Greenways Valley, Caddywell Lane, Torrington EX38 7EW
t (01805) 622153
e enquiries@greenwaysvalley.co.uk
w greenwaysvalley.co.uk

Smytham Manor ★★★★
Holiday & Touring Park
Little Torrington, Torrington EX38 8PU
t (01805) 622110
e info@smytham.co.uk
w smytham.co.uk

HAMWORTHY
Dorset

Rockley Park Holiday Park ★★★★★
Holiday, Touring & Camping Park
Napier Road, Poole BH15 4LZ
t (01202) 679393
e enquiries@british-holidays.co.uk
w british-holidays.co.uk

HAYLE
Cornwall

Atlantic Coast Caravan Park ★★★★
Holiday & Touring Park
53 Upton Towans, Hayle TR27 5BL
t (01736) 752071
e enquiries@atlanticcoast-caravanpark.co.uk
w atlanticcoast-caravanpark.co.uk

Beachside Holiday Park ★★★★
Holiday, Touring & Camping Park
Lethlean Lane, Phillack, Hayle TR27 5AW
t (01736) 753080
e reception@beachside.demon.co.uk
w beachside.co.uk

Churchtown Farm Cvan & Cmpg ★★★
Touring & Camping Park
Gwithian, Hayle TR27 5BX
t (01736) 753219
e caravanning@churchtownfarmgwithian.fsnet.co.uk
w churchtownfarm.org.uk

Riviere Sands Holiday Park ★★★
Holiday Park
Riviere Towans, Hayle TR27 5AX
t (01736) 752132

St Ives Bay Holiday Park ★★★★
Holiday Park
73 Loggans Road, Upton Towans, Hayle TR27 5BH
t (01736) 752274
e stivesbay@dial.pipex.com
w stivesbay.co.uk

Toms Self-Catering Holidays ★★
Holiday Park
3a Riviere Towans, Phillack, Hayle TR27 5AT
t (01736) 756086

HELSTON
Cornwall

Poldown Camping & Caravan Park ★★★★
Holiday & Touring Park
Carleen, Breage, Helston TR13 9NN
t (01326) 574560
e info@poldown.co.uk
w poldown.co.uk

Sea Acres Holiday Park ★★★★ ROSE AWARD
Holiday Park
Kennack Sands, Nr Helston TR12 7LT
t 0870 420 2997
e enquiries@parkdeanholidays.co.uk
w parkdeanholidays.co.uk

HIGHBRIDGE
Somerset

Greenacre Place Touring Caravan Park and Holiday Cottage ★★★★
Touring Park
Bristol Road, Edithmead, Highbridge TA9 4HA
t (01278) 785227
e sm.alderton@btopenworld.com
w greenacreplace.com

HIGHCLIFFE
Dorset

Cobb's Holiday Park ★★★★
Holiday Park
32 Gordon Road, Highcliffe-on-Sea, Christchurch BH23 5HN
t (01425) 273301
e enquiries@cobbsholidaypark.co.uk
w cobbsholidaypark.co.uk

HOLTON HEATH
Dorset

Sandford Holiday Park ★★★★
Holiday, Touring & Camping Park
Organford Road, Holton Heath, Poole BH16 6JZ
t 0870 444 7774
e bookings@weststarholidays.co.uk
w weststarholidays.co.uk

Tanglewood Holiday Park Ltd ★★★★★
Holiday Park
Organford Road, Holton Heath, Poole BH16 6JY
t (01202) 632618

HORN'S CROSS
Devon

Steart Farm Touring Park ★★★
Touring & Camping Park
Horns Cross, Bideford EX39 5DW
t (01237) 431836
e steart@tiscali.co.uk

ILFRACOMBE
Devon

Beachside Holiday Park
★★★★★
Holiday Park
33 Beach Road, Hele,
Ilfracombe EX34 9QZ
t (01271) 863006
e enquiries@beachsidepark.
co.uk
w beachsidepark.co.uk

Hele Valley Holiday Park
★★★★
*Holiday, Touring & Camping
Park*
Hele Bay, Ilfracombe EX34 9RD
t (01271) 862460
e holidays@helevalley.co.uk
w helevalley.co.uk

**Hidden Valley Touring &
Camping Park** ★★★★
Touring & Camping Park
West Down, Ilfracombe
EX34 8NU
t (01271) 813837
e relax@hiddenvalleypark.com
w hiddenvalleypark.com

Mullacott Park ★★★★
ROSE AWARD
Holiday Park
Mullacott Cross, Ilfracombe
EX34 8NB
t (01271) 862212
e info@mullacottpark.co.uk
w mullacottpark.co.uk

IPPLEPEN
Devon

Ross Park ★★★★★
Touring Park
Moor Road, Ipplepen, Newton
Abbot TQ12 5TT
t (01803) 812983
e enquiries@
rossparkcaravanpark.co.uk
w rossparkcaravanpark.co.uk

**Woodville Touring Caravan
Park** ★★★★
Touring Park
Totnes Road, Ipplepen,
Newton Abbot TQ12 5TN
t (01803) 812240
e jo@woodvillepark.co.uk
w caravan-sitefinder.co.uk/
sthwest/devon/woodville.html

ISLES OF SCILLY

St. Martin's Campsite
★★★★
Camping Park
Middle Town, St Martin's
TR25 0QN
t (01720) 422888
e chris@stmartinscampsite.
freeserve.co.uk
w stmartinscampsite.co.uk

Troytown Farm Campsite
★★★
Camping Park
St Agnes TR22 0PL
t (01720) 422360
e troytown@talk21.com
w st-agnes-scilly.org

KENNFORD
Devon

**Exeter Racecourse Caravan
Club Site** ★★★
Touring & Camping Park
Kennford, Exeter EX6 7XS
t (01392) 832107
w caravanclub.co.uk

KENTISBEARE
Devon

Forest Glade Holiday Park
★★★★ **ROSE AWARD**
Holiday & Touring Park
Kentisbeare, Cullompton
EX15 2DT
t (01404) 841381
e nwellard@forest-glade.co.uk
w forest-glade.co.uk

KEWSTOKE
Somerset

Ardnave Holiday Park ★★★
Holiday & Touring Park
Crookes Lane, Kewstoke,
Weston-super-Mare BS22 9XJ
t (01934) 622319

Kewside Caravans ★★
Holiday Park
Crookes Lane, Kewstoke,
Weston-super-Mare BS22 9XF
t (01934) 521486

KINGSBRIDGE
Devon

**Challaborough Bay Holiday
Park** ★★★★ **ROSE AWARD**
Holiday Park
Challaborough Beach, Nr
Bigbury-on-Sea TQ7 4HU
t 0870 420 2997
e enquiries@
parkdeanholidays.co.uk
w parkdeanholidays.co.uk

KINGTON LANGLEY
Wiltshire

Plough Lane Caravan Site
★★★★★
Touring Park
Plough Lane, Kington Langley,
Chippenham SN15 5PS
t (01249) 750146
e ploughlane@lineone.net
w ploughlane.co.uk

LACOCK
Wiltshire

Piccadilly Caravan Park
★★★★★
Touring & Camping Park
Folly Lane (West), Lacock,
Chippenham SN15 2LP
t (01249) 730260
e piccadillylacock@aol.com

LANDRAKE
Cornwall

**Dolbeare Caravan and
Camping Park** ★★★★
Touring & Camping Park
St Ive Road, Landrake, Saltash
PL12 5AF
t (01752) 851332
e dolbearepark@btconnect.
com
w dolbeare.co.uk

LAND'S END
Cornwall

**Cardinney Caravan and
Camping Park** ★★★
Touring & Camping Park
Penberth Valley, St Buryan,
Penzance TR19 6HJ
t (01736) 810880
e cardinney@btinternet.com
w cardinney-camping-park.co.
uk

LANGPORT
Somerset

**Bowdens Crest Caravan and
Camping Park** ★★★
*Holiday, Touring & Camping
Park*
Bowdens, Langport TA10 0DD
t (01458) 250553
e bowcrest@btconnect.com
w Bowdenscrest.co.uk

LANGTON MATRAVERS
Dorset

**Tom's Field Campsite &
Shop** ★★★
Camping Park
Tom's Field Road, Langton
Matravers, Swanage
BH19 3HN
t (01929) 427110
e tomsfield@hotmail.com
w tomsfieldcamping.co.uk

LANIVET
Cornwall

Kernow Caravan Park ★★★
Holiday Park
Clann Lane, Lanivet, Bodmin
PL30 5HD
t (01208) 831343

LOOE
Cornwall

Looe Bay Holiday Park
★★★★
Holiday Park
St Martins, East Looe, Looe
PL13 1NX
t 0870 444 7774
e LouiseNickels@
WeststarHolidays.co.uk
w weststarholidays.co.uk/ic

**Polborder House Caravan
and Camping Park** ★★★★
Holiday & Touring Park
Bucklawren Road, St Martin
PL13 1NZ
t (01503) 240265
e reception@peaceful-
polborder.co.uk
w peaceful-polborder.co.uk

Seaview Holiday Village
★★★★
Holiday Park
Polperro, Looe PL13 2JE
t (01503) 272335
e reception@
seaviewholidayvillage.co.uk
w seaviewholidayvillage.co.uk

Tencreek Holiday Park
★★★★
Holiday & Touring Park
Polperro Road, Looe PL13 2JR
t (01503) 262447
e reception@tencreek.co.uk
w dolphinholidays.co.uk

Tregoad Park Quality Family
Touring Site ★★★★
*Holiday, Touring & Camping
Park*
St Martins, Looe PL13 1PB
t (01503) 262718
e info@tregoadpark.co.uk
w tregoadpark.co.uk

LOWER METHERELL
Cornwall

**Trehorner Farm Holiday
Park** ★★★★
Holiday Park
Lower Metherell, Callington
PL17 8BJ
t (01579) 351122
w trehorner.co.uk

LUXULYAN
Cornwall

Croft Farm Holiday Park
★★★★
*Holiday, Touring & Camping
Park*
Luxulyan PL30 5EQ
t (01726) 850228
e lynpick@ukonline.co.uk
w croftfarm.co.uk

LYDFORD
Devon

**Camping & Caravanning
Club Site – Lydford** ★★★★
Touring & Camping Park
Lydford, Okehampton
EX20 4BE
t (01822) 820275
w campingandcaravanning
club.co.uk

LYME REGIS
Dorset

Shrubbery Caravan Park
★★★
Touring & Camping Park
Rousdon, Lyme Regis
DT7 3XW
t (01297) 442227
w ukparks.co.uk/shrubbery

LYNTON
Devon

**Camping & Caravanning
Club Site – Lynton** ★★★★
Touring & Camping Park
Caffyn's Cross, Lynton
EX35 6JS
t (01598) 752379
w campingandcaravanning
club.co.uk

**Channel View Caravan and
Camping Park** ★★★★
ROSE AWARD
Holiday & Touring Park
Manor Farm, Lynton EX35 6LD
t (01598) 753349
e relax@channel-view.co.uk
w channel-view.co.uk

MALMESBURY
Wiltshire

**Burton Hill Caravan and
Camping Park** ★★★
Touring & Camping Park
Burton Hill Caravan Park,
Arches Lane, Malmesbury
SN16 0EH
t (01666) 826880
e stay@burtonhill.co.uk
w burtonhill.co.uk

MARAZION
Cornwall

Mounts Bay Caravan Park
★★★★★
Holiday Park
Green Lane, Marazion
TR17 0HQ
t (01736) 710307
e mountsbay@onetel.com
w mountsbay-caravanpark.co.
uk

MARLDON
Devon

Widend Touring Park
★★★★
Holiday, Touring & Camping
Park
Totnes Road, Marldon,
Paignton TQ3 1RT
t (01803) 550116

MARTOCK
Somerset

Southfork Caravan Park
★★★★
Holiday, Touring & Camping
Park
Parrett Works, Martock
TA12 6AE
t (01935) 825661
e southforkcaravans@
btconnect.com
w southforkcaravans.co.uk

MAWGAN PORTH
Cornwall

Marver Holiday Park ★★★
Holiday, Touring & Camping
Park
Marver Chalets, Mawgan
Porth, Newquay TR8 4BB
t (01637) 860493
e familyholidays@AOL.com
w marverholidaypark.co.uk

**Sun Haven Valley Holiday
Park** ★★★★★
Holiday, Touring & Camping
Park
Mawgan Porth, Newquay
TR8 4BQ
t (01637) 860373
e traceyhealey@hotmail.com
w sunhavenvalley.co.uk

MEVAGISSEY
Cornwall

Sea View International
★★★★★
Holiday, Touring & Camping
Park
Boswinger, Gorran, St Austell
PL26 6LL
t (01726) 843425
e holidays@
seaviewinternational.com
w seaviewinternational.com

MINEHEAD
Somerset

Beeches Holiday Park
★★★★
Holiday Park
Blue Anchor Bay, Minehead
TA24 6JW
t (01984) 640391
e info@beeches-park.co.uk
w beeches-park.co.uk

**Camping and Caravanning
Club Site Minehead** ★★★★
Camping Park
Hill Road, North Hill, Minehead
TA24 5SF
t (01643) 704138
w campingandcaravanning
club.co.uk

MODBURY
Devon

**Broad Park Caravan Club
Site** ★★★★
Touring Park
Higher East Leigh, Modbury,
Ivybridge PL21 0SH
t (01548) 830714
w caravanclub.co.uk

**Camping & Caravanning
Club Site – California Cross**
★★★★
Touring & Camping Park
Modbury, Ivybridge PL21 0SG
t (01548) 821297
w campingandcaravanning
club.co.uk

Moor View Touring Park
★★★★
Touring & Camping Park
Modbury, Ivybridge PL21 0SG
t (01548) 821485
e info@moorviewtouringpark.
co.uk
w moorviewtouringpark.co.uk

**Pennymoor Camping and
Caravan Park** ★★★★
Holiday, Touring & Camping
Park
Modbury, Ivybridge PL21 0SB
t (01548) 830542
e enquiries@pennymoor-
camping.co.uk
w pennymoor-camping.co.uk

MOORSHOP
Devon

**Higher Longford Caravan &
Camping Park** ★★★★
Touring & Camping Park
Moorshop, Tavistock PL19 9LQ
t (01822) 613360
e stay@higherlongford.co.uk
w higherlongford.co.uk

MORETON
Dorset

**Moreton Camping &
Caravanning Club Site**
★★★★★
Holiday Park
Station Road, Moreton,
Dorchester DT2 8BB
t (01305) 853801
w campingandcaravanning
club.co.uk

MORETON-IN-MARSH
Gloucestershire

**Moreton-in-Marsh Caravan
Club Site** ★★★★★
Touring & Camping Park
Bourton Road, Moreton-in-
Marsh GL56 0BT
t (01608) 650519
w caravanclub.co.uk

MORTEHOE
Devon

**Easewell Farm Holiday Parc
& Golf Club** ★★★★
Holiday, Touring & Camping
Park
Mortehoe, Woolacombe
EX34 7EH
t (01271) 870343
w woolacombe.com

**North Morte Farm Caravan
and Camping Park** ★★★★
Holiday, Touring & Camping
Park
North Morte Road, Mortehoe,
Woolacombe EX34 7EG
t (01271) 870381
e info@northmortefarm.co.uk
w northmortefarm.co.uk

Twitchen Parc ★★★★
Holiday, Touring & Camping
Park
Mortehoe Station Road,
Woolacombe EX34 7ES
t (01271) 870343
e goodtimes@woolacombe.
com
w woolacombe.com

**Warcombe Farm Camping
Park** ★★★★
Touring & Camping Park
Station Road, Woolacombe
EX34 7EJ
t (01271) 870690

MUCHELNEY
Somerset

**Thorney Lakes and Caravan
Park** ★★★
Touring & Camping Park
Thorney West Farm, Langport
TA10 0DW
t (01458) 250811
e enquiries@thorneylakes.co.
uk
w thorneylakes.co.uk

MULLION
Cornwall

**Criggan Mill Caravan and
Camping** ★★★★★
Holiday Park
Mullion, Helston TR12 7EU
t (01326) 240496

Mullion Holiday Park
★★★★
Holiday, Touring & Camping
Park
Ruan Minor, Helston TR12 7LJ
t 0870 444 5344

NANCLEDRA
Cornwall

Higher Chellew Camp Site
★★★
Touring & Camping Park
Nancledra, Penzance
TR20 8BD
t (01736) 364532
e camping@higherchellew.co.
uk
w higherchellewcamping.co.uk

NEWENT
Gloucestershire

**Pelerine Caravan and
Camping Park** ★★★
Touring & Camping Park
Ford House Road, Newent
GL18 1LQ
t (01531) 822761
e pelerine@hotmail.com
w newent.biz

NEWQUAY
Cornwall

**Crantock Beach Holiday
Park** ★★★★ ROSE AWARD
Holiday Park
Crantock, Newquay TR8 5RH
t 0870 420 2997
e enquiries@
parkdeanholidays.co.uk
w parkdeanholidays.co.uk

Hendra Holiday Park
★★★★
Holiday, Touring & Camping
Park
Lane, Newquay TR8 4NY
t (01637) 875778
e hendra.cornwall@dial.pipex.
com

Holywell Bay Holiday Park
★★★★ ROSE AWARD
Holiday Park
Holywell Bay, Newquay
TR8 5PR
t 0870 420 2997
e enquiries@
parkdeanholidays.co.uk
w parkdeanholidays.co.uk

Mawgan Porth Holiday Park
★★★★★
Holiday Park
Mawgan Porth, Newquay
TR8 4BD
t (01637) 860322

Nancolleth Caravan Gardens
★★★★
Holiday Park
Summercourt, Newquay
TR8 4PN
t (01872) 510236
e nancolleth@summercourt.
freeserve.co.uk
w nancolleth.co.uk

Newperran Holiday Park
★★★★ ROSE AWARD
Holiday Park
Rejerrah, Newquay TR8 5QJ
t (01872) 572407
e holidays@newperran.co.uk
w newperran.co.uk

Newquay Holiday Park
★★★★ ROSE AWARD
Holiday Park
Newquay TR8 4HS
t 0870 420 2997
e enquiries@
parkdeanholidays.co.uk
w parkdeanholidays.co.uk

Porth Beach Tourist Park
★★★★
Touring Park
Porth, Newquay TR7 3NH
t (01637) 876531
e info@porthbeach.co.uk
w porthbeach.co.uk

Riverside Holiday Park
★★★★
Holiday Park
Gwills Lane, Newquay TR8 4PE
t (01637) 873617
e info@riversideholidaypark.
co.uk
w riversideholidaypark.co.uk

Trekenning Tourist Park
★★★
Touring & Camping Park
Newquay TR8 4JF
t (01637) 880462
e holidays@trekenning.co.uk
w trekenning.co.uk

Treloy Touring Park ★★★★
Touring & Camping Park
Newquay TR8 4JN
t (01637) 872063 &
(01637) 876279
e treloy.tp@btconnect.com
w treloy.co.uk

Trenance Holiday Park
★★★
Holiday Park
Edgcumbe Avenue, Newquay
TR7 2JY
t (01637) 873447
e tony.hoyte@virgin.net
w trenanceholidaypark.co.uk

Trethiggey Touring Park
★★★★
Holiday Park
Quintrell Downs, Newquay
TR8 4QR
t (01637) 877672
e enquiries@trethiggey.co.uk
w trethiggey.co.uk

**Trevella Caravan & Camping
Pk** ★★★★★
*Holiday, Touring & Camping
Park*
Crantock, Newquay TR8 5EW
t (01637) 830308
e holidays@trevella.co.uk
w trevella.co.uk

Trevornick Holiday Park
★★★★★
Holiday Park
Holywell Bay, Newquay
TR8 5PW
t (01637) 830531
e paul@trevornick.co.uk
w trevornick.co.uk

NEWTON ABBOT
Devon

Dornafield ★★★★★
Touring & Camping Park
Two Mile Oak, Newton Abbot
TQ12 6DD
t (01803) 812732
e enquiries@dornafield.com
w dornafield.com

NORTH PETHERTON
Somerset

Somerset View Caravan Park
★★★
Touring Park
Taunton Road, North
Petherton, Bridgwater
TA6 6NW
t (01278) 661294 &
07767 032687
e qcs@somersetview.co.uk
w somersetview.co.uk

OARE
Wiltshire

Hill-View Park ★★★
Touring & Camping Park
Sunnyhill Lane, Oare,
Marlborough SN8 4JG
t (01672) 563151

ORCHESTON
Wiltshire

Stonehenge Touring Park
★★★
Touring & Camping Park
Stonehenge Park, Orcheston,
Salisbury SP3 4SH
t (01980) 620304
e stay@
stonehengetouringpark.com
w stonehengetouringpark.com

ORGANFORD
Dorset

**Organford Manor Caravans
& Holidays** ★★★
*Holiday, Touring & Camping
Park*
The Lodge, Organford, Poole
BH16 6ES
t (01202) 622202
e organford@lds.co.uk
w organfordmanor.co.uk

OSMINGTON
Dorset

White Horse Holiday Park
★★★
Holiday Park
Osmington Hill, Osmington,
Weymouth DT3 6ED
t (01305) 832164
e enquiries@whitehorsepark.
co.uk
w whitehorsepark.co.uk

OWERMOIGNE
Dorset

Sandyholme Holiday Park
★★★★
*Holiday, Touring & Camping
Park*
Moreton Road, Owermoigne,
Dorchester DT2 8HZ
t (01305) 852677
e smeatons@sandyholme.co.
uk
w sandyholme.co.uk

PADSTOW
Cornwall

Carnevas Farm Holiday Park
★★★★ ROSE AWARD
*Holiday, Touring & Camping
Park*
St Merryn, Padstow PL28 8PN
t (01841) 520230
e carnevascampsite@aol.com
w carnevasholidaypark.com

**Mother Iveys Bay Caravan
Park** ★★★★★
*Holiday, Touring & Camping
Park*
Trevose Head, Padstow
PL28 8SL
t (01841) 520990
e info@motheriveysbay.com
w motheriveysbay.com

Padstow Touring Park
★★★★
Touring & Camping Park
Padstow PL28 8LE
t (01841) 532061
e mail@padstowtouringpark.
co.uk
w padstowtouringpark.co.uk

PAIGNTON
Devon

Ashvale Holiday Park
★★★★
Holiday Park
Goodrington Road, Paignton
TQ4 7JD
t (01803) 843887
e info@beverley-holidays.co.
uk
w beverley-holidays.co.uk

Beverley Park ★★★★★
*Holiday, Touring & Camping
Park*
Goodrington Road, Paignton
TQ4 7JE
t (01803) 843887
e info@beverley-holidays.co.
uk
w beverley-holidays.co.uk

**Byslades International
Touring Park** ★★★★
Touring & Camping Park
Totnes Road, Paignton
TQ4 7PY
t (01803) 555072
e info@byslades.co.uk
w byslades.co.uk

**Higher Well Farm Holiday
Park** ★★★★
*Holiday, Touring & Camping
Park*
Waddeton Road, Stoke
Gabriel, Totnes TQ9 6RN
t (01803) 782289
e higherwell@talk21.com
w higherwellfarmholidaypark.
co.uk

Hoburne Torbay ★★★★
Holiday & Touring Park
Grange Road, Paignton
TQ4 7JP
t (01803) 558010
e enquiries@hoburne.com
w hoburne.com

Marine Park Holiday Centre
★★★★
Holiday & Touring Park
Grange Road, Paignton
TQ4 7JR
t (01803) 843887
e info@beverley-holidays.co.
uk
w beverley-holidays.co.uk

Waterside Holiday Park
★★★★
Holiday Park
Three Beaches, Dartmouth
Road, Paignton TQ4 6NS
t (01803) 842400
w watersidepark.co.uk

Whitehill Country Park
★★★★
*Holiday, Touring & Camping
Park*
Stoke Road, Paignton TQ4 7PF
t (01803) 782338
e info@whitehill-park.co.uk
w whitehill-park.co.uk

PAR
Cornwall

Par Sands Holiday Park
★★★★
*Holiday, Touring & Camping
Park*
Par Beach, Par PL24 2AS
t (01726) 812868
e holiday@parsands.co.uk
w parsands.co.uk

PELYNT
Cornwall

Trelay Farm Park ★★★★
Holiday & Touring Park
Pelynt, Looe PL13 2JX
t (01503) 220900
w trelay.co.uk

PENTEWAN
Cornwall

**Pentewan Sands Holiday
Park** ★★★★
*Holiday, Touring & Camping
Park*
Mevagissey, St Austell
PL26 6BT
t (01726) 843485
e info@pentewan.co.uk
w pentewan.co.uk

PENZANCE
Cornwall

**Tower Park Caravans and
Camping** ★★★
Holiday & Touring Park
St Buryan, Penzance TR19 6BZ
t (01736) 810286
e enquiries@
towerparkcamping.co.uk
w towerparkcamping.co.uk

PERRANPORTH
Cornwall

**Perranporth Caravan
Holidays** ★★★
Holiday Park
1 Crow Hill, Bolingey,
Perranporth TR6 0DG
t (01872) 572385
w caravanscornwall.co.uk

PERROTTS BROOK
Gloucestershire

Mayfield Touring Park
★★★★
Touring Park
Cheltenham Road, Perrotts
Brook, Cirencester GL7 7BH
t (01285) 831301
e Mayfield-park@cirencester.
fsbusiness.co.uk
w mayfieldpark.co.uk

PLYMOUTH
Devon

Plymouth Sound Caravan Club Site ★★★★
Holiday & Touring Park
Bovisand Lane, Down Thomas, Plymouth PL9 0AE
t (01752) 862325
w caravanclub.co.uk

POLGOOTH
Cornwall

Saint Margaret's Holiday Bungalows ★★★★★
Holiday Park
Tregongeeves Lane, St Austell PL26 7AX
t (01726) 74283
e reception@stmargaretsholidays.co.uk
w stmargaretsholidays.co.uk

POLRUAN-BY-FOWEY
Cornwall

Polruan Holidays (Camping & Caravanning) ★★★★
Holiday, Touring & Camping Park
Townsend, Polruan PL23 1QH
t (01726) 870263
e polholiday@aol.com

POLZEATH
Cornwall

Polzeath Beach Holiday Park ★★★★
Holiday Park
Trenant Nook, Polzeath, Wadebridge PL27 6ST
t (01208) 863320

Valley Caravan Park ★★
Holiday, Touring & Camping Park
Polzeath, Wadebridge PL27 6SS
t (01208) 862391
e martin@valleycaravanpark.co.uk
w valleycaravanpark.co.uk

POOLE
Dorset

Beacon Hill Touring Park ★★★
Touring & Camping Park
Blandford Road North, Nr Lytchett Minster, Poole BH16 6AB
t (01202) 631631
e bookings@beaconhilltouringpark.co.uk
w beaconhilltouringpark.co.uk

POOLE
Somerset

Cadeside Caravan Club Site ★★★★
Touring Park
Nynehead Road, Wellington TA21 9HN
t (01823) 663103
w caravanclub.co.uk

PORLOCK
Somerset

Burrowhayes Farm Caravan and Camping Site and Riding Stables ★★★★
Holiday, Touring & Camping Park
West Luccombe, Porlock, Minehead TA24 8HT
t (01643) 862463
e info@burrowhayes.co.uk
w burrowhayes.co.uk

Porlock Caravan Park ★★★★ ROSE AWARD
Holiday, Touring & Camping Park
High Bank, Porlock, Minehead TA24 8ND
t (01643) 862269
e info@porlockcaravanpark.co.uk
w porlockcaravanpark.co.uk

PORTH
Cornwall

Trevelgue Holiday Park ★★★
Holiday, Touring & Camping Park
Trevelgue Road, Porth, Newquay TR8 4AS
t (01637) 851850

PORTHTOWAN
Cornwall

Porthtowan Tourist Park ★★★★
Touring & Camping Park
Mile Hill, Porthtowan, Truro TR4 8TY
t (01209) 890256
e admin@porthtowantouristpark.co.uk
w porthtowantouristpark.co.uk

PORTLAND
Dorset

Cove Holiday Park ★★★★★
Holiday Park
Pennsylvania Road, Portland DT5 1HU
t (01305) 821286
e enquiries@coveholidaypark.co.uk
w coveholidaypark.co.uk

PORTREATH
Cornwall

Cambrose Touring Park ★★★
Touring & Camping Park
Portreath Road, Cambrose, Redruth TR16 4HT
t (01209) 890747
e cambrosetouringpark@supanet.com
w cambrosetouringpark.co.uk

Tehidy Holiday Park ★★★★
Holiday Park
Harris Mill, Illogan, Redruth TR16 4JQ
t (01209) 216489
e holiday@tehidy.co.uk
w tehidy.co.uk

PRAA SANDS
Cornwall

Lower Pentreath Caravan & Campsite ★★★
Holiday, Touring & Camping Park
Praa Sands, Penzance TR20 9TL
t (01736) 763221
e andrew.wearne1@btinternet.com

PRESTON
Dorset

Weymouth Bay Holiday Park ★★★★
Holiday Park
Preston Road, Preston, Weymouth DT3 6BQ
t (01305) 832271
w havenholidays.com

RATTERY
Devon

Edeswell Farm ★★★
Holiday Park
Rattery, South Brent TQ10 9LN
t (01364) 72177
e welcome@edeswellfarm.co.uk
w edeswellfarm.co.uk

REDHILL
Somerset

Brook Lodge Farm Touring Caravan & Tent Park ★★★
Touring & Camping Park
Cowslip Green, Bristol BS40 5RB
t (01934) 862311

REDRUTH
Cornwall

Lanyon Caravan & Camping Park ★★★★ ROSE AWARD
Holiday, Touring & Camping Park
Loscombe Lane, Four Lanes, Redruth TR16 6LP
t (01209) 313474
e jamierielly@btconnect.com
w lanyoncaravanandcamping park.co.uk

RELUBBUS
Cornwall

River Valley Country Park ★★★★★ ROSE AWARD
Holiday Park
Relubbus, Penzance TR20 9ER
t (01736) 763398
e rivervalley@surfbay.dircon.co.uk
w surfbayholidays.co.uk

RODNEY STOKE
Somerset

Bucklegrove Caravan & Camping Park ★★★★
Holiday, Touring & Camping Park
Wells Road, Rodney Stoke, Cheddar BS27 3UZ
t (01749) 870261

ROSUDGEON
Cornwall

Kenneggy Cove Holiday Park ★★★★ ROSE AWARD
Holiday, Touring & Camping Park
Higher Kenneggy, Rosudgeon, Penzance TR20 9AU
t (01736) 763453
e enquiries@kenneggycove.co.uk
w kenneggycove.co.uk

ROUSDON
Devon

Pinewood Homes ★★★★★
Holiday Park
Sidmouth Road, Rousdon, Lyme Regis DT7 3RD
t (01297) 22055
e info@pinewood.uk.net
w pinewood.uk.net

RUAN MINOR
Cornwall

Silver Sands Holiday Park ★★★★
Holiday, Touring & Camping Park
Gwendreath, Kennack Sands, Ruan Minor, Helston TR12 7LZ
t (01326) 290631
e enquiries@silversandsholidaypark.co.uk
w silversandsholidaypark.co.uk

ST AGNES
Cornwall

Beacon Cottage Farm Touring Park ★★★★
Touring Park
Beacon Drive, St Agnes TR5 0NU
t (01872) 552347
e beaconcottagefarm@lineone.net
w beaconcottagefarmholidays.co.uk

ST AUSTELL
Cornwall

Carlyon Bay Caravan & Camping ★★★★★
Touring & Camping Park
Cypress Avenue, Carlyon Bay, St Austell PL25 3RE
t (01726) 812735
e holidays@carlyonbay.net
w carlyonbay.net

River Valley Holiday Park ★★★★★ ROSE AWARD
Holiday, Touring & Camping Park
Pentewan Road, London Apprentice, St Austell PL26 7AP
t (01726) 73533
w cornwall-holidays.co.uk

Trencreek Farm Country Holiday Park ★★★
Holiday, Touring & Camping Park
Hewas Water, St Austell PL26 7JG
t (01726) 882540
e reception@trencreek.co.uk
w surfbayholidays.co.uk

Trewhiddle Village
Holiday, Touring & Camping Park
Pentewan Road, St Austell
PL26 7AD
t (01726) 879420
e holidays@trewhiddle.co.uk
w trewhiddle.co.uk

ST BURYAN
Cornwall

Camping & Caravanning Club (Sennen Cove) ★★★★
Touring Park
Higher Tregiffian Farm, St Buryan, Penzance TR19 6JB
t (01736) 871588
w campingandcaravanning club.co.uk

ST EWE
Cornwall

Heligan Woods Camping & Caravan Park - ★★★★
Holiday, Touring & Camping Park
Mevagissey, St Austell
PL26 6BT
t (01726) 843485
e info@pentewan.co.uk
w pentewan.co.uk

ST GENNYS
Cornwall

Camping & Caravanning Club (Bude) ★★★★
Touring & Camping Park
Gillards Moor, St Gennys, Bude
EX23 0BG
t (01840) 230650
w campingandcaravanning club.co.uk

ST HILARY
Cornwall

Threeways Caravan Club site ★★★★
Holiday & Touring Park
St Hilary, Goldsithney, Penzance TR20 9DU
t (01342) 336842
w caravanclub.co.uk

Wayfarers Caravan Park ★★★★
Touring Park
Relubbus Lane, St Hilary, Penzance TR20 9EF
t (01736) 763326
e elaine@wayfarerspark.co.uk
w wayfarerspark.co.uk

ST IVES
Cornwall

Ayr Holiday Park ★★★★
Holiday, Touring & Camping Park
Higher Ayr, St Ives TR26 1EJ
t (01736) 795855
e recept@ayrholidaypark.co.uk
w ayrholidaypark.co.uk

Little Trevarrack Touring Park ★★★★
Touring & Camping Park
Laity Lane, Carbis Bay, St Ives
TR26 3HW
t (01736) 797580
e littletrevarrack@hotmail.com
w littletrevarrack.co.uk

Polmanter Touring Park ★★★★★
Touring & Camping Park
St Ives TR26 3LX
t (01736) 795640
e reception@polmanter.com
w polmanter.com

Trevalgan Touring Park ★★★★
Touring & Camping Park
St Ives TR26 3BJ
t (01736) 796433
e reception@
trevalgantouringpark.co.uk
w trevalgantouringpark.co.uk

ST JUST-IN-PENWITH
Cornwall

Roselands Caravan Park ★★★★
Holiday, Touring & Camping Park
Dowran, St Just, Penzance
TR19 7RS
t (01736) 788571

ST JUST IN ROSELAND
Cornwall

Trethem Mill Touring Park ★★★★★
Touring & Camping Park
Trethem, St Just in Roseland
TR2 5JF
t (01872) 580504
e reception@trethem.com
w trethem.com

ST LEONARDS
Dorset

Back-of-Beyond Touring Park ★★★★
Touring & Camping Park
234 Ringwood Road, St Leonards, Ringwood BH24 2SB
t (01202) 876968
e melandsuepike@aol.com
w backofbeyondtouringpark. co.uk

Forest Edge Holiday Park ★★★
Touring & Camping Park
229 Ringwood Road, St Leonards, Ringwood BH24 2SD
t (01590) 648331
e holidays@shorefield.co.uk
w shorefield.co.uk

Oakdene Forest Park ★★★★
Holiday, Touring & Camping Park
St Leonards, Ringwood
BH24 2RZ
t (01590) 648331
e holidays@shorefield.co.uk
w shorefield.co.uk

ST MERRYN
Cornwall

Trethias Farm Caravan Park ★★★
Touring Park
Trethias, St Merryn, Padstow
PL28 8PL
t (01841) 520323

Trevean Farm ★★★★
Touring & Camping Park
St Merryn, Padstow PL28 8PR
t (01841) 520772
e trevean.info@virgin.net

ST MINVER
Cornwall

Dinham Farm Family Cvn & Cmp Park ★★★
Holiday, Touring & Camping Park
St Minver, Wadebridge
PL27 6RH
t (01208) 812878
w dinhamfarm.co.uk

Little Dinham Woodland Caravan Park ★★★★
Holiday Park
St Minver, Wadebridge
PL27 6RH
t (01208) 812538
e littledinham@hotmail.com
w littledinham.co.uk

St Minver Holiday Park ★★★★ ROSE AWARD
Holiday, Touring & Camping Park
St Minver, Wadebridge
PL27 6RR
t 0870 420 2997
e enquiries@
parkdeanholidays.co.uk
w parkdeanholidays.co.uk

ST STEPHEN
Cornwall

Court Farm Caravan/ Camping Park ★★★
Touring & Camping Park
Court Farm, St Stephen, St Austell PL26 7LE
t (01726) 823684
e truscott@ctfarm.freeserve. co.uk
w courtfarmcornwall.co.uk

ST TUDY
Cornwall

Hengar Manor Country Park ★★★★★
Holiday Park
St Tudy, Bodmin PL30 3PL
t (01208) 850382
e holidays@hengarmanor.co. uk
w hengarmanor.co.uk

Michaelstow Manor Holiday Park ★★★★
Holiday Park
Michaelstow, St Tudy, Bodmin
PL30 3PB
t (01208) 850244
e michaelstow@eclipse.co.uk
w michaelstow-holidays.co.uk

SALCOMBE
Devon

Bolberry House Farm ★★★
Holiday, Touring & Camping Park
Bolberry, Malborough, Kingsbridge TQ7 3DY
t (01548) 561251
e bolberry.house@virgin.net
w bolberryparks.co.uk

Higher Rew Touring Caravan & Camping Park ★★★★
Touring & Camping Park
Higher Rew, Malborough, Kingsbridge TQ7 3DW
t (01548) 842681
e enquiries@higherrew.co.uk
w higherrew.co.uk

Karrageen Caravan and Camping Park ★★★★
Holiday, Touring & Camping Park
Bolberry, Malborough, Kingsbridge TQ7 3EN
t (01548) 561230
e phil@karrageen.co.uk
w karrageen.co.uk

SALCOMBE REGIS
Devon

Kings Down Tail Caravan & Camping Park ★★★★
Touring & Camping Park
Salcombe Regis, Sidmouth
EX10 0PD
t (01297) 680313
w uk.parks.co.uk/ kingsdowntail

SALISBURY
Wiltshire

Camping And Caravanning Club Site Salisbury ★★★★
Touring & Camping Park
Hudson's Field, Castle Road, Salisbury SP1 3RR
t (01722) 320713
w campingandcaravanning club.co.uk

SANDY BAY
Devon

Devon Cliffs Holiday Park ★★★★
Holiday Park
Sandy Bay, Exmouth EX8 5BT
t (01395) 226226
w havenholiday.co.uk

SEATON
Devon

Axe Vale Caravan Park ★★★★
Holiday Park
Colyford Road, Seaton
EX12 2DF
t (01297) 21342
e info@axevale.co.uk
w axevale.co.uk

SEEND
Wiltshire

Camping and Caravanning Club Site Devizes ★★★★★
Touring & Camping Park
Spout Lane, Seend, Melksham
SN12 6RN
t (01380) 828839
w campingandcaravanning club.co.uk

SENNEN
Cornwall

Sea View Holiday Park ★★★★
Holiday, Touring & Camping Park
Sennen, Penzance TR19 7AD
t (01736) 871266

SHALDON
Devon

Coast View Holiday Park
★★★★
Holiday, Touring & Camping Park
Torquay Road, Shaldon,
Teignmouth TQ14 0BG
t (01626) 872392
e info@coast-view.co.uk
w coast-view.co.uk

Devon Valley Holiday Village ★★★★
Holiday Park
Coombe Road, Ringmore,
Teignmouth TQ14 0EY
t 0870 442 9750
e info@devonvalley.biz
w southdevonholidays.biz

SIDBURY
Devon

Putts Corner Caravan Club Site ★★★★★
Touring Park
Sidbury, Sidmouth EX10 0QQ
t (01404) 42875
w caravanclub.co.uk

SIDMOUTH
Devon

Salcombe Regis Camping and Caravan Park ★★★★★
ROSE AWARD
Holiday, Touring & Camping Park
Salcombe Regis, Sidmouth
EX10 0JH
t (01395) 514303
e info@salcombe-regis.co.uk
w salcombe-regis.co.uk

SIXPENNY HANDLEY
Dorset

Church Farm Caravan & Camping Park ★★★
Touring & Camping Park
High Street, Sixpenny Handley,
Salisbury SP5 5ND
t (01725) 552563
e churchfarmcandcpark@yahoo.co.uk
w churchfarmcandcpark.co.uk

SLAPTON
Devon

Camping & Caravanning Club Site – Slapton Sands ★★★★
Touring & Camping Park
Middle Grounds, Slapton,
Kingsbridge TQ7 2QW
t (01548) 580538
w campingandcaravanningclub.co.uk

SOUTH CERNEY
Gloucestershire

Hoburne Cotswold ★★★★
Holiday Park
Broadway Lane, South Cerney,
Cirencester GL7 5UQ
t (01285) 860216
e cotswold@hoburne.com
w hoburne.com

SOUTH MOLTON
Devon

Yeo Valley Holiday Park
Holiday, Touring & Camping Park
c/o Blackcock Inn, Molland,
South Molton EX36 3NW
t (01769) 550297
e info@yeovalleyholidays.com
w yeovalleyholidays.com

SWANAGE
Dorset

Cauldron Barn Farm Caravan Park ★★★★
Holiday, Touring & Camping Park
Cauldron Barn Road, Swanage
BH19 1QQ
t (01929) 422080
e info@cauldronbarncaravanpark.co.uk
w cauldronbarncaravanpark.co.uk

Haycraft Caravan Club Site
★★★★★
Touring Park
Haycrafts Lane, Swanage
BH19 3EB
t (01929) 480572
w caravanclub.co.uk

Herston Caravan & Camping Park
Rating Applied For
Holiday, Touring & Camping Park
Washpond Lane, Swanage
BH19 3DJ
t (01929) 422932
e office@herstonleisure.co.uk
w herstonleisure.co.uk

Swanage Caravan Park
★★★★
Holiday Park
Panorama Road, Swanage
BH19 2QS
t (01929) 422130

Swanage Coastal Park ★★★
Holiday, Touring & Camping Park
Priests Way, Swanage
BH19 2RS
t (01590) 648331
e holidays@shorefield.co.uk
w shorefield.co.uk

Ulwell Cottage Caravan Park
★★★★
Holiday, Touring & Camping Park
Ulwell, Swanage BH19 3DG
t (01929) 422823
e enq@ulwellcottagepark.co.uk
w ulwellcottagepark.co.uk

Ulwell Farm Caravan Park
★★★
Holiday Park
Ulwell, Swanage BH19 3DG
t (01929) 422825
e ulwell.farm@virgin.net
w ukparks.co.uk/ulwellfarm

TAUNTON
Somerset

Ashe Farm Caravan and Campsite ★★★
Holiday, Touring & Camping Park
Thornfalcon, Taunton
TA3 5NW
t (01823) 442567
e camping@ashe-farm.fsnet.co.uk

Holly Bush Park ★★★★
Touring & Camping Park
Culmhead, Taunton TA3 7EA
t (01823) 421515
e info@hollybushpark.com
w hollybushpark.com

Tanpits Cider Farm Camping and Caravan Park ★★
Holiday & Touring Park
Dyers Lane, Bathpool, Taunton
TA2 8BZ
t (01823) 270663

TAVISTOCK
Devon

Harford Bridge Holiday Park
★★★★
Holiday, Touring & Camping Park
Peter Tavy, Tavistock PL19 9LS
t (01822) 810349
e enquiry@harfordbridge.co.uk
w harfordbridge.co.uk

Langstone Manor Caravan and Camping Park ★★★★
ROSE AWARD
Holiday, Touring & Camping Park
Moortown, Tavistock PL19 9JZ
t (01822) 613371
e jane@langstone-manor.co.uk
w langstone-manor.co.uk

Woodovis Park ★★★★★
Holiday, Touring & Camping Park
Gulworthy, Tavistock PL19 8NY
t (01822) 832968
e info@woodovis.com
w woodovis.com

TEDBURN ST MARY
Devon

Springfield Holiday Park
★★★
Holiday, Touring & Camping Park
Tedburn St Mary, Exeter
EX6 6EW
t (01647) 24242
e enquiries@springfieldholidaypark.co.uk
w springfieldholidaypark.co.uk

TEIGNGRACE
Devon

Twelve Oaks Farm Caravan Park ★★★★
Touring & Camping Park
Teigngrace, Newton Abbot
TQ12 6QT
t (01626) 352769
e info@twelveoaksfarm.co.uk
w twelveoaksfarm.co.uk

TEWKESBURY
Gloucestershire

Croft Farm Leisure and Water Park ★★★
Holiday & Touring Park
Bredons Hardwick,
Tewkesbury GL20 7EE
t (01684) 772321
e alan@croftfarmleisure.co.uk
w croftfarmleisure.co.uk

Tewkesbury Abbey Caravan Club Site ★★★★
Touring & Camping Park
Gander Lane, Tewkesbury
GL20 5PG
t (01684) 294035
w caravanclub.co.uk

THREE LEGGED CROSS
Dorset

Woolsbridge Manor Farm Caravan Park ★★★
Touring & Camping Park
Ringwood Road, Three Legged
Cross, Wimborne BH21 6RA
t (01202) 826369
e woolsbridge@btconnect.com
w woolsbridgemanorcaravanpark.co.uk

TINTAGEL
Cornwall

Trewethett Farm Caravan Club Site ★★★★★
Touring Park
Trethevy, Tintagel PL34 0BQ
t (01840) 770222
w caravanclub.co.uk

TORQUAY
Devon

Torquay Holiday Park
Rating Applied For
Touring & Camping Park
Kingskerswell Road, Torquay
TQ2 8JU
t 0870 420 2997
e enquiries@parkdeanholidays.co.uk
w parkdeanholidays.co.uk

Widdicombe Farm Touring Park ★★★★
Touring & Camping Park
Marldon, Paignton TQ3 1ST
t (01803) 558325
e info@widdicombefarm.co.uk
w torquaytouring.co.uk

TOTNES
Devon

Broadleigh Farm Park
★★★★
Touring & Camping Park
Coombe House Lane, Aish,
Stoke Gabriel, Totnes TQ9 6PU
t (01803) 782309
e enquiries@broadleighfarm.co.uk
w gotorbay.com/accommodation

TREGURRIAN
Cornwall

Camping and Caravanning Club Site Tregurrian ★★★★
Touring & Camping Park
Newquay TR8 4AE
t (01637) 860448
w campingandcaravanning
club.co.uk

TRURO
Cornwall

Summer Valley Touring Park ★★★★
Touring Park
Shortlanesend, Truro
TR4 9DW
t (01872) 277878
e res@summervalley.co.uk
w summervalley.co.uk

UMBERLEIGH
Devon

Camping & Caravanning Club Site Umberleigh ★★★★
Touring & Camping Park
Over Weir, Umberleigh
EX37 9DU
t (01769) 560009
w campingandcaravanning
club.co.uk

UPTON
Somerset

Lowtrow Cross Caravan & Camping Site ★★★★
Holiday, Touring & Camping Park
Upton, Taunton TA4 2DB
t (01398) 371199
e info@lowtrowcross.co.uk
w lowtrowcross.co.uk

VERYAN
Cornwall

Camping & Caravanning Club (Veryan) ★★★★
Holiday Park
Tretheake Manor, Veryan,
Truro TR2 5PP
t (01872) 501658
w campingandcaravanning
club.co.uk

WADEBRIDGE
Cornwall

Little Bodieve Holiday Park ★★★★
Holiday, Touring & Camping Park
Bodieve Road, Wadebridge
PL27 6EG
t (01208) 812323
e berry@
littlebodieveholidaypark.fsnet.
co.uk
w littlebodieve.co.uk

WARDON HILL
Dorset

Clay Pigeon Caravan Park ★★★
Touring & Camping Park
Wardon Hill, Dorchester
DT2 9PW
t (01935) 83492

WAREHAM
Dorset

Birchwood Tourist Park ★★★★
Touring & Camping Park
Bere Road, Coldharbour,
Wareham BH20 7PA
t (01929) 554763
e birchwoodtouristpark@
hotmail.com

The Lookout Holiday Park ★★★★
Holiday, Touring & Camping Park
Corfe Road, Stoborough,
Wareham BH20 5AZ
t (01929) 552546
e enquiries@caravan-sites.co.
uk
w caravan-sites.co.uk

Wareham Forest Tourist Park Ltd ★★★★★
Touring & Camping Park
Bere Road, North Trigon,
Wareham BH20 7NZ
t (01929) 551000
e holiday@wareham-forest.co.
uk
w wareham-forest.co.uk

WARMINSTER
Wiltshire

Longleat Caravan Club Site ★★★★★
Touring Park
Longleat, Warminster
BA12 7NL
t (01985) 844663
w caravanclub.co.uk

WARMWELL
Dorset

Warmwell Caravan Park ★★★★
Holiday, Touring & Camping Park
Warmwell, Dorchester
DT2 8JD
t (01305) 852313
e stay@warmwellcaravanpark.
co.uk
w warmwellcaravanpark.co.uk

Warmwell Holiday Park ★★★★
Holiday Park
Warmwell, Nr Weymouth
DT2 8JE
t 0870 420 2997
e enquiries@
parkdeanholidays.co.uk
w parkdeanholidays.co.uk

WATCHET
Somerset

Lorna Doone Holiday Park ★★★★★
Holiday Park
Watchet TA23 0BJ
t (01984) 631206
e mail@lornadoone.co.uk
w lornadoone.co.uk

WATERROW
Somerset

Waterrow Touring Park ★★★★★ **ROSE AWARD**
Touring & Camping Park
Waterrow, Taunton TA4 2AZ
t (01984) 623464
w waterrowpark.co.uk

WEMBURY
Devon

Churchwood Valley Holiday Cabins ★★★★
Holiday Park
Churchwood Valley, Wembury
Bay, Plymouth PL9 0DZ
t (01752) 862382
e churchwoodvalley@
btinternet.com
w churchwoodvalley.com

WEST BAY
Dorset

West Bay Holiday Park ★★★★
Holiday, Touring & Camping Park
West Bay, Bridport DT6 4HB
t 0870 420 2997
e enquiries@
parkdeanholidays.co.uk
w parkdeanholidays.co.uk

WEST BEXINGTON
Dorset

Gorselands Caravan Park ★★★★
Holiday Park
West Bexington Road, West
Bexington, Dorchester
DT2 9DJ
t (01308) 897232
w gorselands.co.uk

WEST DOWN
Devon

Brook Lea
Rating Applied For
Touring Park
Brooklea Caravan Club Site,
Ilfracombe EX34 8NE
t (01271) 862848
e debby.towers@caravanclub.
co.uk

WEST LULWORTH
Dorset

Durdle Door Holiday Park ★★★★
Holiday, Touring & Camping Park
West Lulworth, Wareham
BH20 5PU
t (01929) 400200
e durdle.door@lulworth.com
w lulworth.com

WEST QUANTOXHEAD
Somerset

St Audries Bay Holiday Club ★★★★
Holiday & Touring Park
West Quantoxhead, Taunton
TA4 4DY
t (01984) 632515
e mrandle@staudriesbay.
demon.co.uk
w staudriesbay.co.uk

WESTON
Devon

Oakdown Touring and Holiday Home Park ★★★★★
Holiday & Touring Park
Weston, Sidmouth EX10 0PH
t (01297) 680387
e enquiries@oakdown.co.uk
w oakdown.co.uk

Stoneleigh Holiday and Leisure Village ★★★★
Holiday Park
Weston, Sidmouth EX10 0PJ
t (01395) 513619
w stoneleighholidays.co.uk

WESTON-SUPER-MARE
Somerset

Camping and Caravanning Club Site Weston-Super-Mare ★★★
Touring Park
West End Farm, Locking,
Weston-super-Mare BS24 8RH
t (01934) 822548
w campingandcaravanning
club.co.uk

Carefree Holiday Park ★★★★★
Holiday Park
12 Beach Road, Kewstoke,
Weston-super-Mare BS22 9UZ
t (01934) 624541
e crichardson@hotmail.co.uk

Country View Holiday Park ★★★★
Holiday, Touring & Camping Park
29 Sand Road, Sand Bay,
Weston-super-Mare BS22 9UJ
t (01934) 627595
w cvhp.co.uk

Dulhorn Farm Camping Site ★★★
Touring & Camping Park
Weston Road, Lympsham,
Weston-super-Mare BS24 0JQ
t (01934) 750298

WESTWARD HO!
Devon

Beachside Holiday Park ★★★★
Holiday Park
Merley Road, Westward Ho!,
Bideford EX39 1JX
t 0845 601 2541 &
0845 601 2541
e beachside@surfbay.dircon.
co.uk
w beachsideholidays.co.uk

Surf Bay Holiday Park ★★★★
Holiday Park
Golf Links Road, Westward
Ho!, Bideford EX39 1HD
t 0845 601132 &
0845 601 1132
e surfbayholidaypark@
surfbay.dircon.co.uk
w surfbay.co.uk

WEYMOUTH
Dorset

Chesil Beach Holiday Park
★★★★
Holiday Park
Chesil Beach, Portland Road,
Weymouth DT4 9AG
t (01305) 773233
e info@chesilholidays.co.uk
w chesilholidays.co.uk

**Crossways Caravan Club
Site** ★★★★
Touring Park
Moreton, Dorchester DT2 8BE
t (01305) 852032
w caravanclub.co.uk

East Fleet Farm Touring Park
★★★★
Touring & Camping Park
Fleet Lane, Chickerell,
Weymouth DT3 4DW
t (01305) 785768
e enquiries@eastfleet.co.uk
w eastfleet.co.uk

Littlesea Holiday Park
★★★★
*Holiday, Touring & Camping
Park*
Lynch Lane, Weymouth
DT4 9DT
t (01305) 774414
e david.bennett@bourne-
leisure.co.uk

Pebble Bank Caravan Park
★★
*Holiday, Touring & Camping
Park*
90 Camp Road, Wyke Regis,
Weymouth DT4 9HF
t (01305) 774844
e info@pebblebank.co.uk
w pebblebank.co.uk

Seaview Holiday Park ★★★
*Holiday, Touring & Camping
Park*
Preston, Weymouth DT3 6DZ
t (01305) 833037
w havenholidays.com

Waterside Holiday Park
★★★★★
Holiday & Touring Park
Bowleaze Coveway,
Weymouth DT3 6PP
t (01305) 833103
e info@watersideholidays.co.
uk
w watersideholidays.co.uk

WHITE CROSS
Cornwall

White Acres Country Park
★★★★★ ROSE AWARD
Holiday Park
White Cross, Newquay
TR8 4LW
t 0870 420 2997
e enquiries@
parkdeanholidays.co.uk
w parkdeanholidays.co.uk

WHITECROSS
Cornwall

The Laurels ★★★★
Touring & Camping Park
Padstow Road, Whitecross,
Wadebridge PL27 7JQ
t (01209) 313474
e jamierielly@btconnect.com
w thelaurelsholidaypark.co.uk

WIMBORNE MINSTER
Dorset

Merley Court Touring Park
★★★★★
Touring Park
Merley Court, Merley,
Wimborne BH21 3AA
t (01590) 648331
e holidays@shorefield.co.uk
w shorefield.co.uk

Springfield Touring Park
★★★★★
Touring & Camping Park
Candys Lane, Corfe Mullen,
Wimborne BH21 3EF
t (01202) 881719

**Wilksworth Farm Caravan
Park** ★★★★★
Touring & Camping Park
Cranborne Road, Furzehill,
Wimborne BH21 4HW
t (01202) 885467
e rayandwendy@
wilksworthfarmcaravanpark.co.
uk
w wilksworthfarmcaravanpark.
co.uk

WINCANTON
Somerset

**Wincanton Racecourse
Caravan Club Site** ★★★
Touring & Camping Park
Wincanton BA9 8BJ
t (01963) 34276
w caravanclub.co.uk

WINCHCOMBE
Gloucestershire

**Camping and Caravanning
Site Winchcombe** ★★★★
Touring & Camping Park
Brooklands Fram, Alderton,
Tewkesbury GL20 8NX
t (01242) 620259
w campingandcaravanning
club.co.uk

WINSFORD
Somerset

**Halse Farm Caravan & Tent
Park** ★★★★
Touring & Camping Park
Winsford, Minehead TA24 7JL
t (01643) 851259
e brit@halsefarm.co.uk
w halsefarm.co.uk

WOODBURY
Devon

Castle Brake Holiday Park
★★★★
Holiday & Touring Park
Castle Lane, Woodbury, Exeter
EX5 1HA
t (01395) 232431
e reception@castlebrake.co.uk
w castlebrake.co.uk

WOODLANDS
Dorset

**Camping & Caravanning
Club Site Verwood, New
Forest** ★★★★
Touring & Camping Park
Sutton Hill, Woodlands,
Wimborne BH21 8NQ
t (01202) 822763
w campingandcaravanning
club.co.uk

WOOL
Dorset

Whitemead Caravan Park
★★★★
Touring & Camping Park
East Burton Road, Wool,
Wareham BH20 6HG
t (01929) 462241
e whitemeadcp@aol.com
w whitemeadcaravanpark.co.
uk

WOOLACOMBE
Devon

**Golden Coast Holiday
Village** ★★★★
Holiday Park
Station Road, Woolacombe
EX34 7HW
t (01271) 870343
e goodtimes@woolacombe.
com
w woolacombe.com

**Woolacombe Bay Holiday
Parcs** ★★★★
*Holiday, Touring & Camping
Park*
Morthoe Station Road,
Woolacombe EX34 7AH
t (01271) 870343

**Woolacombe Bay Holiday
Village** ★★★★
*Holiday, Touring & Camping
Park*
Seymour, Sandy Lane,
Woolacombe EX34 7AH
t (01271) 870343
e goodtimes@woolacombe.
com
w woolacombe.com

**Woolacombe Sands Holiday
Park** ★★★★
*Holiday, Touring & Camping
Park*
Beach Road, Woolacombe
EX34 7AF
t (01271) 870569
e lifesabeach@woolacombe-
sands.co.uk
w woolacombe-sands.co.uk

YEOVIL
Somerset

Long Hazel Park ★★★★
*Holiday, Touring & Camping
Park*
High Street, Sparkford, Yeovil
BA22 7JH
t (01963) 440002
e longhazelpark@hotmail.com
w sparkford.f9.co.uk/lhi.htm

Holiday
Villages

Enjoy England has a separate rating scheme of one to five stars for Holiday Villages. Holiday Villages usually comprise a variety of types of accommodation, with the majority provided in custom-built rooms, chalets for example. The option to book a bed and breakfast, or dinner, bed and breakfast basis is normally available. A range of facilities and activities are also provided which may, or may not, be included in the tariff.

Holiday Villages meet requirements for both the provision and quality of facilities and services, including fixtures, fittings, furnishings and decor. Progressively higher levels of quality and customer care are provided for each of the star ratings. Quite simply, the more stars, the higher the overall level of quality you can expect.

What standards to expect at each rating level:

★	Acceptable
★★	Good
★★★	Very good
★★★★	Excellent
★★★★★	Exceptional

BREAN
Somerset

Holiday Resort Unity
★★★
Coast Road, Brean Sands,
Burnham-on-Sea TA8 2RB
t (01278) 751235
f (01278) 751539
e admin@hru.co.uk
w hru.co.uk

BURNHAM-ON-SEA
Somerset

Pontins Ltd ★★★
Brean Sands Family Centre,
South Road, Burnham-on-
Sea TA8 2RJ
t (01278) 751627
f (01278) 751754
e ellie.hindle@pontins.com
w pontins.com

CORTON
Suffolk

**Corton Beach Holiday
Village ★★★**
The Street, Corton,
Lowestoft NR32 5HS
t (01502) 730200

Warner Holidays Ltd ★★
Corton Classic Resort, The
Street, Lowestoft NR32 5HR
t 0870 601 6012
f (01502) 732334
w warnerholidays.co.uk

CROYDE
Devon

**Croyde Bay Holiday
Village (Unison) ★★★**
Croyde, Braunton EX33 1QB
t (01271) 890890
f (01271) 890888
e s.willis@unison.co.uk
w croydeholidays.co.uk

GREAT YARMOUTH
Norfolk

Potters Leisure Resort
★★★★★
Coast Road, Hopton-on-Sea,
Great Yarmouth NR31 9BX
t (01502) 730345
f (01502) 731970
e potters@pottersholidays
.com
w pottersholidays.com

HAYLING ISLAND
Hampshire

Lakeside Classic Resort
★★★
Fishery Lane, Hayling Island
PO11 9NR
t (023) 9246 3976
f (023) 9246 9143
e tina.large@thebourne-
leisure.co.uk

HEMSBY
Norfolk

Pontins Ltd ★★★
Hemsby Family Centre,
Beach Road, Great Yarmouth
NR29 4HL
t 0870 601 0478
f (01493) 384010

LOWESTOFT
Suffolk

Warner Holidays Ltd
★★★
Gunton Hall Classic Resort,
Gunton Avenue, Lowestoft
NR32 5DF
t (01502) 730288
f (01502) 732319

SEATON
Devon

Lyme Bay Holiday Village
★★★
87 Harbour Road, Seaton
EX12 2NE
t (01297) 626800
f (01297) 626801
w lymebayholidayvillage
.co.uk

TORQUAY
Devon

TLH Leisure Resort
★★★★
Belgrave Road, Torquay
TQ2 5HT
t (01803) 400111
f (01803) 400150

WESTON-SUPER-MARE
Somerset

Sand Bay Holiday Village
★★★
67 Beach Road, Kewstoke,
Weston-super-Mare BS22 9UR
t (01934) 428200
f (01934) 428228
w sandbayholidayvillage
.co.uk

WREA GREEN
Lancashire

Ribby Hall Village ★★★
Ribby Road, Wrea Green,
Preston PR4 2PR
t (01772) 671111
f (01772) 673113
e enquiries@ribbyhall.co.uk
w ribbyhall.co.uk

YARMOUTH
Isle of Wight

Warner Holidays Ltd
★★★
Norton Grange Classic
Resort, Yarmouth PO41 0SD
t 0870 601 6012
f (01983) 760468

Further
information

The British Graded
Holiday Parks Scheme

When you're looking for a place to stay, you need a rating system you can trust. The British Graded Holiday Parks Scheme, operated jointly by the national tourist boards for England, Scotland, Wales and Northern Ireland, was devised in association with the British Holiday and Home Parks Association and the National Caravan Council. It gives you a clear guide of what to expect in an easy-to-understand form.

The process to arrive at a star rating is very thorough to ensure that when you make a booking you can be confident it will meet your expectations. Professional assessors visit parks annually and take into account over 50 separate aspects, from landscaping and layout to maintenance, customer care and, most importantly, cleanliness.

Strict guidelines are in place to ensure that every park is assessed to the same criteria. A random check is made of a sample of accommodation provided for hire (caravans, chalets etc) but the quality of the accommodation itself is not included in the grading assessment.

In addition to The British Graded Holiday Parks Scheme, VisitBritain operates a rating scheme for Holiday Villages. The assessor stays on the site overnight and grades the overall quality of the visitor experience, including accommodation, facilities, cleanliness, service and food.

So you can rest assured that when you choose a star-rated park or holiday village you won't be disappointed.

Star ratings

Parks are required to meet progressively higher standards of quality as they move up the scale from one to five stars:

ONE STAR Acceptable
To achieve this grade, the park must be clean with good standards of maintenance and customer care.

TWO STAR Good
All the above points plus an improved level of landscaping, lighting, refuse disposal and maintenance. May be less expensive than more highly rated parks.

THREE STAR Very good
Most parks fall within this category; three stars represent the industry standard. The range of facilities provided may vary from park to park, but they will be of a very good standard and will be well maintained.

FOUR STAR Excellent
You can expect careful attention to detail in the provision of all services and facilities. Four star parks rank among the industry's best.

FIVE STAR Exceptional
Highest levels of customer care will be provided. All facilities will be maintained in pristine condition in attractive surroundings.

Advice and information

Making a booking

When enquiring about a place to stay, make sure you check prices, the quality rating, and other important details. You will also need to state your requirements clearly and precisely.

Booking by letter or email
Misunderstandings can easily happen over the telephone, so do request a written confirmation together with details of any terms and conditions.

Deposits and advance payments
In the case of caravan, camping and touring parks, and holiday villages the full charge often has to be paid in advance. This may be in two instalments – a deposit at the time of booking and the balance by, say, two weeks before the start of the booked period.

Cancellations

Legal contract
When you accept a booking that is offered to you, by telephone or in writing, you enter a legally binding contract with the proprietor. This means that if you cancel or fail to take up your booking or leave early, the proprietor may be entitled to compensation if he or she cannot re-let for all or a good part of the booked period. You will probably forfeit any deposit you have paid and may well be asked for an additional payment.

At the time of booking you should be advised of what charges would be made in the event of cancelling the accommodation or leaving early. If this is not mentioned you should ask so that future disputes can be avoided. The proprietor cannot make a claim until after the booked period, and during that time he or she should make every effort to re-let the accommodation. If there is a dispute it is sensible for both sides to seek legal advice on the matter. If you do have to change your travel plans, it is in your own interests to let the proprietor know in writing as soon as possible, to give them a chance to re-let your accommodation.

And remember, if you book by telephone and are asked for your credit card number, you should check whether the proprietor intends charging your credit card account should you later cancel your booking. A proprietor should not be able to charge your credit card account with a cancellation fee unless he or she has made this clear at the time of your booking and you have agreed. However, to avoid later disputes, we suggest you check whether this is the intention.

Insurance
A travel or holiday insurance policy will safeguard you if you have to cancel or change your holiday plans. You can arrange a policy quite cheaply through your insurance company or travel agent.

Finding a park

Tourist signs similar to the one shown here are designed to help visitors  find their park. They clearly show whether the park is for tents or caravans or both.

Tourist information centres throughout Britain are able to give campers and caravanners information about parks in their areas. Some tourist information centres have camping and caravanning advisory services that provide details of park availability and often assist with park booking.

Electric hook-up points

Most parks now have electric hook-up points for caravans and tents. Voltage is generally 240v AC, 50 cycles. Parks may charge extra for this facility, and it is advisable to check rates when making a booking.

Avoiding peak season

In the summer months of June to September, parks in popular areas such as North Wales, Cumbria, the West Country or the New Forest in Hampshire may become full. Campers should aim to arrive at parks early in the day or, where possible, should book in advance. Some parks have overnight holding areas for visitors who arrive late. This helps to prevent disturbing other campers and caravanners late at night and means that fewer visitors are turned away. Caravans or tents are directed to a pitch the following morning.

Other caravan and camping places

If you enjoy making your own route through Britain's countryside, it may interest you to know that the Forestry Commission operates campsites in Britain's Forest Parks as well as in the New Forest. Some offer reduced charges for youth organisations on organised camping trips, and all enquiries about them should be made, well in advance of your intended stay, to the Forestry Commission.

Bringing pets to Britain

Dogs, cats, ferrets and some other pet mammals can be brought into the UK from certain countries without having to undertake six months' quarantine on arrival provided they meet all the rules of the Pet Travel Scheme (PETS).

For full details, visit the PETS website at
w defra.gov.uk/animalh/quarantine/index.htm
or contact the PETS Helpline
t +44 (0)870 241 1710
e quarantine@defra.gsi.gov.uk
Ask for fact sheets which cover dogs and cats, ferrets or domestic rabbits and rodents.

What to expect at caravan & camping parks

In addition to fulfilling its statutory obligations, including having applied for a certificate under the Fire Precautions Act 1971 (if applicable) and holding public liability insurance, and ensuring that all caravan holiday homes/chalets for hire and the park and all buildings and facilities thereon, the fixtures, furnishings, fittings and decor are maintained in sound and clean condition and are fit for the purposes intended, the management is required to undertake the following:

- To ensure high standards of courtesy, cleanliness, catering and service appropriate to the type of park;

- To describe to all visitors and prospective visitors the amenities, facilities and services provided by the park and/or caravan holiday homes/chalets whether by advertisement, brochure, word of mouth or other means;

- To allow visitors to see the park or caravan holiday homes/chalets for hire, if requested, before booking;

- To present grading awards and/or any other national tourist board awards unambiguously;

- To make clear to visitors exactly what is included in prices quoted for the park or caravan holiday homes/chalets, meals and refreshments, including service charge, taxes and other surcharges. Details of charges, if any, for heating or for additional services or facilities available should also be made clear;

- To adhere to, and not to exceed, prices current at time of occupation for caravan holiday homes/chalets or other services;

- To advise visitors at the time of booking, and subsequently if any change, if the caravan holiday home/chalet or pitch offered is in a different location or on another park, and to indicate the location of this and any difference in comfort and amenities;

- To give each visitor, on request, details of payments due and a receipt if required;

- To advise visitors at the time of booking of the charges that might be incurred if the booking is subsequently cancelled;

- To register all guests on arrival;

- To deal promptly and courteously with all visitors and prospective visitors, including enquiries, requests, reservations, correspondence and complaints;

- To allow a national tourist board representative reasonable access to the park and/or caravan holiday homes/chalet whether by prior appointment or on an unannounced assessment, to confirm that the VisitBritain Code of Conduct is being observed and that the appropriate quality standard is being maintained;

- The operator must comply with the provision of the caravan industry Codes of Practice.

What to expect at holiday villages

The operator/manager is required to undertake the following:

- To maintain standards of guest care, cleanliness, and service appropriate to the type of establishment;

- To describe accurately in any advertisement, brochure, or other printed or electronic media, the facilities and services provided;

- To make clear to visitors exactly what is included in all prices quoted for accommodation, including taxes, and any other surcharges. Details of charges for additional services/facilities should also be made clear;

- To give a clear statement of the policy on cancellations to guests at the time of booking ie by telephone, fax, email as well as information given in a printed format;

- To adhere to, and not to exceed prices quoted at the time of booking for accommodation and other services;

- To advise visitors at the time of booking, and subsequently of any change, if the accommodation offered is in an unconnected annexe or similar, and to indicate the location of such accommodation and any difference in comfort and/or amenities from accommodation in the establishment;

- To give each visitor, on request, details of payments due and a receipt, if required;

- To register all guests on arrival;

- To deal promptly and courteously with all enquiries, requests, bookings and correspondence from visitors;

- Ensure complaint handling procedures are in place and that complaints received are investigated promptly and courteously and that the outcome is communicated to the visitor;

- To give due consideration to the requirements of visitors with special needs, and to make suitable provision where applicable;

- To provide public liability insurance or comparable arrangement and to comply with applicable planning, safety and other statutory requirements;

- To allow a national tourist board representative reasonable access to the establishment, on request, to confirm the VisitBritain Code of Conduct is being observed.

Comments and complaints

Information

The proprietors themselves supply the descriptions of their establishments and other information for the entries (except ratings). They have all signed a declaration that their information conforms to the Trade Description Acts 1968 and 1972. VisitBritain cannot guarantee the accuracy of information in this guide, and accepts no responsibility for any error or misrepresentation.

All liability for loss, disappointment, negligence or other damage caused by reliance on the information contained in this guide, or in the event of bankruptcy or liquidation or cessation of trade of any company, individual or firm mentioned, is hereby excluded. We strongly recommend that you carefully check prices and other details when you book your accommodation.

Problems

Of course, we hope you will not have cause for complaint, but problems do occur from time to time.

If you are dissatisfied with anything, make your complaint to the management immediately. Then the management can take action at once to investigate the matter and put things right. The longer you leave a complaint, the harder it is to deal with it effectively.

In certain circumstances, VisitBritain may look into complaints. However, VisitBritain has no statutory control over establishments or their methods of operating. VisitBritain cannot become involved in legal or contractual matters or in seeking financial compensation.

If you do have problems that have not been resolved by the proprietor and which you would like to bring to our attention, please write to: Quality in Tourism, Farncombe House, Broadway, Worcestershire WR12 7LJ.

Useful contacts

British Holiday & Home Parks Association

Chichester House, 6 Pullman Court,
Great Western Road, Gloucester GL1 3ND
t (01452) 526911 (enquiries and brochure requests)

Professional UK park owners are represented by the British Holiday and Home Parks Association. Almost 2,000 parks are in membership, and each year welcome millions of visitors seeking quality surroundings in which to enjoy a good value stay.

Parks provide caravan holiday homes and lodges for hire, and pitches for your own touring caravan, motor home or tent. On many, you can opt to buy your own holiday home.

A major strength of the UK's park industry is its diversity. Whatever your idea of holiday pleasure, there's sure to be a park which can provide it. If your preference is for a quiet, peaceful holiday in tranquil rural surroundings, you'll find many idyllic locations.

Alternatively, many parks are to be found at our most popular resorts – and reflect the holiday atmosphere with plenty of entertainment and leisure facilities. And for more adventurous families, parks often provide excellent bases from which to enjoy outdoor activities.

Literature available from BH&HPA includes a guide to over 500 parks which have this year achieved the David Bellamy Conservation Award for environmental excellence.

The Camping and Caravanning Club

Greenfields House, Westwood Way,
Coventry CV4 8JH
t 0845 130 7631
t 0845 130 7633 (advance bookings)
w campingandcaravanningclub.co.uk

Discover the peace and quiet of 100 award-winning Club Sites. Experience a different backdrop to your holiday every time you go away, with a choice of sites in the lakes and mountains, coastal and woodland glades or cultural and heritage locations.

The Club is proud of its prestigious pedigree and regularly achieves awards for spotless campsites, friendly service and caring for the environment – a guarantee that you will enjoy your holiday.

Non-members are welcome at the majority of our sites and we offer special deals for families, backpackers, overseas visitors and members aged 55 and over.

For more details please refer to our entries listed at the back of this publication or telephone (02476) 856797 to request a free guide.

The Caravan Club

East Grinstead House, East Grinstead,
West Sussex RH19 1UA
t (01342) 326944
w caravanclub.co.uk

The Caravan Club offers around 200 sites in the UK and Ireland. These include city locations such as London, Edinburgh, York and Chester, plus sites near leading heritage attractions such as Longleat, Sandringham, Chatsworth and Blenheim Palace. A further 20 sites are in National Parks.

Over 95% of pitches have an electric hook-up point and many sites offer emptying points for motor caravanners. Most Caravan Club Sites are graded four or five stars according to The British Graded Holiday Parks Scheme, run by Quality in Tourism, so that you can be assured of quality at all times. Over 130 sites are open to non-members, but why not become a member and gain access to all sites, plus a further 2,500 Certificated Locations, rural sites for no more than five vans. Tent campers are welcome at over 60 sites. Join The Club and you can save the cost of your subscription fee in just five nights with member discounts on site fees!

Forestry Commission

Heart of the National Forest, Bath Yard, Moira, Derbyshire DE12 6BD
t 0845 130 8223 (cabins)
t 0845 130 8224 (campsites)
w forestholidays.co.uk

Forest Holidays, a new partnership between the Forestry Commission and the Camping and Caravanning Club, have over 20 camping and caravan sites in stunning forest locations throughout Great Britain. Choose from the Scottish Highlands, the New Forest, Snowdonia National Park, the Forest of Dean, or the banks of Loch Lomond. Some sites are open all year and dogs are welcome at most. Advance bookings are accepted for many sites.

For a unique forest experience, call Forest Holidays for a brochure on 0845 130 8224 or visit our website.

The Motor Caravanners' Club Ltd

22 Evelyn Close, Twickenham TW2 7BN
t (020) 8893 3883
e info@motorcaravanners.org.uk
w motorcaravanners.org.uk

The Motor Caravanners' Club is authorised to issue the Camping Card International (CCI). It also produces a monthly magazine, Motor Caravanner, for all members. Member of The Federation Internationale de Camping et de Caravanning (FICC).

The National Caravan Council

The National Caravan Council, Catherine House, Victoria Road, Aldershot, Hampshire GU11 1SS
t (01252) 318251
e info@nationalcaravan.co.uk
w thecaravan.net

The National Caravan Council (NCC) is the trade body for the British caravan industry – not just touring caravans and motor homes but also caravan holiday homes. It has in its membership parks, manufacturers, dealers and suppliers to the industry – all NCC member companies are committed continually to raise standards of technical and commercial excellence.

So, if you want to know where to buy a caravan, where to find a caravan holiday park or simply need advice on caravans and caravanning, see the website thecaravan.net where there is lots of helpful advice including:

- How to check whether the caravan, motor home or caravan holiday home you are buying complies with European Standards and essential UK health and safety regulations (through the Certification scheme that the NCC operates).
- How to contact NCC members – dealers, manufacturers, parks and more.
- Where to find quality parks to visit on holiday.
- Where to find approved caravan and motor home workshops.

Caravan holidays are one of the most popular choices for holidaymakers in Britain – the NCC works closely with VisitBritain to promote caravan holidays in all their forms and parks that are part of the British Graded Quality Parks Scheme.

Country ways

The Countryside Rights of Way Act gives people new rights to walk on areas of open countryside and registered common land.

To find out where you can go and what you can do, as well as information about taking your dog to the countryside, go online at countrysideaccess.gov.uk.

And when you're out and about...

Always follow the Country Code
- Be safe – plan ahead and follow any signs
- Leave gates and property as you find them
- Protect plants and animals, and take your litter home
- Keep dogs under close control
- Consider other people

About the
guide entries

Entries

All the sites featured in this guide have been assessed or has applied for assessment under The British Graded Holiday Parks Scheme. Assessment automatically entitles sites to a listing in this guide. Additionally proprietors may pay to have their site featured in either a standard entry (includes description, facilities and prices) or an enhanced entry (photograph and extended details).

Locations

Places to stay are listed under the town, city or village where they are located. If a place is in the countryside, you may find it listed under a nearby village or town (providing it is within a seven-mile radius). Place names are listed alphabetically within each regional section of the guide, along with the name of the ceremonial county they are in and their map reference.

Map references

These refer to the colour location maps at the front of the guide. The first figure shown is the map number, the following letter and figure indicate the grid reference on the map. Only place names under which standard or enhanced entries (see above) feature appear on the maps. Some entries were included just before the guide went to press, so they do not appear on the maps.

Addresses

County names, which appear in the place headings, are not repeated in the entries. When you are writing, you should of course make sure you use the full address and postcode.

Telephone numbers

Booking telephone numbers are listed below the contact address for each entry. Area codes are shown in brackets.

Prices

The prices shown are only a general guide and include VAT where applicable; they were supplied to us by proprietors in summer 2006. Remember, changes may occur after the guide goes to press, so we strongly advise you to check prices when you book your accommodation.

Touring pitch prices are based on the minimum and maximum charges for one night for two persons, car and either caravan or tent. (Some parks may charge separately for car, caravan or tent, and for each person and there may be an extra charge for caravan awnings.) Minimum and maximum prices for caravan holiday homes are given per week.

Prices often vary through the year, and may be significantly lower outside peak holiday weeks. You can get details of other bargain packages that may be available from the sites themselves, regional tourism organisations or your local tourist information centre (TIC). Your local travel agent may also have information, and can help you make bookings.

Opening period

If an entry does not indicate an opening period, please check directly with the site.

Symbols

The at-a-glance symbols included at the end of each entry show many of the services and facilities available at each site. You will find the key to these symbols on the back-cover flap. Open out the flap and you can check the meanings of the symbols as you go.

Pets

Many places accept visitors with dogs, but we do advise that you check this when you book, and ask if there are any extra charges or rules about exactly where your pet is allowed. The acceptance of dogs is not always extended to cats, and it is strongly advised that cat owners contact the site well in advance. Some sites do not accept pets at all. Pets are welcome where you see this symbol 🛪.

The quarantine laws have changed in England, and dogs, cats and ferrets are able to come into Britain from over 50 countries. For details of the Pet Travel Scheme (PETS) please turn to page 280.

Chalets/villas for hire

Where a site has chalets or villas for hire this is indicated by this symbol ⬥. Please note that this type of accommodation is not necessarily included within the official quality rating for the park and it is advisable to contact the proprietor directly if you require further information.

Payment accepted

The types of payment accepted by a site are listed in the payment accepted section. If you plan to pay by card, check that your particular card is acceptable before you book. Some proprietors will charge you a higher rate if you pay by credit card rather than cash or cheque. The difference is to cover the percentage paid by the proprietor to the credit card company. When you book by telephone, you may be asked for your credit card number as confirmation. But remember, the proprietor may then charge your credit card account if you cancel your booking. See under Cancellations on page 279.

Awaiting confirmation of rating

At the time of going to press some parks featured in this guide had not yet been assessed for their rating for the year 2007 and so their new rating could not be included. Rating Applied For indicates this.

Walkers and cyclists welcome

Look out for quality-assessed accommodation displaying the Walkers Welcome and Cyclists Welcome signs.

Participants in this scheme actively encourage and support walking and cycling. In addition to special meal arrangements and helpful information, they'll provide a water supply to wash off the mud, an area for drying wet clothing and footwear, maps and books to look up cycling and walking routes and even an emergency puncture-repair kit! Bikes can also be locked up securely undercover.

The standards for the scheme have been developed in partnership with the tourist boards in Northern Ireland, Scotland and Wales, so wherever you're travelling in the UK you'll receive the same welcome.

Getting around
Britain

Britain is a place of perfect proportions – big enough to find a new place to discover, yet small enough to guarantee it's within easy reach. Getting from A to B can be easier than you think...

Planning your journey

Make transportdirect.info your first portal of call! It's the ultimate journey-planning tool to help you find the best way from your home to your destination by car or public transport. Decide on the quickest way to travel by comparing end-to-end journey times and routes. You can even buy train and coach tickets and find out about flights from a selection of airports.

With so many low-cost domestic flights, flying really is an option. Just imagine, you could finish work in Bishop's Stortford and be in Newquay just three hours later for a fun-packed weekend!

You can island hop too, to the Isle of Wight or the Isles of Scilly for a relaxing break. No worries.

If you're travelling by car and want an idea of distances check out the mileage chart overleaf. Or let the train take the strain – the National Rail network is also shown overleaf.

Think green

If you'd rather leave your car behind and travel by 'green transport' when visiting some of the attractions highlighted in this guide you'll be helping to reduce congestion and pollution as well as supporting conservation charities in their commitment to green travel.

The National Trust encourages visits made by non-car travellers. It offers admission discounts or a voucher for the tea room at a selection of its properties if you arrive on foot, cycle or public transport. (You'll need to produce a valid bus or train ticket if travelling by public transport.)

More information about The National Trust's work to encourage car-free days out can be found at nationaltrust.org.uk. Refer to the section entitled Information for Visitors.

> **To help you on your way you'll find a list of useful contacts at the end of this section.**

In which region is the
English county I wish to visit?

If you know what English county you wish to visit you'll find it in the
regional section shown below.

county	region	county	region
Bedfordshire	East of England	Leicestershire	East Midlands
Berkshire	South East England	Lincolnshire	East Midlands
Bristol	South West England	Merseyside	England's Northwest
Buckinghamshire	South East England	Norfolk	East of England
Cambridgeshire	East of England	North Yorkshire	Yorkshire
Cheshire	England's Northwest	Northamptonshire	East Midlands
Cornwall	South West England	Northumberland	North East England
County Durham	North East England	Nottinghamshire	East Midlands
Cumbria	England's Northwest	Oxfordshire	South East England
Derbyshire	East Midlands	Rutland	East Midlands
Devon	South West England	Shropshire	Heart of England
Dorset	South West England	Somerset	South West England
East Riding of Yorkshire	Yorkshire	South Yorkshire	Yorkshire
East Sussex	South East England	Staffordshire	Heart of England
Essex	East of England	Suffolk	East of England
Gloucestershire	South West England	Surrey	South East England
Greater Manchester	England's Northwest	Tees Valley	North East England
Hampshire	South East England	Tyne and Wear	North East England
Herefordshire	Heart of England	Warwickshire	Heart of England
Hertfordshire	East of England	West Midlands	Heart of England
Isle of Wight	South East England	West Sussex	South East England
Isles of Scilly	South West England	West Yorkshire	Yorkshire
Kent	South East England	Wiltshire	South West England
Lancashire	England's Northwest	Worcestershire	Heart of England

To help readers we do not refer to unitary authorities in this guide.

By **car** and by **train**

Distance chart

The distances between towns on the chart below are given to the nearest mile, and are measured along routes based on the quickest travelling time, making maximum use of motorways or dual-carriageway roads. The chart is based upon information supplied by the Automobile Association.

To calculate the distance in kilometres multiply the mileage by 1.6

For example: Brighton to Dover
82 miles x 1.6 =131.2 kilometres

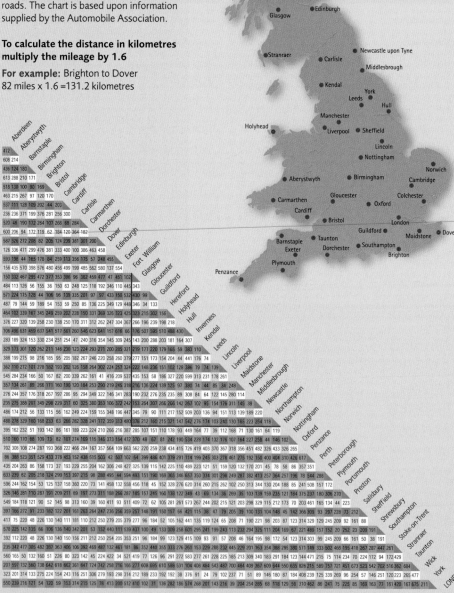

Distance chart (distances in miles). Column/diagonal towns in order: Aberdeen, Aberystwyth, Barnstaple, Birmingham, Brighton, Bristol, Cambridge, Cardiff, Carlisle, Carmarthen, Dorchester, Dover, Edinburgh, Exeter, Fort William, Glasgow, Gloucester, Guildford, Hereford, Holyhead, Hull, Inverness, Kendal, Leeds, Lincoln, Liverpool, Maidstone, Manchester, Middlesbrough, Newcastle, Northampton, Norwich, Nottingham, Oxford, Penzance, Perth, Peterborough, Plymouth, Portsmouth, Preston, Salisbury, Sheffield, Shrewsbury, Southampton, Stoke-on-Trent, Stranraer, Taunton, Wick, York, LONDON.

```
Aberystwyth      472
Barnstaple       608 214
Birmingham       436 124 180
Brighton         613 288 210 171
Bristol          518 130 100 90 169
Cambridge        463 215 267 97 120 170
Cardiff          537 111 128 109 202 44 203
Carlisle         236 236 371 199 376 281 256 300
Carmarthen       520 46 190 172 264 107 266 68 284
Dorchester       600 206 94 172 119 62 184 120 364 182
Dover            587 326 272 208 82 205 124 239 381 301 200
Edinburgh        126 336 471 299 476 381 333 400 100 386 463 458
Exeter           593 198 44 165 178 84 259 113 356 175 57 248 455
Fort William     156 435 570 398 576 480 456 499 199 485 562 580 137 554
Glasgow          150 332 467 295 472 377 353 396 96 382 459 477 47 451 102
Gloucester       484 113 126 56 155 36 150 63 248 125 118 192 346 110 445 343
Guildford        571 224 175 128 44 106 96 139 335 201 97 97 433 150 532 430 99
Hereford         487 79 144 59 189 54 153 59 250 85 136 225 349 129 448 346 34 133
Holyhead         464 102 330 167 345 249 259 202 228 150 331 369 326 323 425 323 215 302 156
Hull             376 227 320 139 258 230 138 250 170 311 312 262 247 304 367 266 196 239 198 218
Inverness        106 496 631 459 637 541 517 561 260 546 623 641 157 616 66 157 507 595 510 488 430
Kendal           283 189 324 153 330 234 251 254 47 240 316 354 145 309 245 143 200 288 203 181 164 307
Leeds            329 173 301 120 262 211 146 230 123 224 293 271 200 285 321 219 177 220 179 165 59 383 110
Lincoln          388 199 275 98 216 185 95 205 182 267 246 220 258 260 379 277 151 173 154 204 44 441 176 74
Liverpool        362 110 272 101 278 182 193 202 126 158 264 302 224 257 324 222 148 236 151 102 128 386 79 74 139
Maidstone        545 284 234 166 50 167 82 200 339 262 161 41 416 209 537 435 153 58 186 327 220 599 313 231 178 261
Manchester       357 134 261 89 266 171 160 190 120 184 253 290 219 245 350 216 136 224 139 125 97 380 74 44 85 34 248
Middlesbrough    276 244 357 176 318 267 197 286 95 294 349 322 146 341 283 190 232 276 235 235 89 308 84 64 122 145 280 114
Newcastle        235 275 388 207 349 298 229 317 60 325 380 353 106 372 242 153 264 307 266 266 142 267 102 95 154 176 311 39 45
Northampton      486 174 212 56 133 115 56 162 249 224 159 155 348 196 447 345 79 90 111 217 152 509 203 136 94 151 113 139 189 220
Norwich          488 278 329 160 168 233 63 266 282 328 241 172 359 313 480 378 212 160 215 321 147 542 276 174 103 240 130 165 223 254 118
Nottingham       395 162 232 51 193 142 86 161 189 223 224 210 266 216 387 285 107 151 110 178 93 449 164 77 39 112 168 71 130 161 64 119
Oxford           510 160 170 68 109 73 82 107 274 169 115 146 373 154 472 370 40 67 81 242 130 512 176 107 164 127 22 44 146 102 270
Penzance         702 308 108 274 287 193 368 222 466 284 167 357 564 109 663 562 220 259 238 434 415 726 419 403 370 367 318 356 451 482 326 433 326 265
Perth            86 388 523 351 529 433 378 453 152 438 515 503 42 507 102 64 399 486 401 379 291 114 199 245 303 278 461 275 192 100 426 617
Peterborough     435 204 263 86 158 173 37 193 229 255 204 162 306 248 427 325 139 115 142 225 110 489 223 121 51 159 120 132 170 201 45 78 58 86 357 351
Plymouth         633 239 60 205 218 124 299 153 397 215 98 288 494 49 594 493 151 190 169 365 346 657 350 334 301 296 249 287 382 413 257 364 257 196 78 564 248
Portsmouth       596 244 162 154 53 125 137 158 360 220 73 141 458 132 558 456 118 45 152 328 276 620 314 260 215 262 102 250 313 344 130 204 188 85 241 508 157 172
Preston          326 146 281 110 287 191 209 211 89 197 273 311 198 266 287 185 157 245 160 138 122 349 43 69 134 26 293 53 103 139 159 125 121 184 375 237 180 306 270
Salisbury        549 184 118 121 90 52 145 98 313 160 39 160 411 93 511 409 72 62 105 281 261 573 267 244 202 215 121 203 298 329 115 212 173 70 203 461 165 134 144 23
Sheffield        397 166 272 91 233 182 122 201 161 263 264 247 236 266 359 277 161 184 191 150 67 66 421 115 38 47 79 66 131 104 148 45 142 360 93 297 228 73 212 429
Shrewsbury       417 75 220 48 226 130 140 111 181 110 212 250 279 205 379 277 96 184 52 105 162 441 135 119 124 65 208 71 190 221 98 203 87 123 314 329 129 245 209 92 161 88
Southampton      578 225 142 136 35 108 127 139 342 201 53 142 440 111 539 437 100 49 133 309 258 595 311 244 199 243 113 232 296 315 111 204 169 67 221 489 157 152 20 202 52 229 191
Stoke-on-Trent   392 112 220 48 226 130 140 150 156 211 212 250 254 205 353 251 96 164 99 123 175 415 109 93 91 57 208 46 164 195 98 172 54 123 314 303 99 245 209 66 161 50 38 191
Stranraer        235 342 477 305 482 387 363 406 106 392 469 487 132 461 181 86 352 440 355 333 276 261 153 229 288 232 445 229 201 163 354 388 295 380 571 149 333 502 466 395 418 267 287 447 261
Taunton          560 165 50 132 160 64 246 98 313 160 56 131 451 65 547 419 77 126 96 291 272 583 277 261 228 255 183 213 309 340 183 291 184 123 144 471 215 75 174 60 70 224 172 94 172 429
Wick             207 597 732 560 738 642 618 662 361 647 724 742 258 716 166 277 608 695 610 585 531 104 408 484 543 487 700 466 367 609 644 550 635 826 215 589 757 721 451 673 623 604 702 516 362 684
York             323 201 314 133 275 224 154 243 116 251 306 279 193 298 314 212 189 233 192 192 38 376 91 24 79 102 237 71 51 89 146 180 87 184 408 239 125 339 269 96 254 57 146 251 120 223 265 477
LONDON           550 239 216 121 54 120 59 153 314 215 125 78 413 200 512 410 102 31 136 282 186 574 268 201 143 216 39 204 254 285 68 118 129 56 310 462 86 241 75 225 85 169 163 77 161 420 167 675 211
```

288

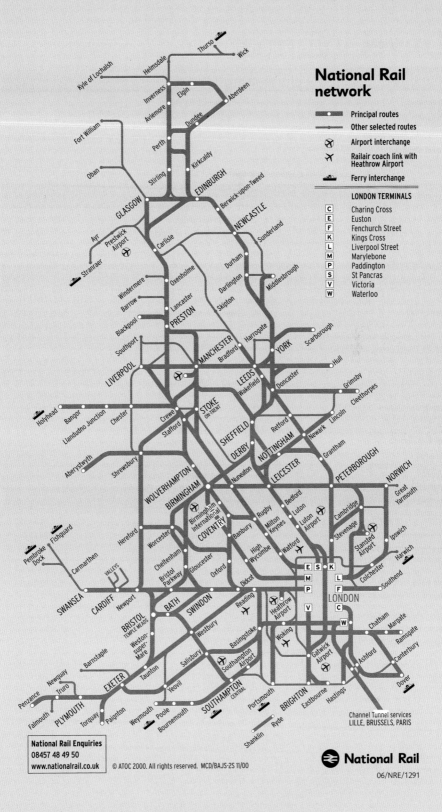

National Rail network

—— Principal routes
—— Other selected routes

⊗ Airport interchange

✈ Railair coach link with Heathrow Airport

⊨ Ferry interchange

LONDON TERMINALS

C	Charing Cross
E	Euston
F	Fenchurch Street
K	Kings Cross
L	Liverpool Street
M	Marylebone
P	Paddington
S	St Pancras
V	Victoria
W	Waterloo

Channel Tunnel services
LILLE, BRUSSELS, PARIS

National Rail Enquiries
08457 48 49 50
www.nationalrail.co.uk

© ATOC 2000. All rights reserved. MCD/BAJS-2S 11/00

National Rail

06/NRE/1291

Travel information

general travel information

Streetmap	streetmap.co.uk	
Transport Direct	transportdirect.info	
Transport for London	tfl.gov.uk	(020) 7222 5600
Travel Services	departures-arrivals.com	
Traveline	traveline.org.uk	0870 608 2608

bus & coach

Megabus	megabus.com	0901 331 0031
National Express	nationalexpress.com	0870 580 8080
WA Shearings	washearings.com	(01942) 824824

car & car hire

AA	theaa.com	0870 600 0371
Green Flag	greenflag.co.uk	0845 246 1557
RAC	rac.co.uk	0870 572 2722
Alamo	alamo.co.uk	0870 400 4562
Avis	avis.co.uk	0870 010 0287
Budget	budget.co.uk	0844 581 2231
Easycar	easycar.com	0906 333 3333
Enterprise	enterprise.com	0870 350 3000*
Hertz	hertz.co.uk	0870 844 8844*
Holiday Autos	holidayautos.co.uk	
National	nationalcar.co.uk	0870 400 4581
Thrifty	thrifty.co.uk	(01494) 751500*

air

Airport information	a2btravel.com/airports	0870 888 1710
Air Southwest	airsouthwest.com	0870 043 4553
Blue Islands (Channel Islands)	blueislands.com	(01481) 727567
BMI	flybmi.com	0870 607 0555
BMI Baby	bmibaby.com	0871 224 0224
BNWA (Isle of Man to Blackpool)	flybnwa.co.uk	0800 083 7783
British Airways	ba.com	0870 850 9850
British International (Isles of Scilly to Penzance)	islesofscillyhelicopter.com	(01736) 363871
Eastern Airways	easternairways.com	0870 366 9100
Easyjet	easyjet.com	0871 244 2366
Flybe	flybe.com	0871 700 0535
Jet2.com	jet2.com	0871 226 1737
Ryanair	ryanair.com	0871 246 0000
Skybus (Isles of Scilly)	islesofscilly-travel.com	0845 710 5555
VLM	flyvlm.com	0871 666 5050

train

National Rail Enquiries	nationalrail.co.uk	0845 748 4950
The Trainline	trainline.co.uk	
UK train operating companies	rail.co.uk	
Arriva Trains	arriva.co.uk	0845 748 4950
c2c	c2c-online.co.uk	0845 601 4873*
Central Trains	centraltrains.co.uk	(0121) 634 2040
Chiltern Railways	chilternrailways.co.uk	0845 600 5165
First Capital Connect	firstcapitalconnect.co.uk	0845 748 4950
First Great Western	firstgreatwestern.co.uk	0845 700 0125*
Gatwick Express	gatwickexpress.co.uk	0845 850 1530
GNER	gner.co.uk	0845 722 5333
Heathrow Express	heathrowexpress.com	0845 600 1515
Hull Trains	hulltrains.co.uk	0845 071 0222
Island Line	island-line.co.uk	0845 748 4950
Merseyrail	merseyrail.org	0845 748 4950
Midland Mainline	midlandmainline.com	0845 712 5678
Northern Rail	northernrail.org	0845 748 4950
One Railway	onerailway.com	0845 600 7245
Silverlink	silverlink-trains.com	0845 601 4868
South Eastern Trains	southeasternrailway.co.uk	0845 748 4950
South West Trains	southwesttrains.co.uk	0845 600 0650
Southern	southernrailway.com	0845 127 2920
Stansted Express	stanstedexpress.com	0845 600 7245
Transpennine Express	tpexpress.co.uk	0845 748 4950
Virgin Trains	virgintrains.co.uk	0870 789 1234

ferry

Ferry information	sailanddrive.com	
Condor Ferries (Channel Islands)	condorferries.co.uk	0870 243 5140*
Steam Packet Company (Isle of Man)	steam-packet.com	0870 552 3523
Isles of Scilly Travel	islesofscilly-travel.co.uk	0845 710 5555
Red Funnel (Isle of Wight)	redfunnel.co.uk	0870 444 8898
Wight Link (Isle of Wight)	wightlink.co.uk	0870 582 7744

Phone numbers listed are for general enquiries unless otherwise stated.

* Booking line only

National cycle network

Sections of the National Cycle Network are shown on the maps in this guide. The numbers on the maps will appear on the signs along your route **3**. Here are some tips about finding and using a route.

- **Research and plan your route online**
  Log on to **sustrans.org.uk** and clink on 'Get cycling' to find information about routes in this guide or other routes you want to use.

- **Order a route map**
  Useful, easy-to-use maps of many of the most popular routes of the National Cycle Network are available from Sustrans, the charity behind the Network. These can be purchased online or by mail order – visit sustransshop.co.uk or call 0845 113 0065.

- **Order Cycling in the UK**
  The official guide to the National Cycle Network gives details of rides all over the UK, detailing 148 routes and profiles of 43 days rides on traffic-free paths and quiet roads. Perfect for those new to cycling or with young families.

ROUTE NUMBER	ROUTE/MAP NAME	START/END OF ROUTE
South West		
3	The West Country Way	Bath & Bristol – Padstow
3 & 32	The Cornish Way	Bude – Land's End
South East		
5	West Midlands	Oxford – Derby via Birmingham
1, 2 & 18	Garden of England	Dover – London – Hastings
East of England		
1	East of England pack	Harwich – Fakenham – Hull
Heart of England		
5 & 54	West Midlands	Oxford – Derby via Birmingham
North East England		
1	Coast & Castles	Newcastle upon Tyne – Berwick-upon-Tweed – Edinburgh
10	Reivers	Tyne – Kielder – Cumbria
68	Pennine Cycleway (North)	Appleby-in-Westmorland or Penrith – Berwick-upon-Tweed
7, 14 & 71	C2C – Sea to Sea	Whitehaven/Workington – Sunderland or Newcastle upon Tyne
72	Hadrian's Cycleway	Ravenglass to Tynemouth/South Shields
Yorkshire and North West England		
62 & 65	Trans Pennine Trail Pack	Yorkshire – North Sea
		Irish Sea – Yorkshire
		Derbyshire – Yorkshire

To order any of the above maps call Sustrans **0845 113 0065** or visit **sustransshop.co.uk**.

A selection of events for 2007

This is a selection of the many cultural, sporting and other events that will be taking place throughout Britain during 2007. For a more comprehensive list, of English events, visit **enjoyengland.com/events**.

Please note, as changes often occur after press date, it is advisable to confirm the date and location before travelling.

January

1–31 Jan
Turner Exhibition
National Gallery, Edinburgh, Scotland
(0131) 624 6200
natgalscot.ac.uk

1 Jan
New Year's Day Parade
Parliament Square to Berkeley Street, London SW1 to W1
(020) 8566 8586
londonparade.co.uk

2–7 Jan
Swan Lake on Ice
Wales Millennium Centre, Cardiff, Wales
0870 040 2000

5–14 Jan
London Boat Show
ExCeL London, Royal Victoria Dock, London E16
londonboatshow.com

11–14 Jan
Autosport International
National Exhibition Centre, Birmingham, West Midlands
0870 909 4133
autosport-international.com

17 Jan–4 Feb
Celtic Connections
Glasgow, Scotland
(0141) 353 8000
celticconnections.com

21–24 Jan
Wales Spring Fair
North Wales Conference Centre, Llandudno, Wales
artswales.org.uk

25 Jan
Burns Night
Various venues, Scotland

February

1–28 Feb
Darwin Festival
Various venues, Shrewsbury, Shropshire
(01743) 281200
darwinshrewsbury.org

2 Feb
World Wetlands Day
Newport Wetlands Reserve, Wales
(01633) 275567
rspb.org.uk

3, 10 & 16 Feb, 1 & 3 Mar
Madam Butterfly
Wales Millennium Centre, Cardiff, Wales
0870 040 2000
wmc.org.uk

4 Feb
Wales v Ireland Six Nations Championships
Millennium Stadium, Cardiff, Wales
millenniumstadium.co.uk

14–18 Feb
Jorvik Viking Festival
Various venues, York, North Yorkshire
(01904) 543413

March

Mar
Scottish Wheelchair Curling Championships
Inverness, Scotland
highland2007.com

Mar*
**Tenby Annual Festival
of Daffodils**
St John's Church, Tenby, Wales
(01834) 844905
stjohnstenby.co.uk

2–4 Mar
Celtic Festival of Wales
Trecco Bay, Porthcawl, Wales
(01656) 766667
cwlwmceltaidd.com

8–11 Mar
Crufts
National Exhibition Centre,
Birmingham, West Midlands
the-kennel-club.org.uk

9 Mar–1 Apr
Ideal Home Show
Earls Court Exhibition Centre,
London SW5
idealhomeshow.co.uk

14–18 Mar
Lord of the Dance
Cardiff International Arena, Wales
cclive.co.uk

16–18 Mar
**The Ordnance Survey
Outdoors Show**
National Exhibition Centre,
Birmingham, West Midlands
(020) 7471 1082
theoutdoorsshow.co.uk

17 Mar
**Wales v England Six Nations
Championships**
Millennium Stadium, Cardiff,
Wales
millenniumstadium.com

24–25 Mar
St David's Day Food Festival
Saundersfoot, Wales
(01834) 812304
visit-saundersfoot.co.uk

26 Mar
Conwy Seed Fair
Conwy, Wales
(01492) 650851
conwybeekeepers.org.uk

28–29 Mar
**Somerley Park International
Horse Trials**
Somerley, Ringwood, Hampshire
(01425) 461744
eleda.co.uk

April

Apr/May*
**Peak District Walking
Festival**
Various venues
(01298) 25106
visitpeakdistrict.com

Apr*
Glasgow International
Scotland
glasgowinternational.org

5–9 Apr
**Nantwich Jazz, Blues
& Music Festival**
Various venues, Nantwich,
Cheshire
(01270) 610983
nantwichjazz.com

6–9 Apr
Easter Festival
Edinburgh, Scotland
edinburgheaster.co.uk

7–22 Apr
Taste Lancashire
Various venues
(01995) 642255
visitlancashire.com

7–9 Apr
**Chester Food and Drink
Festival**
Various venues, Chester, Cheshire
(01244) 402111
chesterfoodanddrink.com

7 Apr
**Oxford and Cambridge
Boat Race**
River Thames, London
theboatrace.org

22 Apr
Flora London Marathon
Greenwich Park to The Mall,
London
(020) 7902 0200
london-marathon.co.uk

26–29 Apr
**Harrogate Spring Flower
Show**
Great Yorkshire Showground,
Harrogate, North Yorkshire
(01423) 561049
flowershow.org.uk

May

1–31 May*
**International Cider & Perry
Competition**
Hereford Cider Museum,
Herefordshire
(01432) 354207
cidermuseum.co.uk

1 May
**King's Lynn May Garland
Procession**
Various venues, King's Lynn,
Norfolk
(01553) 768930
thekingsmorris.co.uk

5–27 May
Brighton Festival
Various venues, Brighton,
East Sussex
(01273) 709709
brighton-festival.org.uk

5–7 May
**Dales Festival of Food
and Drink**
Various venues, Leyburn,
North Yorkshire
(01969) 624761
dalesfestivaloffood.org

5 May
Spalding Flower Parade
Spalding, Lincolnshire
(01775) 724843
flowerparade.org

8 May
Helston Flora Day
Cornwall
(01326) 572082
helstonfloraday.org.uk

10–13 May
Royal Windsor Horse Show
Windsor Home Park, Berkshire
(01753) 860633
royal-windsor-horse-show.co.uk

12–20 May
Aviemore Walking Festival
Scotland
aviemorewalking.com

12–18 May
Royal Deeside Golf Week
Ballater, Scotland
ballatergolfclub.co.uk

13 May
Northumbrian Water University Boat Race
River Tyne, Quayside, Newcastle upon Tyne, Tyne and Wear
(0191) 433 3820
gateshead.gov.uk

17–19 May
Devon County Show
Westpoint Exhibition Centre, Clyst St Mary
(01392) 446000
devoncountyshow.co.uk

18 May–3 Jun
Bath International Music Festival
Various venues, Bath, Somerset
(01225) 463362
bathmusicfest.org.uk

19 May–3 Jun
Lincolnshire Wolds Walking Festival
Various venues
(01507) 609289
lincswolds.org.uk

19–20 May
Haworth 1940s Festival
Various venues, Haworth, West Yorkshire
(01535) 642329
haworth-village.org.uk

22–26 May
Chelsea Flower Show
Royal Hospital, London SW3
(020) 7649 1885
rhs.org.uk

25 May–10 Jun
Salisbury Festival
Various venues, Wiltshire
(01722) 332977
salisburyfestival.co.uk

26–27 May
Hertfordshire County Show
Herts County Showground, Redbourn
(01582) 792676
hertsshow.com

28 May–2 Jun
Urdd National Eisteddfod
Carmarthen, Wales
(01970) 613110
urdd.org.uk

28 May
Luton International Carnival
Hertfordshire
(01582) 728121
luton.gov.uk

28 May
Northumberland County Show
Tynedale Park, Corbridge
(01697) 747848
northcountyshow.co.uk

30 May–2 Jun
Royal Bath & West Show
Bath & West Showground, Shepton Mallet, Somerset
(01749) 822200
bathandwest.com

30–31 May
Suffolk Show
Trinity Park, Ipswich
(01473) 707110
suffolkshow.co.uk

June

Jun*
Isle of Wight Festival
Seaclose Park, Newport
0870 532 1321
isleofwightfestival.com

1 Jun–31 Aug
South Tyneside Summer Festival
Various venues, South Shields
(01914) 247985
southtyneside.info

1–3 Jun
Gardening Scotland
Edinburgh, Scotland
(0131) 333 0969
gardeningscotland.com

1–2 Jun
Vodafone Derby
Epsom Downs Racecourse, Epsom, Surrey
(01372) 470047
epsomderby.co.uk

4 Jun–25 Aug
Stamford Shakespeare Festival
Rutland Open Air Theatre, Tolethorpe Hall, Little Casterton, Rutland
(01780) 756133
stamfordshakespeare.co.uk

7–9 Jun
Royal Cornwall Show
Royal Cornwall Showground, Wadebridge
(01208) 812183
royalcornwall.co.uk

9–10 Jun
Durham Regatta
River Wear, Durham, County Durham
(0191) 386 4118

10 Jun
The Cosford Air Show
Royal Air Force Museum, Cosford, Suffolk
(01902) 377922
cosfordairshow.co.uk

11 Jun–19 Aug
Royal Academy Summer Exhibition
Burlington House, Piccadilly, London W1
(020) 7300 8000
royalacademy.org.uk

15–17 Jun
Three Counties
Countryside Show
Three Counties Showground,
Malvern, Worcestershire
(01684) 584900
threecounties.co.uk

16–24 Jun
Golowan Festival
Incorporating Mazey Day
Various venues, Penzance,
Cornwall
(01736) 332211
golowan.com

16–17 Jun
Althorp Literary Festival
Althorp, Northampton,
Northamptonshire
(01604) 770107
althorp.com

16 Jun
Trooping the Colour
Horseguards Parade, Whitehall,
London SW1
royal.gov.uk

19–24 Jun*
Royal Ascot
Ascot Racecourse, Berkshire
0870 727 1234
royalascot.co.uk

19–20 Jun
Cheshire County Show
Tabley, Knutsford
(01565) 722050
cheshirecountyshow.org.uk

21–24 Jun
Royal Highland Show
Edinburgh, Scotland
(0131) 335 6200
royalhighlandshow.org

25 Jun–8 Jul
Wimbledon Lawn Tennis
Championships
All England Lawn Tennis Club,
London SW19
(020) 8946 2244
wimbledon.org

26 Jun–8 Jul
International Byron Festival
Various venues, Hucknall,
Nottinghamshire
(01159) 664367
internationalbyronsociety.org

27 Jun–1 Jul
Alnwick Fair
Alnwick, Northumberland
(01665) 711397

27–28 Jun
Royal Norfolk Show
Norfolk Showground,
New Costessey, Norwich
(01603) 748931
royalnorfolkshow.co.uk

30 Jun–1 Jul
Sunderland International
Kite Festival
Northern Area Playing Fields,
Washington, Sunderland,
Tyne and Wear
(01915) 148443
sunderland-kites.co.uk

30 Jun
Pride 2007
Various venues, London
pridelondon.org

July

Jul/Aug*
Cardiff Festival
Wales
cardiff-festival.com

Jul*
Goodwood Festival of Speed
Goodwood Park, Chichester,
West Sussex
(01243) 755055
goodwood.co.uk

4–8 Jul
Henley Royal Regatta
Henley-on-Thames, Oxfordshire
(01491) 572153
hrr.co.uk

6–22 Jul
Buxton Festival
Various venues, Buxton, Derbyshire
(01298) 70395
buxtonfestival.co.uk

6–9 Jul*
121st Wenlock Olympian
Games Weekend
Various venues, Shropshire
(01952) 727679
wenlock-olympian-society.org.uk

6–8 Jul
The Grand Départ –
Tour de France
Central and South East London
london.gov.uk/mayor/culture
/tour_de_france

7–8 Jul
City Of Durham
Summer Festival
Various venues, Durham,
County Durham
(0191) 301 8819
durhamtourism.co.uk

8 Jul
Tour de France Stage 1
London to Canterbury
Various venues, Canterbury, Kent
(020) 7222 1234
tourdefrancelondon.com

10–15 Jul
Llangollen International
Musical Eisteddfod
Llangollen, Wales
(01978) 862000
international-
eisteddfod.co.uk

10–12 Jul
The Great Yorkshire Show
Great Yorkshire Showground,
Harrogate, North Yorkshire
(01423) 541000
greatyorkshireshow.com

13 Jul–8 Sep
The Proms
Royal Albert Hall, London SW7
(020) 7765 5575
bbc.co.uk/proms

13–15 Jul
Whitley Bay International
Jazz Festival
Menzies Silverlink Hotel,
Wallsend, Tyne and Wear
(0191) 252 3505
whitleybayjazzfest.org

14 Jul
Barnsley Summer Carnival and Parade
Various venues, Barnsley,
South Yorkshire
barnsley.gov.uk/council/sum
mercarnival

14 Jul
Durham Miners Gala
Various venues, Durham,
County Durham
(01913) 833379

15 Jul
Burton Constable Hall Country Fair
Burton Constable, Hull,
East Riding of Yorkshire
(01964) 562400
burtonconstable.com

16–17 Jul*
Godiva Festival
Memorial Park, Coventry,
West Midlands
(024) 7622 7264
visitcoventry.co.uk/godiva

19–22 Jul
The Open Championship
Carnoustie, Scotland
opengolf.com

20–22 Jul
Royal Lancashire Agricultural Show
Salesbury Hall, Ribchester
(01254) 813769
visitlancashire.com

20–21 Jul
World Highland Games Heavy Championships
Inverness, Scotland
invernesshighlandgames.com

25–29 Jul
Longines Royal International Horse Show
All England Jumping Course,
Hickstead, Haywards Heath,
West Sussex
(01273) 834315
hickstead.co.uk

25 Jul
Nantwich South Cheshire Show
Dorfold Hall, Nantwich, Cheshire
(01457) 876198
nantwichshow.co.uk

27–29 Jul
Gateshead Summer Flower Show
Gateshead Central Nurseries,
Tyne and Wear
(0191) 433 3838
gateshead.gov.uk

28–29 Jul
Sunderland International Air Show
Seafront, Sunderland,
Tyne and Wear
(0191) 553 2000
sunderland.gov.uk/airshow

28–29 Jul*
WOMAD Festival
Rivermead, Reading, Berkshire
(0118) 960 6060
womad.org/reading

28 Jul
Cleveland Show
Stewart Park, Middlesbrough,
Tees Valley
(01642) 312231
middlesbrough.gov.uk

28 Jul
European Pipe Band Championships
Inverness, Scotland
highland2007.com

30 Jul–5 Aug
Robin Hood Festival
Sherwood Forest Visitor Centre,
Edwinstowe, Nottinghamshire
(01623) 823202
robinhood.co.uk

31 Jul–4 Aug*
Glorious Goodwood
Goodwood Racecourse,
Chichester, West Sussex
0800 018 8191
goodwood.co.uk

August

2–5 Aug
The Big Chill Festival
Eastnor Castle, Ledbury,
Herefordshire
(020) 7684 2020
bigchill.net

3–25 Aug
Edinburgh Military Tattoo
Scotland
0870 7555 1188
edintattoo.co.uk

3–10 Aug
Sidmouth Folk Week
Various venues, Sidmouth,
Devon
(01395) 516441
sidmouthfolkweek.co.uk

3–5 Aug
Glastonbury Abbey Musical Extravaganza
Glastonbury, Somerset
(01458) 834596
glastonburyfestivals.co.uk

4–11 Aug
Cowes Week
The Solent, Cowes, Isle of Wight
(01983) 295744
skandiacowesweek.co.uk

4–11 Aug
National Eisteddfod of Wales
Mold, Wales
(029) 2076 3777
eisteddfod.org.uk

12 Aug–2 Sep
Edinburgh Imternational Festival
Scotland
(0131) 473 2001
eif.co.uk

18–19 Aug*
**Northampton Balloon
Festival**
Racecourse Park, Northampton,
Northamptonshire
(01604) 838222
northamptonballoonfestival.com

18–19 Aug
V Festival
Weston Park, Weston-under-
Lizard, Shifnal, Shropshire
0871 220 0260
vfestival.com

23–26 Aug*
**Bowmore Blair Castle
Horse Trials**
Blair Atholl, Scotland
(01796) 481207
blairhorsetrials.co.uk

24–26 Aug*
**Carling Weekend Leeds
Festival**
Bramham Park, Leeds,
West Yorkshire
0870 060 3775

25 Aug–1 Sep*
Shetland Walking Week
Scotland
(01595) 693434
visitshetland.com

25–26 Aug
**Saddleworth Rushcart
Festival**
Uppermill, Greenfield, Dobcross
and Delph, Saddleworth,
West Riding of Yorkshire
(01457) 876198
morrismen.saddleworth.org.uk

26–27 Aug
Notting Hill Carnival
Ladbroke Grove area,
London W11
(020) 8964 0544

29 Aug–2 Sep
Great Dorset Steam Fair
South Down Farm, Tarrant Hinton
(01258) 860361
gdsf.co.uk

31 Aug–3 Sep
Pendle Walking Festival
Various venues, Pendle,
Lancashire
(01282) 661685
visitlancashire.com

September

Sep*
Abergavenny Food Festival
Abergavenny, Wales
abergavennyfoodfestival.com

Sep*
Artsfest
Various venues, Birmingham,
West Midlands
0870 225 0127
artsfest.org.uk

Sep*
**Ludlow & the Marches Food
and Drink Festival**
Various venues, Ludlow,
Shropshire
(01584) 873957
foodfestival.co.uk

1–3 Sep
Jazz in the Park
Pontypool, Wales
(01495) 792615
torfaenjazz.org.uk

1–2 Sep
English Wine Festival
New Hall Vineyard, Purleigh,
Maldon, Essex
(01621) 828343
newhallwines.co.uk

1–2 Sep
MELA
Edinburgh, Scotland
(0131) 557 1400
edinburgh-mela.co.uk

1 Sep
Oyster Festival
The Waterfront, Maldon, Essex
(01621) 856503
hidden-treasures.co.uk

3–9 Sep
**UCI Mountain Bike and
Trials World Championships**
Fort William, Scotland
fortwilliamworldchamps.co.uk

6–9 Sep
**The 2nd Pennine Lancashire
Festival of Food & Drink**
Various venues across the West
Pennine Moors
(01254) 683563
visitlancashire.com

7–23 Sep
Wirksworth Festival
Various venues, Wirksworth,
Derbyshire
(01629) 824003
wirksworthfestival.co.uk

8–9 Sep
Stanhope Agricultural Show
Unthank Park, Stanhope, Bishop
Auckland, County Durham
(01388) 529118

9 Sep
**Massed Morris Dancing
in Thornham**
Various venues, Thornham,
Hunstanton, Norfolk
(01553) 768930
thekingsmorris.co.uk

14–23 Sep
Southampton Boat Show
Mayflower Park, Southampton,
Hampshire
(01784) 472222
southamptonboatshow.com

14–22 Sep
Hexham Abbey Festival
Tynedale, Northumberland
(01661) 843347
hexhamabbey.org.uk/festival

15–16 Sep
**The Mayor's Thames
Festival**
Westminster Bridge to Tower
Bridge, London SW1 & SE1
thamesfestival.org

15–16 Sep
Open House Weekend
Various venues, London
londonopenhouse.org

22 Sep–1 Oct
**York Festival of Food
and Drink**
Various venues, York,
North Yorkshire
(01904) 466688
yorkfestivaloffoodanddrink.com

October

Oct–Nov*
London Film Festival
Various venues, London
(020) 7928 3232
lff.org.uk

Oct–Nov*
State Opening of Parliament
Houses of Parliament,
Westminster, London SW1
parliament.uk

Oct*
East Midlands Food Festival
Various venues, Leicestershire
(01664) 562971
eastmidlandsfoodfestival.co.uk

5–14 Oct
Ideal Home Show
Earls Court Exhibition Centre,
London SW5
idealhomeshow.co.uk

5–7 Oct
**Stoke on Trent Ceramics
Festival**
Various venues, Stoke-on-Trent,
Staffordshire
(01782) 236000
visitstoke.co.uk

6–14 Oct
Hull Fair
Hull, East Riding of Yorkshire
(01482) 615624

12–20 Oct
The Royal National MOD
Lochaber, Scotland
(01463) 709705
the-mod.co.uk

31 Oct–4 Nov
Blackpool Illuminations
Blackpool Promenade, Lancashire
visitblackpool.com

November

5 Nov
Tar Barrels
Ottery St Mary, Devon
(01404) 813964
otterytourism.org.uk

9 Nov
**Bridgwater Guy Fawkes
Carnival**
Various venues, Bridgwater,
Somerset
(01278) 421795
bridgwatercarnival.org.uk

10 Nov
Lord Mayor's Show
City of London
(020) 7606 3030
lordmayorsshow.org

16 Nov–23 Dec
Frankfurt Christmas Market
Various venues, Birmingham,
West Midlands
(0121) 202 5000
beinbirmingham.com

23–26 Nov
St Nicholas Fayre
Various venues, York,
North Yorkshire
(01904) 554427

27–28 Oct
**Glenfiddich Piping
& Fiddling Championships**
Blair Atholl, Scotland
(01698) 573536
glenfiddich.com

29 Nov–2 Dec
Worcester Christmas Fayre
Various venues, Worcester,
Worcestershire
(01905) 726311
worcestershire-tourism.org

30 Nov
St Andrew's Day
Various venues, Scotland

December

Dec*
Masters Tennis
Royal Albert Hall, London SW7
(020) 7589 8212
themasterstennis.com

1–2 Dec*
**City of Durham
Christmas Festival**
Various venues, Durham,
County Durham
(0191) 301 8819
durhamtourism.co.uk

6–9 Dec
Lincoln Christmas Market
Lincoln Market, Lincolnshire
(01522) 873213
lincoln.gov.uk

29 Dec–1 Jan 08
Edinburgh's Hogmany
Scotland
visitscotland.com

* provisional date at time of going
to press

2007 Calendar

JANUARY
M	T	W	T	F	S	S
1	2	3	4	5	6	7
8	9	10	11	12	13	14
15	16	17	18	19	20	21
22	23	24	25	26	27	28
29	30	31				

FEBRUARY
M	T	W	T	F	S	S
			1	2	3	4
5	6	7	8	9	10	11
12	13	14	15	16	17	18
19	20	21	22	23	24	25
26	27	28				

MARCH
M	T	W	T	F	S	S
			1	2	3	4
5	6	7	8	9	10	11
12	13	14	15	16	17	18
19	20	21	22	23	24	25
26	27	28	29	30	31	

APRIL
M	T	W	T	F	S	S
						1
2	3	4	5	6	7	8
9	10	11	12	13	14	15
16	17	18	19	20	21	22
23	24	25	26	27	28	29
30						

MAY
M	T	W	T	F	S	S
	1	2	3	4	5	6
7	8	9	10	11	12	13
14	15	16	17	18	19	20
21	22	23	24	25	26	27
28	29	30	31			

JUNE
M	T	W	T	F	S	S
				1	2	3
4	5	6	7	8	9	10
11	12	13	14	15	16	17
18	19	20	21	22	23	24
25	26	27	28	29	30	

JULY
M	T	W	T	F	S	S
						1
2	3	4	5	6	7	8
9	10	11	12	13	14	15
16	17	18	19	20	21	22
23	24	25	26	27	28	29
30	31					

AUGUST
M	T	W	T	F	S	S
		1	2	3	4	5
6	7	8	9	10	11	12
13	14	15	16	17	18	19
20	21	22	23	24	25	26
27	28	29	30	31		

SEPTEMBER
M	T	W	T	F	S	S
					1	2
3	4	5	6	7	8	9
10	11	12	13	14	15	16
17	18	19	20	21	22	23
24	25	26	27	28	29	30

OCTOBER
M	T	W	T	F	S	S
1	2	3	4	5	6	7
8	9	10	11	12	13	14
15	16	17	18	19	20	21
22	23	24	25	26	27	28
29	30	31				

NOVEMBER
M	T	W	T	F	S	S
			1	2	3	4
5	6	7	8	9	10	11
12	13	14	15	16	17	18
19	20	21	22	23	24	25
26	27	28	29	30		

DECEMBER
M	T	W	T	F	S	S
					1	2
3	4	5	6	7	8	9
10	11	12	13	14	15	16
17	18	19	20	21	22	23
24	25	26	27	28	29	30
31						

2008 Calendar

JANUARY
M	T	W	T	F	S	S
	1	2	3	4	5	6
7	8	9	10	11	12	13
14	15	16	17	18	19	20
21	22	23	24	25	26	27
28	29	30	31			

FEBRUARY
M	T	W	T	F	S	S
				1	2	3
4	5	6	7	8	9	10
11	12	13	14	15	16	17
18	19	20	21	22	23	24
25	26	27	28	29		

MARCH
M	T	W	T	F	S	S
					1	2
3	4	5	6	7	8	9
10	11	12	13	14	15	16
17	18	19	20	21	22	23
24	25	26	27	28	29	30
31						

APRIL
M	T	W	T	F	S	S
	1	2	3	4	5	6
7	8	9	10	11	12	13
14	15	16	17	18	19	20
21	22	23	24	25	26	27
28	29	30				

MAY
M	T	W	T	F	S	S
			1	2	3	4
5	6	7	8	9	10	11
12	13	14	15	16	17	18
19	20	21	22	23	24	25
26	27	28	29	30	31	

JUNE
M	T	W	T	F	S	S
						1
2	3	4	5	6	7	8
9	10	11	12	13	14	15
16	17	18	19	20	21	22
23	24	25	26	27	28	29
30						

JULY
M	T	W	T	F	S	S
	1	2	3	4	5	6
7	8	9	10	11	12	13
14	15	16	17	18	19	20
21	22	23	24	25	26	27
28	29	30	31			

AUGUST
M	T	W	T	F	S	S
				1	2	3
4	5	6	7	8	9	10
11	12	13	14	15	16	17
18	19	20	21	22	23	24
25	26	27	28	29	30	31

SEPTEMBER
M	T	W	T	F	S	S
1	2	3	4	5	6	7
8	9	10	11	12	13	14
15	16	17	18	19	20	21
22	23	24	25	26	27	28
29	30					

OCTOBER
M	T	W	T	F	S	S
		1	2	3	4	5
6	7	8	9	10	11	12
13	14	15	16	17	18	19
20	21	22	23	24	25	26
27	28	29	30	31		

NOVEMBER
M	T	W	T	F	S	S
					1	2
3	4	5	6	7	8	9
10	11	12	13	14	15	16
17	18	19	20	21	22	23
24	25	26	27	28	29	30

DECEMBER
M	T	W	T	F	S	S
1	2	3	4	5	6	7
8	9	10	11	12	13	14
15	16	17	18	19	20	21
22	23	24	25	26	27	28
29	30	31				

David Bellamy
Conservation Award

"These well-deserved awards are a signpost to parks which are making real achievements in protecting our environment. Go there and experience wrap-around nature....you could be amazed at what you find!" says Professor David Bellamy.

Many of Britain's holiday parks have become 'green champions' of conservation in the countryside, according to leading conservationist David Bellamy. More than 500 gold, silver and bronze parks were this year named in the David Bellamy Conservation Awards, organised in conjunction with the British Holiday and Home Parks Association. These parks are recognised for their commitment to conservation and the environment through their management of landscaping, recycling policies, waste management, the cultivation of flora and fauna and the creation of habitats designed to encourage a variety of wildlife onto the park. Links with the local community and the use of local materials is also an important consideration.

Parks participating in the scheme are assessed for the awards by holidaymakers who complete postcards to be returned to David Bellamy, an inspection by a local, independent Environmental Consultant and David Bellamy's own study of the parks' environmental audit completed when joining the scheme. Parks with Bellamy Awards offer a variety of accommodation from pitches for touring caravans, motor homes and tents, to caravan holiday homes, holiday lodges and cottages for rent. Holiday parks with these awards are not just those in quiet corners of the countryside. Amongst the winners are much larger centres in popular holiday areas that offer a wide range of entertainments and attractions.

The following parks, which all have a detailed entry in this guide, have received a Gold, Silver or Bronze David Bellamy Conservation Award. Use the park index to find the page number.

For a free brochure featuring a full list of award-winning parks please contact:
BH&HPA, 6 Pullman Court, Great Western Road, Gloucester GL1 3ND
t (01452) 526911
e enquiries@bhhpa.org.uk
w ukparks.com/bellamy

Castlerigg Hall Caravan & Camping Park	GOLD	Keswick	England's Northwest
Church Stile Holiday Park	GOLD	Wasdale	England's Northwest
Crake Valley Holiday Park	GOLD	Coniston	England's Northwest
Flusco Wood Caravan Park	GOLD	Penrith	England's Northwest
Hill of Oaks and Blakeholme Caravans	GOLD	Windermere	England's Northwest
Solway Holiday Village	BRONZE	Silloth	England's Northwest
Waterfoot Caravan Park	GOLD	Ullswater	England's Northwest
Woodclose Caravan Park	GOLD	Kirby Lonsdale	England's Northwest
Causey Hill Caravan Park	SILVER	Hexham	North East England
Seafield Caravan Park	GOLD	Seahouses	North East England
Allerton Park Caravan Park	GOLD	York	Yorkshire
Cayton Village Caravan Park	GOLD	Scarborough	Yorkshire
Golden Square Caravan and Camping Park	GOLD	Helmsley	Yorkshire
Jasmine Park	GOLD	Snainton	Yorkshire
Knight Stainforth Hall Caravan and Camping Park	SILVER	Stainforth	Yorkshire
Ladycross Plantation Caravan Park	GOLD	Whitby	Yorkshire
Lebberston Touring Park	GOLD	Scarborough	Yorkshire
Middlewood Farm Holiday Park	GOLD	Whitby	Yorkshire
Rudding Holiday Park	GOLD	Harrogate	Yorkshire
Slenningford Watermill Caravan & Camping	GOLD	Ripon	Yorkshire
Upwood Holiday Park	GOLD	Haworth	Yorkshire
York House Caravan Park	GOLD	Thirsk	Yorkshire
Fernwood Caravan Park	GOLD	Ellesmere	Heart of England
Island Meadow Caravan Park	GOLD	Aston Cantlow	Heart of England
The Millpond	GOLD	Little Tarrington	Heart of England
Ashby Park	GOLD	Horncastle	East Midlands
Lickpenny Caravan Park	SILVER	Tansley	East Midlands
Longnor Wood Caravan Park	GOLD	Buxton	East Midlands
Orchard Caravan Park	GOLD	Boston	East Midlands
Rivendale Caravan and Leisure Park	GOLD	Alsop En le Dale	East Midlands
Cherry Tree Holiday Park	SILVER	Great Yarmouth	East of England
Grasmere Caravan Park	BRONZE	Great Yarmouth	East of England
Sandy Gulls Cliff Top Touring Park	SILVER	Mundesley	East of England
Seacroft Caravan Club Site	BRONZE	Cromer	East of England
Searles Leisure Resort	GOLD	Hunstanton	East of England
Wyton Lakes Holiday Park	SILVER	Wyton	East of England
Bay View Park	GOLD	Pevensey Bay	South East England
Crowhurst Park	GOLD	Battle	South East England
Highclere Farm Country Touring Park	BRONZE	Beaconsfield	South East England
Honeybridge Park	GOLD	Horsham	South East England
Hurley Riverside Park	GOLD	Hurley	South East England
Sumners Ponds Fishery & Campsite	GOLD	Barns Green	South East England
Tanner Farm Touring Caravan & Camping Park	GOLD	Marden	South East England
Whitecliff Bay Holiday Park	SILVER	Bembridge	South East England
Beacon Hill Touring Park	GOLD	Poole	South West England
Broadway House Holiday Touring Caravan & Camping Park	GOLD	Cheddar	South West England
Challaborough Bay Holiday Park	SILVER	Kingsbridge	South West England
Channel View Caravan and Camping Park	GOLD	Lynton	South West England

Coastal Caravan Park	SILVER	Burton Bradstock	South West England
Cofton Country Holidays	GOLD	Dawlish	South West England
Crantock Beach Holiday Park	SILVER	Newquay	South West England
Croft Farm Holiday Park	GOLD	Luxulyan	South West England
Dornafield	GOLD	Newton Abbot	South West England
Forest Glade Holiday Park	GOLD	Kentisbeare	South West England
Freshwater Beach Holiday Park	BRONZE	Bridport	South West England
Golden Cap Holiday Park	GOLD	Bridport	South West England
Halse Farm Caravan & Tent Park	GOLD	Winsford	South West England
Harford Bridge Holiday Park	GOLD	Tavistock	South West England
Higher Longford Caravan & Camping Park	GOLD	Moorshop	South West England
Highlands End Holiday Park	GOLD	Bridport	South West England
Holywell Bay Holiday Park	SILVER	Newquay	South West England
Monkton Wyld Farm Caravan & Camping Park	GOLD	Charmouth	South West England
Newquay Holiday Park	GOLD	Newquay	South West England
Newton Mill Camping	GOLD	Bath	South West England
The Old Oaks Touring Park	GOLD	Glastonbury	South West England
Polruan Holidays (Camping & Caravanning)	SILVER	Polruan-by-Fowey	South West England
Porlock Caravan Park	GOLD	Porlock	South West England
Porthtowan Tourist Park	SILVER	Porthtowan	South West England
River Valley Country Park	SILVER	Relubbus	South West England
River Valley Holiday Park	SILVER	St Austell	South West England
Ruda Holiday Park	SILVER	Croyde Bay	South West England
Saint Margaret's Holiday Bungalows	GOLD	Polgooth	South West England
Sandyholme Holiday Park	GOLD	Owermoigne	South West England
Sea Acres Holiday Park	SILVER	Helston	South West England
Silver Sands Holiday Park	GOLD	Ruan Minor	South West England
Stowford Farm Meadows	GOLD	Combe Martin	South West England
Summer Valley Touring Park	SILVER	Truro	South West England
Torquay Holiday Park	SILVER	Torquay	South West England
Treloy Touring Park	SILVER	Newquay	South West England
Trencreek Farm Country Holiday Park	SILVER	St Austell	South West England
Ulwell Cottage Caravan Park	SILVER	Swanage	South West England
Warmwell Holiday Park	GOLD	Warmwell	South West England
West Bay Holiday Park	SILVER	West Bay	South West England
Westermill Farm	GOLD	Exford	South West England
White Acres Country Park	GOLD	White Cross	South West England
Wood Farm Caravan and Camping Park	SILVER	Charmouth	South West England
Wooda Farm Park	GOLD	Bude	South West England
Yeo Valley Holiday Park	SILVER	South Molton	South West England
Barnsoul Farm	GOLD	Dumfries	Scotland
Belhaven Bay Caravan Park	GOLD	Dunbar	Scotland
Dovecot Caravan Park	SILVER	Laurencekirk	Scotland
Kippford Holiday Park	GOLD	Kippford	Scotland
Linnhe Lochside Holidays	GOLD	Fort William	Scotland
Witches Craig Caravan Park	GOLD	Stirling	Scotland
Kingsbridge Caravan and Camping Park	GOLD	Beaumaris	Wales

National Accessible
Scheme index

Establishments participating in the National Accessible Scheme are listed below. At the front of the guide you can find information about the scheme. Establishments in bold have a detailed entry in this guide. Place names are listed alphabetically within their region.

♿ Mobility Level 1

Armathwaite England's Northwest	**Englethwaite Hall Caravan Club Site ★★★★**	42
Bury England's Northwest	**Burrs Country Park Caravan Club Site ★★★★★**	43
Lamplugh England's Northwest	**Dockray Meadow Caravan Club Site ★★★★**	46
Rothbury North East England	**Nunnykirk Caravan Club Site ★★★**	61
Stockton-on-Tees North East England	**White Water Caravan Club Park ★★★★★**	62
Sneaton Yorkshire	**Low Moor Caravan Club Site ★★★★**	78
Peterborough East of England	**Ferry Meadows Caravan Club Site ★★★★★**	123
Sidbury South West England	**Putts Corner Caravan Club Site ★★★★★**	198

♿ Mobility Level 2

Sandown South East England	**Southland Camping Park ★★★★★**	261

🏛 Category 2 (Scotland)

Dunbar Scotland	**Belhaven Bay Caravan Park ★★★★**	218
Edinburgh Scotland	**Mortonhall Caravan Park ★★★★**	219
North Berwick Scotland	**Tantallon Caravan Park ★★★★★**	223

Quick reference
index

If you're looking for a specific facility use this index to see at-a-glance parks that match your requirement. Establishments are listed alphabetically by place name within each region.

🏊 Indoor pool

Parks listed here have a detailed entry in this guide.

⇲ Outdoor pool

Bamburgh North East England	Meadowhead's Waren Caravan and Camping Park ★★★★ ROSE	58
Harrogate Yorkshire	Rudding Holiday Park ★★★★★ ROSE	74
Roos Yorkshire	Sand-le-Mere Caravan & Leisure Park ★★★★ ROSE	76
Evesham Heart of England	The Ranch Caravan Park ★★★★★	91
Cromer East of England	Seacroft Caravan Club Site Applied	119
Great Yarmouth East of England	Cherry Tree Holiday Park ★★★★	120
Hunstanton East of England	Searles Leisure Resort ★★★★★ ROSE	121
Scratby East of England	Scratby Hall Caravan Park ★★★★	123
Andover South East England	Wyke Down Touring Caravan & Camping Park ★★★	146
Bembridge South East England	Whitecliff Bay Holiday Park ★★★★	148
Canterbury South East England	Yew Tree Park ★★★★	150
Seasalter South East England	Homing Leisure Park ★★★★★	156
Selsey South East England	Warner Farm Touring Park ★★★★★	156
Bridport South West England	Freshwater Beach Holiday Park ★★★★	172
Brixham South West England	Hillhead Holiday Park ★★★★★	173
Bude South West England	Budemeadows Touring Holiday Park ★★★★★	174
Camelford South West England	Juliot's Well Holiday Park ★★★	176
Charmouth South West England	Manor Farm Holiday Centre ★★★	176
Cheddar South West England	Broadway House Holiday Touring Caravan and Camping Park ★★★★ ROSE	177
Dawlish South West England	Cofton Country Holidays ★★★★	179
Hayle South West England	Beachside Holiday Park ★★★★	182
Looe South West England	Tencreek Holiday Park ★★★★	185
Newquay South West England	Holywell Bay Holiday Park ★★★★ ROSE	188
Newquay South West England	Newperran Holiday Park ★★★★ ROSE	188
Newquay South West England	Newquay Holiday Park ★★★★ ROSE	188
Newquay South West England	Treloy Touring Park ★★★★	189
Poole South West England	Beacon Hill Touring Park ★★★	192
Portreath South West England	Cambrose Touring Park ★★★	193
St Austell South West England	Trencreek Farm Country Holiday Park ★★★	196
St Austell South West England	Trewhiddle Village	196
St Ives South West England	Polmanter Touring Park ★★★★★	197
St Ives South West England	Little Trevarrack Touring Park ★★★★	196
Tedburn St Mary South West England	Springfield Holiday Park ★★★	200
Teigngrace South West England	Twelve Oaks Farm Caravan Park ★★★★	200
Weston-super-Mare South West England	Country View Holiday Park ★★★★	202
Aberaeron Wales	Aeron Coast Caravan Park ★★★★	235

index to
display advertisers

Index by
park name

All parks with a detailed entry in this guide are listed below.

Parks listed here have a detailed entry in this guide.

Index by place name

The following places all have detailed park entries in this guide. If the place where you wish to stay is not shown, the location maps (starting on page 17) will help you to find somewhere to stay in the area.

Turn to the pages indicated for detailed park entries in these places.

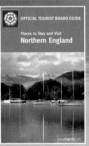

win

a full set of official
tourist board guides

OFFICIAL TOURIST BOARD PUBLICATION
Bed & Breakfast
Guide to quality-assessed accommodation in England
2007

OFFICIAL TOURIST BOARD PUBLICATION
Self Catering
Guide to quality-assessed holiday homes in England
2007

OFFICIAL TOURIST BOARD PUBLICATION
Britain's Camping & Caravan Parks
Guide to quality-assessed sites
2007

OFFICIAL TOURIST BOARD PUBLICATION
Hotels
Guide to quality-assessed accommodation in England
2007

Keep in touch and WIN a full set of 2007 official tourist board accommodation guides

VisitBritain would be delighted to hear what you think of this guide. Please complete the short questionnaire overleaf and send it back to us.

Questionnaires will be entered into a monthly draw to win a full set of 2007 official accommodation guides.

Title _____ First name _____

Surname _____

Address _____

Town/City _____ County _____

Postcode _____ Country _____

Mobile _____ Telephone _____

E-mail _____

Which age group are you in?

16-24 ❑   25-34 ❑   35-44 ❑   45-54 ❑   55-64 ❑   65+ ❑

When do you normally buy accommodation guides? (please tick one box)

❑ Easter holidays
❑ Before main summer season, i.e. May
❑ Christmas / end of the year
❑ Anytime – planning a special occasion

❑ Anytime – planning a spontaneous occasion
❑ Anytime – planning a holiday
❑ Spontaneously purchased

How often do you buy accommodation guides? (please tick one box)

❑ Every year
❑ Every 2 years
❑ Every 3 years

❑ Every 4 years
❑ Every 5 years
❑ Single purchase, i.e. I do not replace guide

Do you regularly use any other accommodation guides? If yes, which ones?

_____

What do you find useful about this official tourist board guide?

_____

Is there any other information you would like to see added to this guide?

_____

Have you booked any accommodation through this guide? If yes, which one (establishment and region)?

_____

Would you like to be contacted by VisitBritain in future with news, ideas and special offers?   Yes ❑ No ❑
Would you like to be contacted by VisitBritain's carefully chosen partners with news of more offers?   Yes ❑ No ❑

Please complete, put in an envelope and return Freepost (no stamp required) **to:**

VisitBritain Commercial Publishing, Freepost RLXU–XLYY–UKLB
Thames Tower, Blacks Road, London W6 9EL

C07-RRC

CUT ALONG LINE